1-15-53

D1625357

INTERNATIONAL SERIES IN PURE AND APPLIED PHYSICS

G. P. HARNWELL, CONSULTING EDITOR

MESONS

A Summary of Experimental Facts

INTERNATIONAL SERIES IN PURE AND APPLIED PHYSICS

G. P. HARNWELL, CONSULTING EDITOR

ADVISORY EDITORIAL COMMITTEE: E. U. Condon, George R. Harrison
Elmer Hutchisson, K. K. Darrow

Allis and Herlin   Thermodynamics and Statistical Mechanics
Cady   Piezoelectricity
Clark   Applied X-rays
Edwards   Analytic and Vector Mechanics
Finkelnburg   Atomic Physics
Gurney   Introduction to Statistical Mechanics
Hardy and Perrin   The Principles of Optics
Harnwell   Electricity and Electromagnetism
Harnwell and Livingood   Experimental Atomic Physics
Houston   Principles of Mathematical Physics
Houston   Principles of Quantum Mechanics
Hughes and DuBridge   Photoelectric Phenomena
Hund   High-frequency Measurements
Ingersoll, Zobel, and Ingersoll   Heat Conduction
Kemble   The Fundamental Principles of Quantum Mechanics
Kennard   Kinetic Theory of Gases
Koller   The Physics of Electron Tubes
Marshak   Meson Physics
Morse   Vibration and Sound
Morse and Feshbach   Methods of Theoretical Physics
Muskat   Physical Principles of Oil Production
Richtmyer and Kennard   Introduction to Modern Physics
Ruark and Urey   Atoms, Molecules, and Quanta
Schiff   Quantum Mechanics
Seitz   The Modern Theory of Solids
Slater   Introduction to Chemical Physics
Slater   Microwave Transmission
Slater   Quantum Theory of Matter
Slater and Frank   Electromagnetism
Slater and Frank   Introduction to Theoretical Physics
Slater and Frank   Mechanics
Smythe   Static and Dynamic Electricity
Stratton   Electromagnetic Theory
Thorndike   Mesons: A Summary of Experimental Facts
White   Introduction to Atomic Spectra

Dr. Lee A. DuBridge was Consulting Editor of the series from 1939 to 1946.

20,552

RADIATION & NUCLEONICS LAB

MESONS,

A Summary of Experimental Facts

ALAN M. THORNDIKE

Associate Physicist, Brookhaven National Laboratory

FIRST EDITION

McGRAW-HILL BOOK COMPANY, INC.

NEW YORK   TORONTO   LONDON

1952

Library
I.U.P.
Indiana, Pa.

539.72 T393m
c. 1

MESONS: A SUMMARY OF EXPERIMENTAL FACTS

Copyright, 1952, by the McGraw-Hill Book Company, Inc. Printed in the
United States of America. All rights reserved. This book, or parts thereof,
may not be reproduced in any form without permission of the publishers.

Library of Congress Catalog Card Number: 52-5343

A000004749226

LE PRESS COMPANY, YORK, PA.

PREFACE

During the second quarter of the twentieth century knowledge of nuclear physics has expanded at an unprecedented rate. With the large-scale release of atomic energy during the Second World War, the technological developments based on this knowledge have become a dominant force in national and international affairs. Everyone knows that atomic energy will have an extensive influence upon the course of human society in years to come. Not everyone knows, however, that the scientific and technical knowledge of nuclear physics overlies a profound ignorance of certain basic principles. In particular we do not really understand the nature of the forces which hold nuclei together and cause them to behave as they do.

Many attempts have been made to rectify this situation, and many are still being made. It appears likely that the mysterious nuclear force field can be quantized and that its quanta appear as particles whose mass is intermediate between that of an electron and that of a proton. These quanta are called mesons. Particles having properties appropriate for mesons have indeed been observed experimentally in cosmic radiation and in energetic nuclear reactions. A great many experimental investigations of them have been made. This book is an attempt to summarize the experimental information now available in such a form that it can be related to the problem of nuclear forces. No attempt is made, however, to present the meson theory of nuclear forces except in a rudimentary qualitative discussion.

The book is descriptive and nonmathematical, and is intended to serve as an introduction to the field of meson physics suitable for use by students in modern physics and nuclear-physics courses. At the same time sufficient detail is given to constitute a useful reference for those engaged in research or teaching in nuclear physics or allied fields. Since many questions relative to mesons have still been answered only provisionally, the approach is partly historical, and an attempt is made to give the developments leading up to the present knowledge of mesons. In this respect it gives a good illustration of the devious processes involved in the growth of scientific knowledge.

Since a large number of the subjects discussed are ones concerning which many investigations are now under way, new and improved results may soon be obtained concerning them. In recognition of this, no attempt has been made to make this book a complete and comprehensive discussion, since it could not possibly remain complete and comprehensive. Instead the attempt has been to select the most important results and those established with the greatest certainty, which may be expected to remain significant regardless of additional information that may be obtained.

Many experiments on mesons have been concerned with those found in cosmic radiation. Consequently the subjects of cosmic rays and mesons are closely interrelated. In the first seven chapters only those results are discussed which bear directly on the existence of mesons, their properties, and behavior. In the final chapter a brief outline is given of information on the occurrence of mesons in cosmic radiation, which represents a rather different aspect of knowledge about mesons.

The author wishes to express his thanks to all those who have contributed material for inclusion. He is especially indebted to R. P. Shutt and E. C. Fowler for many helpful suggestions during the preparation of the manuscript.

Alan M. Thorndike

Upton, N.Y.
August, 1952

CONTENTS

PREFACE   v

CHAPTER 1. EVIDENCE FOR THE EXISTENCE OF MESONS   1

     1. Particles Known before the Discovery of Mesons   1
     2. The Hard and Soft Components of Cosmic Radiation   7
     3. Energy Losses of Charged Particles; Bethe-Heitler Theory   10
     4. Experiments on Energy Losses of Cosmic Rays in Solid
        Plates   15
     5. Meson Theory of Nuclear Forces   19

CHAPTER 2. PROPERTIES OF COSMIC-RAY MESONS   27

     1. Properties of Elementary Particles   27
     2. Mass   28
     3. Charge   37
     4. Spin   39
     5. Summary   44

CHAPTER 3. NEW TYPES OF MESONS   45

     1. The Discovery of the Particle Predicted by Yukawa   45
     2. The λ-meson Hypothesis   59
     3. Heavy Mesons   65

CHAPTER 4. ARTIFICIALLY PRODUCED MESONS   74

     1. Evidence for Artificial Production   74
     2. Description of the Production Process   78
     3. Production as a Function of Bombarding Particle and
        Energy   79
     4. Production as a Function of Meson Charge, Energy, and
        Angle   82
     5. Masses of Artificially Produced Mesons   86
     6. Behavior of Artificial Mesons   89
     7. Evidence for Neutral Mesons   89
     8. Artificial Production of Heavy Mesons   92

CHAPTER 5. DECAY OF MESONS   94

1. Evidence for Decay of the μ Meson   95
2. Direct Measurement of μ-meson Lifetime   99
3. Products of μ-meson Decay   108
4. Decay of π Mesons   118
5. Decay of Heavy Mesons   125
6. Summary   125

CHAPTER 6. INTERACTION OF MESONS WITH MATTER   128

1. Electromagnetic Interactions   128
2. Scattering of Mesons   135
3. Nuclear Interactions of μ Mesons   141
4. Nuclear Interactions of π Mesons   149
5. Nuclear Interactions of Heavy Mesons   159
6. Summary   159

CHAPTER 7. PRODUCTION OF MESONS IN COSMIC RADIATION   163

1. Production of Penetrating Particles by Non-ionizing Radiation   167
2. Penetrating Showers   169
3. Penetrating Particles in Air Showers   180
4. Mesons from Stars   185
5. Summary   196

CHAPTER 8. OCCURRENCE OF MESONS IN COSMIC RADIATION   201

1. Mesons at Sea Level   203
    1.1. Positive Excess   204
    1.2. Energy Spectrum   205
    1.3. Effect of Meteorological Variations   207
    1.4. Variations with Zenith Angle   209
    1.5. Geomagnetic Effects   211
2. Occurrence of Mesons below Ground   213
3. Occurrence of Mesons at High Altitudes   216
    3.1. Positive Excess   218
    3.2. Energy Spectrum   219
    3.3. Effect of Meteorological Variations   222
    3.4. Variations with Zenith Angle   222
    3.5. Geomagnetic Effects   223

GLOSSARY   227

LIST OF SYMBOLS IN EQUATIONS   231

NAME INDEX   233

SUBJECT INDEX   239

CHAPTER 1

EVIDENCE FOR THE EXISTENCE OF MESONS

1. PARTICLES KNOWN BEFORE THE DISCOVERY OF MESONS

Men who have inquired into the nature of the world about them have very often pictured its great diversity as being built up of relatively simple elements of some sort. Such a view is taken by natural scientists today. In a chemical sense, there are some 92 different elements (plus a few more which do not occur naturally in any appreciable quantity but can be made artificially) which can combine in various proportions, more or less complicated, to form all the substances which we know. In any particular chemical compound the ratios between the weights of the elements which comprise it are fixed, and if a different compound can be formed from the same elements, the new ratios are simply related to the original ones. In other words the chemical compounds are built up out of definite numbers of elementary building blocks. This picture was clearly presented in the atomic hypothesis of Dalton in 1802,* which involved "atoms" of each element as the building blocks, the atoms being indivisible and indestructible. Molecules of all substances were thought of as made up by combination of the proper numbers of atoms of the constituent elements. This picture of chemical combination was well established during the nineteenth century and is now taken for granted.

Atoms and molecules serve to present a systematic description of the facts of chemical combination, but to explain phenomena involving the interaction of light or electricity with matter it is necessary to ascribe some sort of structure to the atom. The atom is not completely indestructible and indivisible in such processes; it may, for example, gain or lose one or more electrons and become electrically charged—an ion. The structure of atoms was not understood until the twentieth century. Many features have not yet been worked out in all their complex detail, but the general features appear to be well established along the following lines:

* Detailed references are not given in this section. They can be found in any standard text on atomic structure, modern physics, or nuclear physics.

1

1. The nuclear atom, as proposed by Rutherford in 1911, has a nucleus of positive charge at which most of the weight of the atom is concentrated, and whose diameter is of the order of magnitude of 10^{-13} cm. Electrons of negative charge, which are light in weight, fill the rest of the space occupied by the atom. Its over-all dimensions are of the order of magnitude of 10^{-8} cm. Such a model of the atom was necessary to explain the occasional large-angle scattering which α particles experienced in going through thin metal foils. If the massive positively charged part of the atom were spread out, the α particle could never be close enough to all of it to experience the force necessary for large-angle scattering. Hence the small heavy nucleus was postulated.

2. Quantum theory, first proposed by Bohr in 1913, defines equilibrium states of atomic systems which are characterized by values of the angular momentum of the electrons which are equal to integral multiples of a universal constant, Planck's constant. Line spectra are due to transitions between different states.

3. Nuclear charge is characteristic of an element. Since the atom as a whole is uncharged, the positive charge on the nucleus must be equal to the number of planetary electrons. These electrons then arrange themselves in the most stable way. The number and arrangement of the electrons then determines (in principle) all the optical, electrical, and even chemical properties of the element, since chemical combination is thought of as occurring through the gain or loss of one or more electrons, or the sharing of pairs of electrons in valence bonds.

4. Nuclei of the same charge but different mass exist for most elements. These are called isotopes. The masses are, however, all approximately integer multiples of the lightest nucleus, hydrogen. This suggests strongly that nuclei may be made up of units having approximately the mass of the hydrogen nucleus.

It is, as a matter of fact, quite certain that atomic nuclei are made up of smaller, more fundamental particles. The existence of radioactive nuclei is a convincing indication of this. When a naturally radioactive nucleus emits an α particle and transforms into the nucleus with mass four units lighter and charge less by two units, one feels justified in concluding that the α particle was a constituent of the original nucleus. In addition, other types of nuclear reactions can be produced artificially. Thus neither atoms nor nuclei are true elementary particles since both can be broken down into simpler constituents.

The above outline sketches the facts as they were known at about 1930. It was reasonable to consider the electron and the proton (hydrogen nucleus) to be elementary particles, the first of charge -4.80×10^{-10} esu and mass 9.11×10^{-28} g, the second of equal positive charge and mass about 1840 times that of the electron. Other nuclei might be thought of as made up of electrons and protons with a sufficient excess of the latter to give the net positive charge. A major difficulty with this picture is that of confining the electron to a space of dimensions $\sim 10^{-13}$ cm. According to quantum mechanics a particle confined to a small space must be allowed to have a large energy, and for an electron confined to a nucleus the energy becomes about 10^9 ev. This seems unreasonably high since the binding energies of particles in nuclei are usually only about 10^7 ev.

It was also appropriate to consider the photon as an elementary particle in some sense, since light was known to be quantized. It behaves as though made up of particles with respect to emission by atoms, photoelectric effect, and other interactions with electrons. The photon was, however, unlike the proton and the electron in that it could be emitted and absorbed, and in that it had no rest mass.

It was not long, however, before two additional particles were found, which had not been observed previously because they were produced only in energetic nuclear reactions which had not been available for study until that time. Nuclear physics proper grew out of the study of the naturally radioactive elements and began with Rutherford's discovery of nuclear reactions in 1919. He found that when nitrogen was irradiated by α particles, ionizing particles were produced whose range was much greater than that of the original α particles. The long-range particles were identified as protons which were produced when the α particles collided with the nitrogen nuclei and interacted with them. Many similar nuclear reactions were found, and it is now known that any particle of sufficient energy can cause a nuclear reaction, although the likelihood of doing so and the reaction produced vary widely.* It was found by Bothe and Becker in 1930 that α bombardment of beryllium produced an extremely penetrating radiation which was first thought to consist of γ rays rather than protons. The radiation was shown by the Curie-Joliots and by Chadwick in 1932 to be able to knock protons out of paraffin. The energy of the protons was greater than could be produced by γ rays. Chadwick pointed out that the difficulties could be removed by assuming a neutral particle whose mass was equal to that of the proton. This particle was called a "neutron." Other reactions producing neutrons were soon found, so that the neutron was clearly a common constituent of atomic nuclei.

Two alternatives were then possible: to consider the neutron as a combination of a proton and electron or as an independent elementary

---

* The neutrino (see p. 6), for example, interacts only very weakly with nuclei, and nuclear reactions attributable to neutrinos have not so far been detected.

particle. A strong argument in favor of the latter is provided by the critical difficulty of confining an electron to a space as small as a nucleus without violating the uncertainty principle. If the neutron is thought of as an elementary particle, nuclei can be considered to be composed of protons and neutrons with no electrons existing inside the nucleus. The correctness of this picture is confirmed by data on nuclear spins and statistics. Since proton and electron each have a spin of $\frac{1}{2}$, the deuteron should have a spin of either $\frac{3}{2}$ or $\frac{1}{2}$ if composed of two protons and an electron. Actually its spin is 1. This would be reasonable if the deuteron is composed of proton and neutron each with a spin of $\frac{1}{2}$. Such an assumption also accounts for the observed spins of heavier nuclei and is certainly correct.* Thus the neutron is an elementary particle.

The neutron was not the only new elementary particle discovered in 1932; the other was the positron, a particle of the same mass as the electron, but with a positive charge rather than negative. The existence of the positron was first realized by Anderson while studying cosmic radiation.

Cosmic radiation has also been the source of mesons,† and some aspects of it will accordingly be discussed later in greater detail. A short digression is appropriate at this time to sketch the experiments demonstrating the existence and general nature of cosmic radiation.

In the early 1900's it was generally known that an ionization chamber such as was used to detect ionizing radiation from radioactive substances would discharge slowly when no source was near. This background current could be somewhat reduced by shielding with lead and was therefore caused at least in part by some radiation entering the ionization chamber from outside, and not by leakage at the insulation. It was originally assumed that penetrating γ rays were the cause, coming from radioactive materials in the earth's surface. In this case it would be expected that the intensity of the radiation would decrease at high altitudes. Ionization chambers were flown with balloons by Gockel (1910), Hess (1911), and Kolhörster (1913 to 1914), with just the opposite result. The ionization increased with increasing altitude, and reached a value about twelve times that at sea level when at 9000 m. It was necessary to conclude that the radiation either had its genesis at great heights in the atmosphere or came in to the earth from outside. The latter of these two possibilities was eventually generally accepted.

* Independent confirmation of the spin of $\frac{1}{2}$ for the neutron also exists in experiments on the polarization of neutrons by a magnetic field.

† Variously known as mesons, mesotrons, barytrons, yukons, and heavy electrons during the first years after their discovery.

Cosmic rays are in practically all instances detected by the ionization that they produce. In 1927, Skobelzyn observed the tracks of fast ionizing particles in a cloud chamber although no source of radiation except cosmic rays was present. In 1929, Bothe and Kolhörster showed that cosmic rays discharged two Geiger-Müller counters in coincidence. These and other experiments indicated that the cosmic rays at sea level consisted largely of charged particles.

Confirmation of the idea that cosmic rays consist of charged particles coming from outside the earth's atmosphere was found in the effect of the earth's magnetic field on cosmic-ray intensity. Particles approaching the earth near the magnetic poles move more or less parallel to the earth's magnetic field and are little affected by it. A charged particle moving in the equatorial plane will, however, be deflected away from the earth unless its energy exceeds a certain minimum value. Thus the cosmic-ray intensity is reduced, and the direction of the admitted particles is distorted. These geomagnetic effects have been studied extensively, and the results leave no doubt that the incoming cosmic rays consist largely, perhaps completely, of charged particles, whose energies vary widely, being mainly in the range 1 to 25 Bev. On striking the atmosphere, many secondaries of different sorts are produced in a great variety of ways. In 1932, however, it was considered that the cosmic radiation was made up of positively charged protons and negatively charged electrons.

During 1931 and 1932, Anderson was studying cosmic rays with a cloud chamber which was located in a magnetic field. Curvature of the tracks left by particles could be used to determine their momentum. In a uniform magnetic field the force on a charged particle, being perpendicular to its motion, causes it to move in a circle. The relation between momentum P and radius of curvature ρ is given by Eq. (1).

$$P = \frac{H\rho e}{c} \tag{1}$$

where e is the charge of the particle in electrostatic units, H the magnetic field in gauss, and c the velocity of light. It is often convenient to measure momentum in units of electron volts divided by the velocity of light (ev/c) in which case the momentum is given by Eq. (2).

$$P = 300H\rho \quad \text{ev/c} \tag{2}$$

Positive and negative particles were found. These were at first assumed to be protons and electrons.

For a given momentum, however, a proton would have much less energy than an electron, since the kinetic energy E of a particle of mass m and momentum P is given by Eq. (3)

$$E = \frac{P^2}{2m} \tag{3}$$

for nonrelativistic particles such as those whose range could be measured in the cloud chamber. Hence a proton of a certain curvature would have a much shorter range before stopping than an electron of that curvature. Curved positive tracks were found whose range was too great to be protons. They were, in fact, indistinguishable from electron tracks except in sign, and it was therefore concluded that they were actually positive electrons, which were called positrons. Once the existence of the positron was accepted, it was found to be a fairly common component of cosmic radiation. Positrons are also emitted by many radioactive nuclei which have been produced artificially.

It is, perhaps, not quite right to consider the positron as a new particle since it is extremely closely related to the electron. This relationship is apparent in the relativistic quantum-mechanical treatment of electron spin devised by Dirac. This theory requires that there be states of the electron with negative energy existing symmetrically with the positive states. One may think of the negative states as being normally all occupied and unobservable. If, however, sufficient energy is supplied to move an electron from a negative energy state to a positive one, a "hole" is created in the infinite sea of electrons of negative energy which could be observed as a positron. Such an act would form a positron-electron pair, and the positron can be regarded as another manifestation of the electron rather than an altogether new particle.

There remains only one more particle to be discussed before passing to the meson with which we shall mainly be concerned. This last, and most elusive, is the neutrino, a particle which has not yet really been detected. It is supposed to have no charge, a rest mass which is probably zero, and a weak interaction with electrons and nucleons. The main reason for supposing the existence of such a particle is the fact that when a radioactive nucleus emits a β particle the energy of the β particle is normally less than the full amount available from loss in mass of the parent nucleus. In order not to violate the law of conservation of energy, it is assumed that the practically unobservable neutrino carries off the excess.

At about 1935, then, the list of known elementary particles was as follows: proton, neutron, electron, positron, photon, and neutrino. Within the next few years a new particle was found, the meson, and it has recently become apparent that more than one type of meson exists. The remainder of this chapter will be concerned with the reasons for believing in the existence of mesons.

2. THE HARD AND SOFT COMPONENTS OF COSMIC RADIATION

After the discovery of the positron there was a tendency to consider that the charged particles in the cosmic radiation were all electrons and positrons. Electrons and positrons had been demonstrated to be present

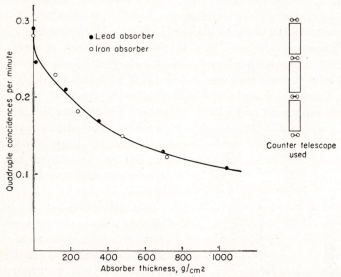

Fig. 1. The absorption of cosmic rays in lead and iron, from Street, Woodward, and Stevenson [3].

in the cosmic radiation. The simplest assumption to make was then that no other types of charged particles were involved. There was, however, no positive evidence supporting such a belief. As a matter of fact, the only particles which had been identified by magnetic-deflection experiments as electrons or positrons were those of relatively low energy— up to about 10 Mev or so. Information could not be obtained easily by deflection measurements about the high-energy particles making up the majority of the cosmic-ray flux. Evidence was accumulated through other types of experiments dealing with the ability of the particles to penetrate matter. These experiments will now be discussed.

While it had been assumed at first that the penetrating cosmic rays were some form of ultra γ radiation which produced ionizing particles of low penetration as secondaries, experiments of Bothe and Kolhörster [1] and Rossi [2] indicated that this was not likely to be the case since the ionizing particles were themselves able to penetrate lead up to a meter or more in thickness. They had, in fact, much the same penetrating ability as had previously been ascribed to the ultra γ rays to explain their penetration through the atmosphere. Not all the ionizing particles had the ability to penetrate large thicknesses of matter, however, since some of them were stopped by a few centimeters of lead. A typical curve for the absorption of cosmic rays is given in Fig. 1 on p. 7, plotted from the data of Street, Woodward, and Stevenson [3]. Quadruple coincidences in the counter telescope are plotted against the absorber thickness in grams per square centimeter. Results for absorbers of different atomic weights fell on a single curve if reduced to this common unit. The measurements extend to a thickness of 91.5 cm of lead. About 15 per cent of the particles are stopped by the first 1.5 cm of lead, but the next 1.5 cm of lead does not stop a tenth as many particles. It was natural, then, to describe the observations in terms of a soft, easily absorbed component and a hard component constituting the penetrating particles. This distinction was emphasized by Auger who suggested that the two components might well actually be different kinds of particles [4].

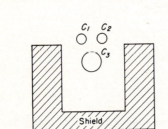

FIG. 2. Counter arrangement for detecting showers used by Rossi [2]. Shield and producing layer, A, are of lead.

This distinction between hard and soft components would seem somewhat artificial if it were not that the two components also act differently in other ways. Multiple events, called showers, are an example. Cloud-chamber pictures had shown that the charged particles sometimes occurred in groups rather than singly, occasionally in groups containing many particles. These were called showers. A counter scheme for detecting showers was devised by Rossi [2] who counted coincidences between all three counters in an arrangement such as that in Fig. 2. Such a coincidence requires two or more particles. If the thickness of the layer A was varied, he obtained the curve shown in Fig. 3. The prominent maximum occurs in just that thickness of lead in which the soft component is absorbed. One can therefore conclude that the soft component produces numerous showers in thin layers of lead, while the hard component produces somewhat fewer in larger thicknesses. Thus the soft component can be characterized as shower-producing.

The two components are also distinguished by different dependence of intensity on altitude and depth under ground.   Auger and Leprince-Ringuet [5] measured the cosmic-ray intensity at the Jungfraujoch

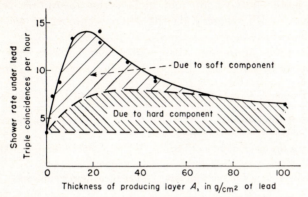

Fig. 3.   Rossi curve giving frequency of showers under lead as a function of thickness of producing layers [2].

(3500 m) in the open and under a layer of ice equivalent to the air between that point and sea level.   The results in Table 1 show a definite change in the fraction of hard particles.

TABLE 1. DIVISION INTO HARD AND SOFT COMPONENT AT 3500 m ACCORDING TO AUGER AND LEPRINCE-RINGUET [5]

	In open	Under ice
Vertical coincidences no absorber (total radiation)	1.9	1.1
Vertical coincidences with 20 cm lead (hard)	1.0	0.76
Difference (soft)	0.9	0.34
Ratio hard/soft	1.1	2.2

Results at sea level were approximately the same as under the ice at the higher elevation,* but under 8 m of soil [4] the hard to soft ratio was up to 15.   At the high altitude it was found that the frequency of showers increased in the same way as the intensity of the soft component. These results have been verified and extended by many subsequent investigations.

Yet another, and one of the most striking, of the distinctions between hard and soft components is the effect of atomic number of the absorbing material on the absorption.   In the case of the hard component it was

* Later more accurate data show a difference between these conditions, which is discussed in Chap. 5.

shown by a number of investigators that equal masses of material were approximately equally effective as absorbers [3,6 to 8]. In the case of the soft component, however, elements of high atomic weight were relatively more effective [8], and in fact the absorption per atom is proportional to Z^2, where Z is the atomic number of the absorbing material [9].

We may then summarize these differences between soft and hard components as in Table 2. These differences suggest some fundamental

TABLE 2. COMPARISON OF SOFT AND HARD COMPONENTS

Soft Component	Hard Component
Absorbed by a few centimeters of lead	Able to penetrate up to 100 cm of lead or more
Produces showers in a few centimeters of lead	Produces fewer showers
Intensity increases rapidly with altitude, and drops rapidly under ground	Slower variation with altitude and depth under ground
Absorption by atom is proportional to Z^2	Absorption per atom proportional to Z

difference in nature between hard and soft components.

3. ENERGY LOSSES OF CHARGED PARTICLES: BETHE-HEITLER THEORY

In order to give a definite interpretation to these and other subsequent experimental results, it is necessary to outline the corresponding theoretical results concerning the ability of charged particles to penetrate matter. The matter itself is made up of charged particles, nuclei and planetary electrons. As a high-speed charged particle flies past the relatively stationary ones, it exerts a force on them as shown in Fig. 4, tending to set the light electrons in more rapid motion. A certain number of the bound electrons will be excited to states of higher energy and some will be removed from their atoms, creating ions. The energy for these processes is supplied by the fast particle, and it loses energy accordingly. In these collisions energy is absorbed by the planetary electrons. The nuclei are too heavy to respond appreciably to the force and do not absorb much energy. If, however, the fast particle passes close to a nucleus, the force may be sufficient to deflect the fast particle. Such a deflection implies that the fast particle has been accelerated, in this case in a direction more or less perpendicular to its path, and this acceleration may be expected to result in electromagnetic radiation. This process, known as "bremsstrahlung," is another way in which a high-energy particle loses energy in passing through matter. A high-energy charged particle will continue until its energy has been absorbed by these two processes.

It is easy to see qualitatively that the energy lost by inelastic collisions will depend on the velocity of the charged particle, since a slow particle exerts a force on each electron for a longer time than does a fast one, and should therefore lose more energy per electron passed. The energy required to ionize the atom will enter in some way, and, in general, the energy lost in any given absorber will be proportional to the number of electrons passed. The energy lost by bremsstrahlung will, on the other hand, be most important if the fast particle is of light weight, i.e., an electron; and would not be of comparable importance for a fast proton whose acceleration due to a given force of interaction with the atomic nuclei would be only $\frac{1}{1800}$ as great. Since collisions with large momentum change are required to produce bremsstrahlung, it is favored by high particle energy. Relativistic effects enhance its probability so that it becomes of special importance for particles whose kinetic energy is much greater than their rest

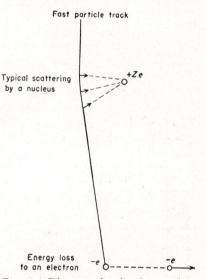

Fig. 4. Diagram showing interactions of a fast charged particle with a nucleus and with an electron.

energy. A high charge on the nucleus is also necessary to have large losses due to bremsstrahlung. Such radiative losses would be large for an electron passing through lead, but not for protons passing through light materials.

The rigorous derivation of the formulas involved is outside the scope of this discussion. The subject is discussed at some length by Heitler [10], Rossi and Greisen [11], Janossy [12], and others. The formulas applicable for cosmic-ray particles were derived in the early 1930's. A summary of them follows.

1. Average energy loss by inelastic collisions:

$$\left(-\frac{dE}{dx}\right)_{\text{coll}} = \frac{3}{4} NZ\Phi_0 m_e c^2 z^2 \frac{1}{\beta^2} \left[\log \frac{m_e c^2 \beta^2 E_{\max}}{(1-\beta^2)I^2 Z^2} + 1 - \beta^2 \right] \qquad (4)$$

Here $\left(-\dfrac{dE}{dx}\right)_{\text{coll}}$ = average energy lost per cm path, E being the kinetic energy of the fast particle

N = number of atoms per cm^3 of material traversed

Z = atomic number of material traversed

Φ_0 = a standard cross section = 6.57×10^{-25} cm^2

m_e = mass of the electron

c = velocity of light

z = charge of high-speed particle in units of electronic charge

$\beta = v/c$, where v is the velocity of the high-speed particle

E_{max} = the maximum energy which can be transferred in a direct collision from the particle to a free electron. If the fast particle is an electron $E_{\text{max}} = E/2$; if it is a meson or proton, $E_{\text{max}} = 2m_e v^2/(1 - \beta^2)$ for all except very high energies

This formula is valid for any particle fast enough that $\beta \gg z/137$. The energy loss is shown graphically in Fig. 5 for mesons.

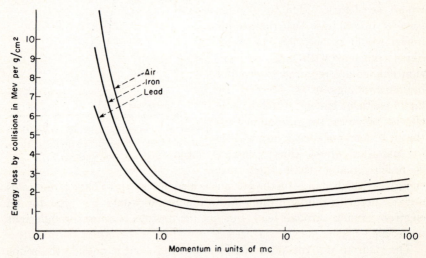

FIG. 5. Total collision loss for mesons in air, iron, and lead, from Rossi and Greisen [11]. Calculated for meson mass = $200m_e$, but practically valid for any mass above about $100m_e$.

2. Average energy loss by radiation for an electron:

$$\left(-\frac{dE}{dx}\right)_{\text{rad}} = NW\Phi_{\text{rad}} \qquad (5)$$

Here $\left(-\dfrac{dE}{dx}\right)_{rad}$ = average energy lost per cm path by radiation

W = total energy of the fast electron

Φ_{rad} = a slowly varying function of energy given in Fig. 6

There are two outstanding characteristics of this formula. The first is the fact that rate of energy loss is proportional to energy, so that the electrons of high energy have a correspondingly high energy loss. The second is that the quantity Φ_{rad} given in Fig. 6 is measured in units proportional to Z^2, so that loss is greatest in elements of high atomic

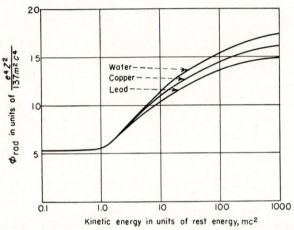

FIG. 6.   Cross section for energy loss of an electron (per centimeter path) by radiation, from Heitler [10].

number, as expected on the basis of qualitative arguments. In heavy absorbers, then, electrons would not be able to penetrate very far. Curves for the ranges of electrons and protons in lead are given in Fig. 7.

If we compare these theoretical predictions on the range of electrons with the observations on the hard and soft components, it is evident that the soft component, with range up to a few centimeters of Pb could readily be considered to be electrons, but the hard component could not easily be if the theory is correct. Furthermore, it was observed that the soft component is absorbed most strongly in elements of high atomic number, as here predicted for electrons, but that this was not so for the hard component.

It is also possible to give an explanation of shower phenomena by using additional theoretical results on the production of electron-positron pairs by high-energy photons. Without going into any details of these considerations, we can state the results as showing that photons of adequate energy ($> 2m_ec^2$) can form an electron-positron pair by raising an electron from a negative to a positive energy level. The probability of this kind of event is about the same as that for the inverse process of bremsstrahlung in which the electron produces a photon. These two processes can therefore occur in cascade, and this involves multiplication, since each photon is likely to produce a pair of particles and each electron or positron is likely to produce more than one photon. As a result, the number of particles increases until their energy is too low for such radiation processes, the remainder then being lost by ionization. The

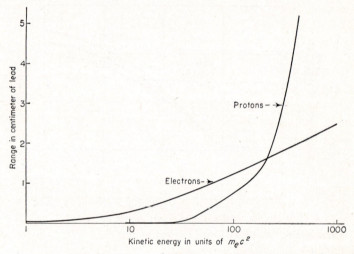

FIG. 7. Average range of protons and electrons of the same energy in lead, from Heitler [10].

mechanism of a cascade shower is shown schematically in Fig. 8. The solid lines represent electrons; the dotted, photons.

Thus electrons would be expected to form cascade showers, and since showers are known to be formed by the soft component, this fact appears to prove quite definitely that electrons do indeed make up the soft component.

It also seems clear that the hard component cannot have radiative effects such as bremsstrahlung. Two alternatives are possible, either to assume that the hard component consists of heavier particles than electrons or that the theory is not really valid at the very high energies involved in cosmic rays, which may be thousands or millions of times those encountered in normal nuclear physics. Such was the situation during 1935; while no clear decision was possible the majority was rather in favor of assuming a breakdown of the theory at very high energies.

4. EXPERIMENTS ON ENERGY LOSSES OF COSMIC RAYS IN SOLID PLATES

The experiments which played the crucial role in distinguishing between the characteristics of hard and soft component were performed during 1934 to 1936 by Anderson and Neddermeyer.* Similar investigations were also carried on in other laboratories. The following discussion does not trace the historial evolution of the results in comprehensive detail, but rather illustrates the growth of evidence for the existence of mesons by a fairly complete description of these experiments. In them the absorbing plate was placed across the middle of a cloud chamber so that the particle could be observed both before and after passing through it. A magnetic field was applied to the chamber so that the momentum of the particle could be determined above and below the plate. For any assumed mass, the corresponding energies are then determined by the relation $W = \sqrt{P^2c^2 + m_e{}^2c^4}$. The difference between the two energies then gives the energy lost.

If the particles involved lose energy by bremsstrahlung in accordance with the Bethe-Heitler theory discussed in Sec. 3, they should lose a substantial fraction of their energy in penetrating a centimeter of heavy material. Moreover, the actual energy lost should be proportional to the initial energy. If, on the other hand, radiative processes are not significant, the energy lost by relativistic particles should be about 15 to 20 Mev/cm of lead, and should not change much with energy. Thus data on energy losses can serve to differentiate between the two possibilities. If the low absorption of the penetrating component is due to a breakdown of the Bethe-Heitler theory at high energies, one would expect the transition between these two situations to occur at some intermediate energy.

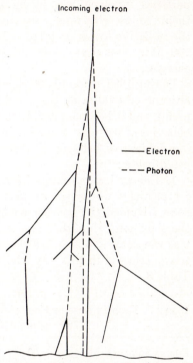

Incoming electron

———Electron

- - - Photon

Fig. 8.   Schematic cascade shower of photons and electrons.

* A general account of these experiments is given by S. H. Neddermeyer and C. D. Anderson, *Revs. Modern Phys.*, **11**, 191 (1939).

The first measurements of Anderson and Neddermeyer were inconclusive. They found that in most cases the energy lost corresponded to ionization loss without radiative effects. In some cases, however, "abnormal" high energy losses were observed which were apparently due to radiative electron impacts [13]. In the majority of cases, however, such losses were *not* observed. The initial energy of the particles involved was in most cases less than 250 Mev (assuming them to be electrons), so that the possibility remained open that the radiative losses occurred only at energies up to some value, perhaps 100 Mev, and ceased, due to some breakdown of the theory, at higher energies.

During 1935, some 10,000 cloud-chamber photographs were taken at an altitude of 4500 m on the summit of Pike's Peak. Many showers were found, and it became possible to make a reliable comparison between the behavior of particles occurring in showers and those that did not. Striking differences between the two were observed, of which the chief are listed below:

1. Energy loss. Energy losses in a 0.35-cm lead plate were measured for particles whose tracks were accompanied by another which could have triggered the counter control. This was done in order to reduce the likelihood that the requirement of discharging the counter would bias the data, and also had the effect of selecting shower particles. For tracks selected in this way, the observed energy losses were as given in Table 3.

TABLE 3. ENERGY LOSS OF COSMIC-RAY SHOWER PARTICLES IN Pb (Mev/cm) [14]
(7900 gauss, 0.35-cm Pb plate, 4500 m)

Energy interval, Mev	<50	50–100	100–150	150–200	200–400
Number of tracks	29	65	18	13	21
Average initial energy	31	75	123	177	272
Observed $\Delta E/d$(av)	42	82	178	191	358
Theoretical $\Delta E/d$(av)	50	110	175	248	378

The theoretical values are calculated for electrons by the Bethe-Heitler theory and agree well with the observations. These particles lost energy as electrons should do, even though the penetrating component did not.

2. Shower production. Particles occurring as a part of a shower were very much more likely to produce showers themselves than were the others. The experimental data were as given in Table 4.

3. Altitude variation. The frequency of both single tracks and showers was found to increase markedly on going from 250 to 4500 m.

TABLE 4. SHOWERS PRODUCED IN 1 cm OF PLATINUM [14]

	Number of primary traversals	Number of showers produced	Fraction producing showers
Particles occurring singly in cloud chamber	1795	12	0.0067
Particles accompanied by one other	33	7	0.21
Particles accompanied by more than one other	33	12	0.36

The increase in showers was much greater than in single tracks, the figures being given in Table 5.

TABLE 5. RATIO OF FREQUENCY OF EVENTS AT 4500 m TO THAT AT 250 m [14]

		Shower size		
	Single tracks	2–4	5–10	11–100
Ratio	2.7	8.6	21	29

This provides further evidence that the particles causing showers are different from the typical single particle, and are more rapidly absorbed in passing through the atmosphere, just as the shower particles are the more strongly absorbed in lead plates.

As a result of these experiments it became quite clear that the shower particles were electrons whose behavior was described by the Bethe-Heitler theory. This gave an adequate qualitative explanation of their absorption and multiplication. The hard component, on the other hand, which makes up most of the cosmic rays at sea level, had no such radiative losses, presumably because it was made up of heavier particles.

In order to make the distinction between shower and nonshower particles completely unambiguous, further data were presented by Anderson and Neddermeyer on the energy dependence of energy losses [15]. It is evident from Fig. 9 that the shower particles have the property of high energy loss and the single particles of low energy loss at all energies up to 500 Mev. Since shower particles have a high energy loss at all energies, including high ones, and nonshower particles have a low energy loss at all energies, including low ones, the difference between shower and nonshower particles cannot be caused by difference in energy.

MESONS

Consequently, the penetration of the hard component cannot be caused by a breakdown of the Bethe-Heitler theory at high energies.

These experiments left no alternative but to accept the idea that the hard component is made up of particles heavier than the electron. It was natural to assume that these particles were protons. This possibility had been suggested some years before by Williams [16]. There were, however, a number of contradictions between such an assumption and the experimental data.

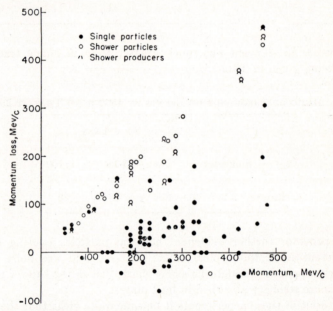

FIG. 9. Momentum loss of particles penetrating 1 cm of platinum as a function of incident momentum [15].

In the first place, identifying the penetrating component as protons would require that there be a considerable number of particles slow enough to ionize noticeably more than the minimum, since any proton of momentum less than about 1 Bev/c would ionize heavily. Heavily ionizing particles are, however, very rare, and many particles of momentum less than 1 Bev/c were observed which were *not* heavily ionizing. This is not consistent with the proton hypothesis.

Further evidence was obtained from the energies of secondary particles knocked out of plates by the particles of the hard component. The knock-on particles were almost universally negative in charge, and were considered to be electrons which had been given high energy by close collisions. The observed distribution of energy of the knock-on electrons contained many more high-energy cases than would be expected if the primary particle were a proton. Many knock-ons occurred with energies higher than could be produced even by a 5000-Mev proton. If, however, the mass of the primary were less than that of the proton, its velocity would be greater, and higher energy knock-ons would be expected.

The final conclusion reached from these experiments was that the penetrating part of the cosmic radiation contained particles heavier than an electron, but lighter than a proton. Such a particle, of mass somewhere in the range 100 to $300m_e$ would be consistent with the observations since:

1. It would be too heavy to suffer much radiative energy loss by bremsstrahlung and would therefore have the required penetration.

2. Tracks heavier than minimum ionization would be rare, since only particles of energy less than about 50 Mev would be heavily ionizing.

3. The expected energy distribution for the secondary electrons would agree well with the experimental measurements.

Thus the evidence for particles of intermediate mass was quite strong, although it was largely of a negative nature, that the observations were not to be explained except by the introduction of such a particle.

As these indirect arguments were being made thoroughly convincing, more positive evidence was found in many laboratories by studying the tracks of particles of momentum low enough that they would be heavily ionizing if they were protons. Many such tracks were soon found to have curvature, ionization, and range of such values that the particle involved must have had a mass intermediate between that of the proton and electron. From data of this sort it was, in fact, possible to make a rough determination of the mass of the particle concerned, which in most cases appeared to be between 100 and 250 electron masses. They will be discussed in more detail in Chap. 2.

It seemed then, that there was persuasive evidence for believing that particles of mass in the range 100 to $300m_e$ existed and were an important part, at least, of the penetrating component of the cosmic radiation. Such a belief would not, perhaps, have been accepted readily except for the fact that certain theoretical arguments had already been advanced by Yukawa [17] which had caused the existence of such a particle to be suspected. These arguments will be discussed very briefly in the next section.

5. MESON THEORY OF NUCLEAR FORCES

At about the same time that direct experimental evidence was being accumulated for the existence in cosmic radiation of particles of mass

intermediate between those of proton and electron, theoretical discussion
of the forces between nucleons was suggesting the existence of just such
a particle.   The idea was first advanced by Yukawa in 1935 [17].   Subsequent contributions to the literature on the subject have been numerous
and often abstruse.   To present a synthesis of them would be a task far
beyond the scope of the present discussion.   Recent reviews have been
prepared by Heisenberg [18], Pauli [19], Wentzel [20,21], Rosenfeld [22],
Yukawa [23], Fermi [24], and Marshak [25].   We shall be content with
sketching the basic problems and ideas in the simplest terms and pointing
out conclusions which may be compared with experimental data on
mesons.

The objective of the theory of nuclear forces is to give a systematic
accounting for the various properties of the forces which hold nucleons
together in nuclei.   These forces are not directly related to electrical
or magnetic forces, since they act on neutrons, which have no electrical
charge, and hold together protons, whose electrostatic forces are strongly
repulsive.   They are very large, nuclear binding energies being from 1
to 10 Mev/nucleon.   They are effective only at short range, as shown
by experiments on nuclear scattering, and become negligible at distances
much in excess of 2×10^{-13} cm.   They have the property of saturation.
That is, each nucleon in a large nucleus is bound only to a small number
of nearby nucleons, much as an atom in a large molecule is bound chemi-
cally to adjacent atoms but not to those at a great distance from it.
Because the nuclear forces are effective only at distances so small that
the uncertainty relation seriously restricts the possibility of measuring
them, it has not been possible to establish the nature of the nuclear force
law by any direct measurements.

We imagine the forces between nucleons to be represented by a field
of some sort which is analogous to the electromagnetic field used to
represent electromagnetic forces.   The simplest type of field is a scalar
potential.   This nuclear potential of unknown nature we will denote by
$U(r)$. $U(r)$ is known to decrease with increasing r in a much more
abrupt fashion than the $1/r$ decline of the electrostatic potential.   The
type of potential which Yukawa introduced had an additional exponential
decrease with r, as given in Eq. (6b)

$$\Phi(r) = \pm \frac{e}{r} \qquad\qquad \text{Coulomb} \qquad\qquad (6a)$$

$$U(r) = \pm \frac{g}{r} \exp(-Kr) \qquad \text{Yukawa} \qquad\qquad (6b)$$

Here e is the electric charge, g is a constant with the same dimensions, and
K is a constant with dimensions cm^{-1}.   The curves in Fig. 10 show that

this U potential drops off with distance very much more rapidly than the Coulomb potential and would give appreciable forces only for ranges up to about $1/K$. Taking $1/K \approx 2 \times 10^{-13}$ cm would, therefore, result in forces of about the range required by scattering experiments.

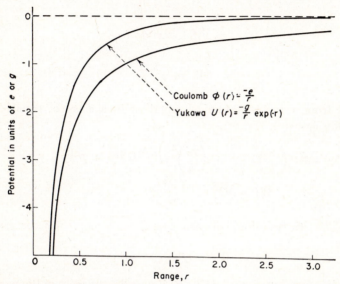

FIG. 10.   Comparison between Coulomb and Yukawa potentials.   Yukawa curve is drawn assuming $K = 1$; that is, the range is measured in units of $1/K$.

The Coulomb potential ($6a$) is a very simple solution of the wave equation ($7a$).   It is spherically symmetrical and time-independent.

$$\nabla^2\Phi - \frac{1}{c^2}\frac{\partial^2\Phi}{\partial t^2} = 0 \qquad (7a)$$

The U potential, Eq. ($6b$), is the corresponding solution of Eq. ($7b$) which has the added term $-K^2U$.   Yukawa then also proceeded to point out

$$\nabla^2 U - \frac{1}{c^2}\frac{\partial^2 U}{\partial t^2} - K^2 U = 0 \qquad (7b)$$

that in general this U field must be considered to be quantized, the quantum being analogous to light quanta.   The quanta of the U field may be thought of as particles for which Eq. ($7b$) is the Schrödinger equation. This may be seen by rewriting Eq. ($7b$) in the form

$$\frac{\partial^2 U}{\partial t^2} = \left[c^2\left(\frac{\partial^2}{\partial x^2} + \frac{\partial^2}{\partial y^2} + \frac{\partial^2}{\partial z^2}\right) - K^2 c^2\right] U$$

One then uses the formal substitutions

$$P_x = \frac{h}{2\pi i} \frac{\partial}{\partial x}$$

$$P_y = \frac{h}{2\pi i} \frac{\partial}{\partial y}$$

$$P_z = \frac{h}{2\pi i} \frac{\partial}{\partial z}$$

and

$$W = \frac{-h}{2\pi i} \frac{\partial}{\partial t}$$

to shift from a wave-mechanical equation to a classical equation with the result shown in Eq. (8).

$$-W^2 \left(\frac{2\pi}{h}\right)^2 = -c^2 \left(\frac{2\pi}{h}\right)^2 (P_x{}^2 + P_y{}^2 + P_z{}^2) - K^2c^2$$

$$W^2 = c^2P^2 + \frac{K^2h^2}{4\pi^2} c^2 \tag{8}$$

The relativistic relation between energy and momentum is given by Eq. (9).

$$W^2 = (Pc)^2 + (mc^2)^2 \tag{9}$$

which corresponds exactly to Eq. (8) if we take the mass of the particle to be $m = Kh/2\pi c$. With $1/K \approx 2 \times 10^{-13}$ cm, the numerical value of the mass m_m turns out to be

$$m_m \approx 1.8 \times 10^{-25} \text{ g}$$

$$m_m \approx 200 m_e$$

At the time of Yukawa's paper, mesons of such a mass had not yet been experimentally demonstrated to exist. He pointed out that they would not be observed directly in nuclear transformations since the energy required for their formation (their rest mass being equivalent to about 100 Mev) was not available.

The value of the mesic charge on a nucleon—the coefficient g in Eq. (6b)—is adjusted so that the forces between nucleons come out to be as observed experimentally. To get an idea of the result, we can calculate g, assuming that if one nucleon is brought within a distance equal to the range of the nucleon forces it will have a potential energy equal to the deuteron binding energy (about 2.2 Mev). Using this extremely crude picture, we have

$$2.2 \text{ Mev} = \frac{g^2}{r} \exp \frac{-r}{2 \times 10^{-13}} \qquad \text{for } r = 2 \times 10^{-13}$$

In cgs units,

$$2.2 \times 10^6 \times 4.8 \times 10^{-10} \times \frac{1}{300} = \frac{g^2}{2 \times 10^{-13}} \times \exp(-1)$$

$$g \approx 15 \times 10^{-10} \text{ cgs units}$$

Thus the mesic charge on a nucleon is about three times as great as its electric charge. An accurate calculation leads to a somewhat higher value.

It is not possible to give such a simple quantitative illustration of the remaining property of the meson field which Yukawa postulated. He assumed that the meson field was the agency responsible for the produc-

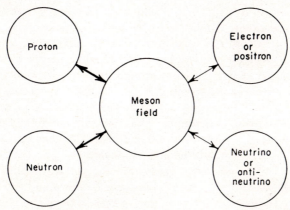

FIG. 11. Schematic role of meson field as a means of interaction between elementary particles.

tion of light particles—electrons, positrons, and neutrinos—in the process of β decay. It was necessary to assume that the light particles also had a certain mesic charge, but smaller than that on the nucleons by about 10^{-8}. The meson field was thus coupled to both nucleons and light particles and could provide a mechanism whereby the heavy nucleons could provide energy to create the light particles observed in β decay. Schematically, the system may be diagramed as in Fig. 11. The interactions between nucleons are strong due to their close coupling to the meson field, as indicated by the heavy lines. Interactions between nucleons and light particles are very much smaller, corresponding to the low probability of β decay on a nuclear time scale. Interactions between the light particles are very small indeed, and have not been found experimentally.

As was previously noted, the meson field may be thought of as the wave function of a particle of mass about $200m_e$. If the nucleons which

are sources of this field are given a sufficiently violent agitation, wave
packets may be established in the meson field which will in fact behave
like such a particle. Until recently cosmic radiation has been the only
place where nuclear reactions energetic enough to create mesons have
been found. Now a few large accelerators can produce the required
energy. The artificial production of mesons will be discussed in Chap. 4.

A somewhat different picture of the meson field is obtained from the
viewpoint of quantum field theory. In this case the field is considered
equivalent to an appropriate assembly of virtual particles. In the
electromagnetic case they would be virtual photons. In the meson case
they would be virtual mesons. One can imagine these particles being
continually emitted and reabsorbed by the source of the field. Only
when emitted into free space independent of the source does the particle
have a real existence. In the case of mesons this requires an energy
source adequate to provide the meson's rest energy, i.e., an energetic
collision. The usual force between a proton and a neutron, for example,
would be thought of as occurring through a process in which the proton
emits a positive meson, becoming a neutron, and the neutron absorbs
the positive meson, becoming a proton which emits a positive meson
becoming a neutron, whereupon the neutron (originally a proton)
reabsorbs the positive meson becoming a proton, and so on.

The interaction between the meson field and light particles which
was postulated to fit nuclear β decay into the picture implies a β decay
for the free meson as well. In a later paper Yukawa and coworkers [26]
estimated the lifetime for a free meson at rest to be in the neighborhood
of 10^{-6} sec. For a rapidly moving meson, the apparent lifetime would
be lengthened by relativistic effects, being actually proportional to the
total energy of the meson.

The foregoing discussion is, however, a vastly oversimplified sketch
of the ideas of meson theory. The meson field has been assumed to be a
scalar, like electrostatic potential. The question of the electrical charge
carried by the meson has been by-passed. In reality, nuclear forces
are dependent upon orientation in space, on the relative orientations of
nuclear spins, for example. To represent such a force, a more complicated field, such as a vector, is required. It is known that mesons
may have positive or negative charges, and the existence of forces
between two protons or two neutrons requires the introduction of neutral
mesons as well.

Unfortunately the introduction of such fields leads not only to greater
complication, but to serious intrinsic difficulties. One of the most
obvious sources of trouble is that the potential energy of interaction
becomes infinite at the origin as $1/r^3$, an infinity of sufficiently high order

Library
I.U.P.
Indiana, Pa.

539.72 T393m
c. 1

that it makes an infinite contribution to the binding energy of the bound particle. This region near the origin must therefore be excluded from consideration by some more or less arbitrary cutoff procedure, which procedure then strongly influences the results obtained from the theory. An alternative procedure is to combine two meson fields suitably chosen so that their infinities cancel out. None of the resulting theories is, however, completely satisfactory, and the reader is referred to the reviews previously mentioned for a discussion of them. We will consider only the experimental information on mesons.

In doing so, however, the major question of interest will be that of whether the mesons studied experimentally are responsible for nuclear forces and β decay in some way such as that suggested by Yukawa. We will give special attention to information bearing on this question.

REFERENCES

1. Bothe, W., and W. Kolhörster, *Z. Physik*, *56*, 751 (1929).
2. Rossi, B., *Z. Physik*, *82*, 151 (1933).
3. Street, J. C., R. H. Woodward, and E. C. Stevenson, *Phys. Rev.*, *47*, 891 (1935).
4. Auger, P., *Compt. rend.*, *200*, 739 (1935).
5. Auger, P., and L. Leprince-Ringuet, "International Conference on Physics," London, 1934, Vol. I, p. 21, Hermann & Cie, Paris, 1936.
6. Steinke, E. G., and Tielsch, *Z. Physik*, *84*, 425 (1933).
7. Alocco, G., *Nature*, *135*, 96 (1935).
8. Auger, P., A. Rosenberg, and F. Bertein, *Compt. rend.*, *200*, 1022 (1935).
9. Rossi, B., and G. Alocco, *Atti accad. nazl. Lincei.*, *21*, 167 (1935).
10. Heitler, W., "The Quantum Theory of Radiation," 2d ed., Oxford University Press, New York, 1944.
11. Rossi, B., and K. Greisen, *Revs. Modern Phys.*, *13*, 240 (1941).
12. Janossy, L., "Cosmic Rays," Oxford University Press, New York, 1948.
13. Anderson, C. D., and S. H. Neddermeyer, "International Conference on Physics," London, 1934, Vol. I, p. 11, Hermann & Cie, Paris, 1936.
14. Neddermeyer, S. H., and C. D. Anderson, *Revs. Modern Phys.*, *11*, 191 (1939).
15. Neddermeyer, S. H., and C. D. Anderson, *Phys. Rev.*, *51*, 884 (1937).
16. Williams, E. J., *Phys. Rev.*, *45*, 729 (1934).
17. Yukawa, H., *Proc. Phys.-Math. Soc. Japan*, *17*, 48 (1935).
18. Heisenberg, W., "Cosmic Radiation," Chap. 10, Dover Publications, New York, 1946.
19. Pauli, W., "Meson Theory of Nuclear Forces," Interscience Publishers, New York, 1946.
20. Wentzel, G., *Revs. Modern Phys.*, *19*, 1 (1947).
21. Wentzel, G., "Quantum Theory of Fields," Interscience Publishers, New York, 1949.

22. Rosenfeld, L., "Nuclear Forces," Interscience Publishers, New York, 1949.
23. Yukawa, H., *Revs. Modern Phys.*, *21*, 474 (1949).
24. Fermi, E., "Elementary Particles," Yale University Press, New Haven, Conn., 1951.
25. Marshak, R. E., "Meson Physics," McGraw-Hill Book Company, Inc., New York, 1952.
26. Yukawa, H., S. Sakata, and M. Taketani, *Proc. Phys.-Math. Soc. Japan*, *20*, 319 (1938).

CHAPTER 2

PROPERTIES OF COSMIC-RAY MESONS

1. PROPERTIES OF ELEMENTARY PARTICLES

There are not very many properties which elementary particles can have compared with the number required to describe an atom or molecule. In spite of this relative simplicity the properties of mesons have not yet been measured with satisfying accuracy.   There have been two main difficulties: the control of the behavior of the mesons in experiments and the construction of theories with which experimental results could be compared.   As a result, obtaining information concerning even the simplest of properties has been a difficult undertaking.

The most obvious property is that of *mass*.   By definition the meson is a particle having a mass intermediate between that of the proton and the electron.   It remains, then, to assign to the mass a definite value somewhere in this range, which covers three orders of magnitude.   It is also necessary to find out whether the meson mass is unique, and, if not, what values or distribution of values exist.

In addition to mass, mesons have, or may have, *electric charge*.   Mesons have been found with both positive and negative charge, and the existence of neutral mesons seems probable theoretically to provide for forces between neutron and neutron or proton and proton, as explained in Chap. 1.   (Experimental evidence concerning neutral mesons is discussed in Chap. 4.)   Fairly accurate estimates of the magnitudes of the electric charges have been made.

The *coupling* between mesons and nucleons is probably the most important property of mesons.   Coupling with light particles is also an important attribute.   While measurements of mass and charge can be made in terms of electromagnetic effects, coupling coefficients can be determined only in terms of meson theory.   Information on the coupling with nucleons is obtained primarily from the production of mesons by the interaction of nucleons and from the interaction of mesons with nuclei. These topics will be discussed in Chaps. 6 and 7.   Similarly, the data on coupling with light particles are mainly derived from experiments on meson decay, which is considered in Chap. 5.

In addition to properties of this type the meson has internal properties such as *spin*. The spin of the meson is of great importance in the construction of meson theories, since the spin is determined by the number of quantities which must be specified to determine the value of the meson field at any point. If the meson has spin, it fairly certainly has a magnetic moment, but no measurements of it have been made. The weakness of magnetic interactions and the lack of convenient sources of mesons have made such measurements impractical.

Once the evidence for the existence of mesons in cosmic rays was accepted, many efforts were made to measure these properties of mesons. The remainder of this chapter will be devoted to a description of measurements of what might be called the static properties of mesons: mass, charge, and spin. These properties do not involve interactions with other particles, as would coupling. As will be seen in Chap. 3, it is now known that more than one kind of meson exists. The measurements which will now be discussed are, however, all concerned with the most common type of meson, that most frequently observed in cosmic rays at sea level. Properties of the rarer types will be discussed in later chapters.

2. MASS

One of the main objects of experiments on mesons has been to determine whether the properties of the particles found in cosmic rays fit the predictions of the meson theory started by Yukawa. Measurements of the mass of the meson provide a direct comparison, since Yukawa predicted a mass $\sim 200 m_e$ for the meson. Accurate mass measurements can be obtained only for mesons whose velocities are substantially less than the velocity of light. Since such slow mesons are quite rare in cosmic radiation, it has been difficult to determine meson masses accurately.

The mass of a meson obviously cannot be measured directly, but must be inferred from its behavior. In general, both mass and velocity of the meson are unknown, while its charge is assumed to be known to be equal to that of an electron. (Such a charge would be expected theoretically and has been demonstrated experimentally as well. The evidence is discussed in the next section.) Measurements are made of quantities of like range and momentum which depend on both mass and velocity, so that from a measurement of two such quantities one has, in effect, two simultaneous equations which can be solved for the mass. A mass determination thus requires a measurement of some two properties such as those listed below.

1. Momentum.   This is usually measured by the curvature of a cloud-chamber track formed in a magnetic field.

2. Range.   Range is measured in cloud-chamber gas, solid plates, or in nuclear emulsions.

3. Density of ionization or energy loss.   It can be estimated in a cloud chamber from the appearance of the track or measured more accurately by droplet count.   Measured by grain counting in an emulsion.   Sometimes also determined for passage through a solid plate by measuring momentum before and after traversal of the plate.

4. Energy.   This may be determined by the small-angle Coulomb scattering in solid foils or plates or in a nuclear emulsion.

5. Velocity.   This can sometimes be determined from range or curvature of a knock-on electron produced in the gas of a cloud chamber.

If range or energy-loss measurements are involved, the theory of energy losses of charged particles must be used to relate the observed data to mass and velocity of the particle.   The accuracy of the theory is quite well established, however, for particles of velocity considerably less than the velocity of light, so that this is not a serious drawback. Determination of the energy through multiple scattering is also possible only by means of a fairly involved theory, but there appears to be no reason to doubt its validity.   In a determination based on the direction and velocity of a knock-on electron in addition to the meson momentum, the meson mass can be calculated without introducing any assumptions except those of conservation of energy and momentum, so that this is, in a sense, the most reliable type of mass measurement.   Unfortunately not many events of this type have been photographed.

Most of the first mass determinations involved momentum and range or density of ionization in a cloud chamber.   The factors involved can be illustrated by the nomograph in Fig. 1, adapted by Hughes [1] from that of Corson and Brode [2].

Figures 2, 3, and 4 show examples of various types of mass determinations.   That shown in Fig. 2a involves the use of curvature and ionization, and was obtained by Street and Stevenson [3].   The track is broadened by allowing a delay of about 1 sec between passage of the particle and expansion of the cloud chamber.   This permits the individual droplets to be counted and improves the accuracy of determining density of ionization.   They obtained a density of ionization about six times minimum, and a curvature 9.5×10^4 gauss-cm, mass $130m_e$. (If the figures in the nomograph of Fig. 1 are used, a mass of $160m_e$ results.   The difference is due to different assumptions concerning energy loss, but is not serious.)   Figure 2b shows a recent photograph of a track of a particle with density of ionization about three times

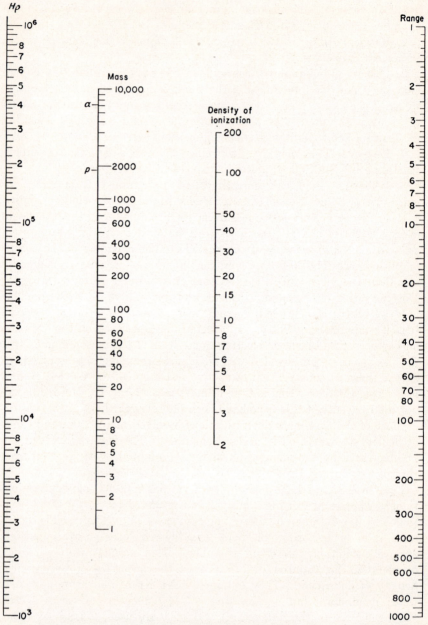

Fig. 1. Nomograph for calculating masses from cloud-chamber data. $H\rho$ is given in gauss-centimeters, mass in electron masses, density of ionization in units of the minimum ionization of a fast single particle, and range in centimeters of air.

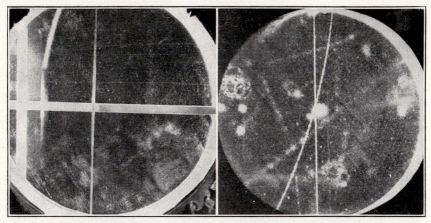

FIG. 2. (a) Cloud-chamber photograph of a cosmic-ray track showing ionization about six times minimum, whose momentum indicates a mass of about $130m_e$, according to Street and Stevenson [3]. (b) Photograph obtained by Nonnemaker of a track showing ionization about three times minimum, whose momentum indicates a mass of about $220m_e$.

FIG. 3. Cloud-chamber photograph obtained by Neddermeyer and Anderson of a track of a cosmic-ray particle which just penetrates the counter in the center of the picture. Its range is thus determined to be 0.99 g/cm³ of air. Its momentum in the region above the counter [4] indicates a mass of about $240m_e$. Two stereoscopic views are shown.

minimum and $H\rho$ of 2×10^5 gauss-cm, mass about $220m_e$, obtained by Nonnemaker.

Figure 3 shows a particle photographed by Anderson and Neddermeyer, the range and curvature of which give a determination of its mass [4]. The horizontal object in the middle of the picture is a counter through which the particle passes. It then stops in the gas below the counter. From the thickness of the counter walls penetrated, the range of the particle in the upper section is found to be 0.99 g/cm² of air or about

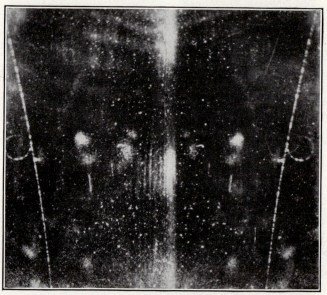

Fɪɢ. 4. Cloud-chamber photograph showing a knock-on electron produced in the gas by a cosmic-ray particle. Both momenta and the initial angle between the tracks can be determined, leading to an estimate of the mass at $240m_e$, according to Leprince-Ringuet, Gorodetzky, Nageotte, and Richard-Foy [5]. Two stereoscopic views are shown.

700 cm of air. From the curvature, $H\rho$ is determined to be 1.74×10^5 gauss-cm. The mass was estimated at $240m_e$. Entering these figures in the nomograph, we obtain a mass of about $225m_e$, showing essential agreement.

Only a few mass measurements have been based on momentum and change of momentum in passing through a plate, and the actual photographs have not been published.

Figure 4 shows a knock-on electron obtained by Leprince-Ringuet, Gorodetzky, Nageotte, and Richard-Foy [5] from which it was possible to calculate the mass of the incoming particle as $240 \pm 20m_e$.

The examples given were among the earliest determinations of meson mass. A considerable number of similar measurements were made by other investigators. A summary of results obtained by 1941 was made by Wheeler and Ladenburg [6] who give complete references to this early work. Table 1 presents a list of results obtained. The values of Nielsen and Powell, which were reported later, have been added. The data included are those considered to have been reliable, but the accuracy of the measurements has undoubtedly been much overestimated in some cases.

TABLE 1. MESON-MASS VALUES AS OF 1945

Reference	Value
J. C. Street and E. C. Stevenson, *Phys. Rev.*, *52*, 1003 (1937)	≈ 130
E. J. Williams and E. Pickup, *Nature*, *141*, 648 (1938)	220 ± 50
	190 ± 60
	160 ± 30
D. R. Corson and R. B. Brode, *Phys. Rev.*, *53*, 773 (1938)	250
P. Ehrenfest, Jr., *Compt. rend.*, *206*, 428 (1938)	≈ 200
S. H. Neddermeyer and C. D. Anderson, *Phys. Rev.*, *54*, 88 (1938)	220 ± 35
A. J. Ruhlig and H. R. Crane, *Phys. Rev.*, *53*, 266 (1938)	120 ± 30
Y. N. Nishina, M. Takeuchi, and I. Ichimiya, *Phys. Rev.*, *55*, 585 (1939)	180 ± 20
	170 ± 8
H. Maier-Leibnitz, *Z. Physik*, *112*, 569 (1939)	20
	100 ± 30
	120 ± 30
	55 ± 35
	170 ± 100
L. Leprince-Ringuet, S. Gorodetzky, E. Nageotte, and R. Richard-Foy, *Phys. Rev.*, *59*, 460 (1941)	240 ± 20
J. G. Wilson, *Proc. Roy. Soc. (London)*, (A)*172*, 521 (1939)	250 ± 50
	170 ± 20
C. E. Nielson and W. M. Powell, *Phys. Rev.*, *63*, 384 (1943)	210 ± 20
	180 ± 20
	190 ± 15
	145 ± 30

The average value is $172 m_e$, but the individual values are quite widely spread about it. Their distribution is shown graphically in Fig. 5.

They indicated quite clearly that the average mass was in the neighborhood of $200m_e$, as predicted by Yukawa, but left undetermined the ques-

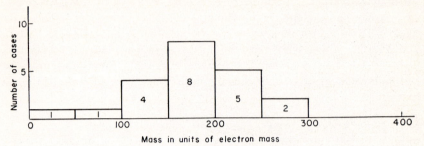

Fɪɢ. 5.   Distribution of 21 early meson-mass measurements.

tion of uniqueness of the mass.   Some of the highest and lowest values obtained did not seem to be compatible with a single mass of about

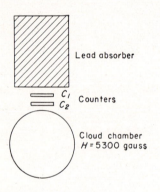

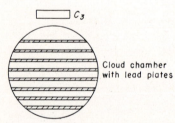

Fɪɢ. 6.   Fretter's apparatus for meson-mass determination [8].

$170m_e$, but it was shown by Bethe that these cases were very probably due to the contribution of scattering in the cloud-chamber gas to the apparent curvature of the particles [7].   His conclusion was that when scattering was properly allowed for "all existing data are compatible with a unique mass of the meson, of about 200 electron masses."   On the other hand, the data were not sufficiently accurate to prove the uniqueness of the mass.

In an attempt to resolve this uncertainty concerning the existence of mesons of various masses, Fretter undertook a systematic series of measurements based on curvature and range [8].   His apparatus involved two cloud chambers as shown in Fig. 6, an arrangement first used by Street [9].   The top cloud chamber had a magnetic field of 5300 gauss and was used to measure the momentum of the particle.   The bottom chamber was larger in size and contained eight $\frac{1}{2}$-in. lead plates.   The range of the particle was determined by the number of plates penetrated.   The plates were large enough to cover the solid angle of the telescope and provided a substantial margin for observing tracks which were somewhat scattered. A total of 2100 pictures were taken, of which only a small fraction showed tracks appearing to stop in the bottom chamber. Of these many had to be excluded because turbulence in the upper chamber distorted the track from the ideal circular arc so that measurement of the curvature was uncertain. Others could not be used because scattering in the lead plates made the range uncertain; many were clearly scattered out of the illuminated region without actually stopping. Twenty-six cases appeared to provide reliable data which led to the masses given in Table 2. The weighted average value of $202m_e$ was obtained for the mass, with an estimated absolute error of ± 5 per cent or somewhat

TABLE 2. MESON-MASS VALUES OBTAINED BY FRETTER [8]

160 ± 26	163 ± 35	258 ± 28
199 ± 33	250 ± 30	143 ± 28
212 ± 35	222 ± 18	228 ± 19
180 ± 33	225 ± 32	237 ± 35
142 ± 32	242 ± 37	258 ± 35
238 ± 30	180 ± 26	183 ± 21
164 ± 38	157 ± 16	230 ± 37
264 ± 28	195 ± 28	244 ± 37
260 ± 42	209 ± 30	

more. Brode has applied a different averaging process in which a curve is fitted to the observed values of curvature and range [10]. With this procedure a mass of $212 \pm 5m_e$ is obtained.

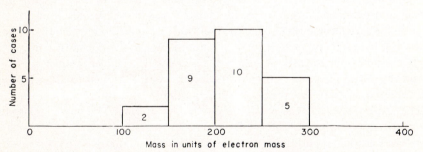

FIG. 7. Distribution of meson-mass values found by Fretter [8].

The distribution of mass values found by Fretter is given in Fig. 7. There are no very high or low mass values, and the spread is very close to that estimated for the errors of the individual values. The conclusion is that only a single meson mass is involved in these measurements, or at any rate, the fraction of mesons whose mass deviated from $200m_e$ by more than 10 to 20 per cent is not large.

The measurements of Fretter have been extended by Brode and coworkers [11,12]. Special attention was paid to reducing turbulence in the top chamber so as to obtain more accurate momentum measurements. The size of the bottom chamber was further increased to include more scattered particles. In the work of Retallack and Brode, the thickness of lead plates was reduced to 0.270 in., and their number was increased to 15. The distribution of meson masses found is shown graphically in Fig. 8. They concluded that the four highest values (474, 538, 588, and 717) were not statistically consistent with the main group, near 200, nor were the two low values (114 and 120). From the remain-

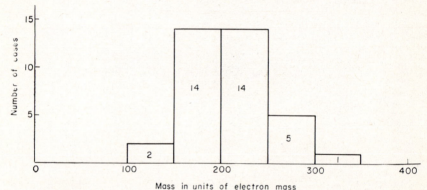

Fig. 8. Distribution of meson-mass values found by Retallack and Brode [11].

ing consistent set of values they obtained a mass of $215 \pm 4m_e$, in excellent agreement with the recalculated value from Fretter's data.

In the measurements of Merkle, Goldwasser, and Brode, turbulence in the top cloud chamber was further reduced by careful thermostatting to give a more accurate momentum measurement. Eleven copper plates and three lead plates were used in the lower chamber, whose thickness was graduated so that the probable error in range was about 3.5 per cent. They estimated that the resolving power of the apparatus was increased by a factor of about 2; 23 positive and 25 negative mesons gave mass determinations in addition to 52 protons. The distribution of mass values for the mesons is given by Fig. 9. No particles were observed with masses higher than those shown, except for the proton group. The average mass deduced for the protons was $1893 \pm 50m_e$; that for the mesons was $196 \pm 3m_e$. It was felt that the difference between this and previous values might be due to uncertainties in the range-energy relation for copper.

Brode has also measured meson masses using an apparatus in which a permanent magnet supplies the magnetic field. Cloud chambers above and below the magnetic field give tracks at an angle due to bending in the field, and this determines momentum. Range is measured in a third cloud chamber with plates. The contribution of turbulence in the cloud chamber to the error in momentum measurement should be further reduced by such apparatus. Preliminary results have been reported [13] which are in good agreement with those of Retallack and Brode. Eighteen mass determinations in the range 150 to 350 give $218 \pm 5m_e$ for the meson mass.

We may conclude that the mass of the commonly occurring cosmic-ray meson has been established at about $215m_e$. If there is a distribution, it

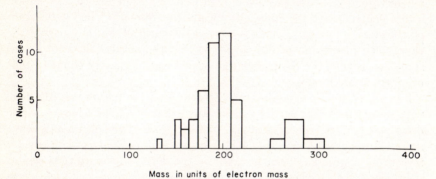

Fig. 9. Distribution of meson-mass values found by Merkle, Goldwasser, and Brode [12].

is masked by the experimental uncertainties of about $\pm 30m_e$ and must be narrower than this. In all probability there is a unique mass. In 1947, however, Powell and coworkers presented persuasive evidence for the existence of a heavier meson of mass about $300m_e$. Such heavier mesons are very rare at sea level, but become more common at high altitudes. Their existence is now definitely established. Since the heavy meson (π meson) is one of the major discoveries in nuclear physics made in the years following the Second World War, it will be discussed in some detail in Chap. 3. The value for its mass obtained in the most accurate experiments so far is $277m_e$. The possible existence of mesons of other masses remains open, and other evidence bearing on this question will be presented in Chap. 3.

3. CHARGE

It is evident that the mesons found experimentally must bear an electric charge, since in practically every experiment they are observed by ionization caused by their electromagnetic field. Early cloud-chamber work established "that with minor variations nearly all the cosmic-ray particles produce about the same density of ionization as found along the tracks of fast electrons, and since for a given velocity the density of ionization should be proportional to the square of the charge, this means that the particles presumably have a charge of one electron" [14]. When it was established that a major fraction of the particles were mesons, it was clear that the electric charge on the meson was not far from the electronic charge and was very likely exactly equal to it.

As a matter of fact, the meson theory of nuclear forces implies strongly that the electric charge of a meson is *exactly* equal to that of a proton or electron. It is assumed that a proton, for example, can transform into a neutron with the emission of a positive meson. The meson takes off the electric charge. There is no reason to believe that any part of the charge can be created or destroyed, so that the natural theoretical presumption is that the electric charge of a meson is exactly equal to that of a proton or electron.

Since it seemed so certain that the charge of the meson was identical with that of the other particles, not many experiments have been made to determine the charge accurately. Those that have been made have served to confirm the theoretical expectations. The procedure for measuring charge has been to measure the density of ionization of particles whose velocity is such as to give the minimum value. For electrons this corresponds to energies of about 2 Mev; for mesons about 200 Mev. As shown in Fig. 5, Chap. 1, the density of ionization does not change rapidly with energy at or near the minimum so that precise energy determination is not necessary. To determine the density of ionization of a single minimum ionization particle is difficult, however, since it is very small and subject to statistical fluctuations. The chief method followed has been actually to count the individual droplets formed along a track in a cloud chamber as a measure of ions formed.

Such a measurement was made by Hazen [15]. He compared the density of ionization of β particles from P^{32} with penetrating cosmic-ray particles of momentum about 400 Mev/c. The cloud chamber had a magnetic field to determine the energy of the particle. The results are given in Table 3. While the number of cases is small, a considerable number of droplets are counted on each track. From these data it seems fairly sure that the ionization of mesons does not differ from that of electrons by more than 10 per cent. Since the ionization is proportional to the square of the charge, the two charges cannot differ by more than 5 per cent.

TABLE 3. IONIZATION BY ELECTRONS AND MESONS ACCORDING TO HAZEN [15]

	Electrons	Mesons
Momentum, Mev/c	1.3–2.1	210–600
No. of cases	20	6
Ions counted per cm at NTP	38.8	42.0
Corrected for overlapping of droplets	42	45
Estimated probable error	2	3

More recent measurements by Frost [16] have reduced the possible difference somewhat further. The same general procedure was used. His data are given in Table 4. The final column gives the ratio of meson charge to electron charge. In no case is it significantly different from

TABLE 4. IONIZATION BY ELECTRONS AND MESONS ACCORDING TO FROST [16]

Gas	Minimum density of ionization for electron	Minimum density of ionization for meson	Ratio of min. density of ionization, meson to electron	Ratio of charge, meson to electron
Hydrogen	6.48	6.78	1.046	1.02 ± 0.03
Helium	8.13	8.20	1.009	1.005 ± 0.02
Argon	53.1	55	1.036	1.017 ± 0.03

unity, and the estimated errors indicate that the difference from unity cannot be greater than about 2 per cent.

Additional data indicating that the meson charge is identical to the electron charge are discussed in Chap. 6. Strong indirect evidence is obtained from the fact that different methods of measuring meson masses give consistent results if the meson charge is assumed equal to that of an electron, and would not be consistent otherwise.

As mentioned in Chap. 1, one would expect neutral mesons to exist as well as charged ones if mesons are responsible for nuclear forces. There is very strong indirect evidence for the existence of neutral mesons, derived chiefly from experiments on the production of mesons. It will accordingly be discussed in Chaps. 4 and 7.

4. SPIN

It has not yet proved possible to make any measurements of meson spin which are as direct and clear-cut as those on the mass and charge.

Theoretical considerations indicate that if the meson is responsible for nuclear forces it may well have a spin, since the nuclear forces are dependent upon the orientation of the spins of the nucleons involved. The meson field must, therefore, take account of these orientations in space. This cannot be done by a purely scalar field, but requires a field for which more than one quantity must be specified at each point. One way of accomplishing this would be to assign an internal coordinate which is to be specified in addition to the meson's position in order that its state be determined; that is, a meson spin.

Most experimental observations of particle spins are really observations of the effect of the magnetic moment associated with the spin. One observes, for atomic electrons, that the spectral lines are split up by applying a magnetic field, and one can then infer values of angular momentum and spin. The effect is observable because of the energy difference between different spin orientations in a magnetic field. The energy differences are small, however, and no one has noticed them in the case of mesons, whose energies, when observed, are usually many orders of magnitude greater than those of atomic electrons. In addition the number of mesons available to observe is usually of the order of 1, whereas in the case of atomic electrons it is 10^{15} or more. The problems involved are quite different, and the methods used for measuring spins of other particles have not so far been applicable to mesons.

As a matter of fact the most convincing information concerning meson spins has been obtained from the interaction of mesons with other particles of known spin. For example, if a meson can be formed by a simple reaction like

$$\text{Proton} \rightarrow \text{neutron} + \text{positive meson}$$

it would seem that the meson could not have a spin of $\frac{1}{2}$, since there would be no way to add its spin to that of the neutron (also $\frac{1}{2}$) to obtain the proton's spin of $\frac{1}{2}$. In such a case the meson would have to have spin 0 or 1. Evidence of this type concerning meson spin will be discussed in subsequent chapters.

In addition, however, efforts have been made to determine meson spin from the electromagnetic effects of its associated magnetic moment. At any considerable distance from the meson these effects are completely negligible compared with the field due to the meson's charge, but at small enough distances the contribution may become appreciable. One might, therefore, expect to find an effect due to the meson's spin in cases where another charged particle comes very close to the meson, for example, in collisions between a meson and an electron where the two come very close together, that is, very high-energy collisions. Such collisions are extremely rare. When a meson passes through matter, its electromagnetic field gives many electrons energies of a few tens of electron volts; only occasionally are high-energy knock-on electrons produced. In a similar way very close collisions may produce energetic photons by bremsstrahlung. When an electron or photon of very high energy is produced, it may start a cascade shower. Bursts have been observed in heavily shielded ionization chambers which are considered to have been formed by such processes. Analysis of these bursts has been the source of some information concerning meson spin.

The general procedure has been the following. One first calculates theoretically the probability that a meson of a given energy produces a high-energy electron or photon in passing through matter. One then calculates the probability that the electron or photon produces a shower of a certain size in the material surrounding the sensitive volume of the ionization chamber. One then estimates the expected ionization (and hence size of burst) to be expected by such a shower. One then takes information on the frequency of incident high-energy mesons, sums over this spectrum, and obtains a theoretically calculated distribution for the frequencies of bursts of various sizes, which can be compared with the observed frequency distribution. Many steps in the theoretical calculation are somewhat uncertain, especially the first two, so that it is by no means sure that the resulting conclusions would be reliable even if the experimental data were perfectly clear-cut and highly accurate.

Theoretical calculations have been made by Christy and Kusaka [17] extending earlier work of Bhabha, Carmichael, and Chou [18]. They showed that there were two processes by which mesons could create large electromagnetic showers, the production of high-energy knock-on electrons and bremsstrahlung photons.* The latter process is the more important one.

The calculations with spin 0 or $\frac{1}{2}$ were a better fit to the experimental values than those with spin 1. They compared their calculations with the data observed by Schein and Gill [19]. The comparison is shown in Fig. 10. The data appear to be in excellent agreement with the spin 0 case, but the accuracy of calculations and data is not such as to rule out spin $\frac{1}{2}$. For one thing, the meson mass assumed in the calculations was $177m_e$. The bremsstrahlung cross section is inversely proportional to the square of the mass, so that use of the currently accepted value of $215m_e$ would reduce the calculated values by about 32 per cent, which would make the spin $\frac{1}{2}$ curve agree best with the experimental data. Other

---

* In passing very close to a nucleus, the meson can produce bremsstrahlung radiation just as an electron does in conventional shower development.

uncertainties render this conclusion uncertain as well. All that can be said is that spin 1 does not appear to be a possibility.

This conclusion has been criticized by Chakrabarty on the basis that radiation damping was neglected in the calculation [20]. It is not certain, however, that the inclusion of radiation damping would alter the conclusions [21]. In the absence of definite conclusions to the contrary,

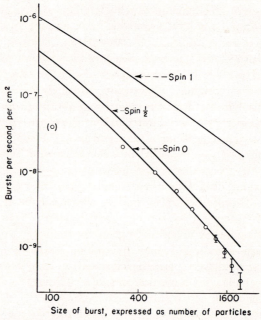

FIG. 10. Calculated and observed burst frequencies for different meson spins, from Christy and Kusaka [17]. Frequencies are given in bursts per sec per cm² from a thick layer of lead. Sizes are given in number of particles, assuming the bursts consist of large numbers of minimum ionization particles. Circles are experimental points of Schein and Gill [19].

we can accept the calculations of Christy and Kusaka as provisionally valid.

The main question concerning the experimental data is that of whether the bursts recorded really *are* showers created by mesons. Qualitatively it is evident that this is the most likely process. There are four main possibilities for the production of bursts: (1) nuclear events (stars) in which heavily ionizing tracks are given off; (2) showers produced by mesons; (3) showers produced by high-energy photons or electrons; (4) groups of particles (air showers) incident on the ion chamber. (1), (3), and (4) are favored by going to high altitude, (1) and (4) tend to be important in thin-walled chambers where there is little chance for shower formation. Showers produced by mesons appear to be the main cause of bursts in well-shielded ion chambers at sea level.

If high-energy mesons were the *only* cause of such bursts, one would expect the burst frequency to change very little between sea level and mountain altitudes. Schein and Gill found, however, that the rate was several times as high at 3350 m as at sea level. They interpreted this as an additional burst formation at the higher altitude, probably due to high-energy photons and electrons. No such assumption is necessary at sea level since the calculations of Christy and Kusaka indicate that mesons can account for all the bursts observed.* If there is really a small contribution to the rate of occurrence of bursts at sea level due to photons, electrons, or nucleonic component, this fact would make even stronger the conclusion that the meson spin is 0 or $\frac{1}{2}$, but not 1 or greater.

These conclusions relative to bursts and meson spin have been substantiated by a more detailed investigation by Lapp [22]. He has shown, in the first place, that it is quite certain that no large fraction of the bursts observed at sea level are caused by high-energy photons and electrons present in air showers. A number of counters were placed in the vicinity of the ion chamber so that an air shower would give counts coincident with the burst in the chamber. About 5 per cent of the bursts were observed to be coincident with air showers, proving that their contribution was a small one. At higher altitudes it would be considerably greater. Bursts in ion chambers at sea level with shielding of 12 cm of lead and 35 cm of iron were both consistent with production by mesons of spin 0 or $\frac{1}{2}$.

Data taken at 3350 m showed a considerably larger frequency of bursts than that calculated for mesons of spin 0 or $\frac{1}{2}$. This probably means that showers produced by mesons were not the only source of bursts at that altitude, and does not imply anything concerning meson spin.

As an over-all conclusion, then, we may say that a spin of 0 or $\frac{1}{2}$ seems to be indicated for the majority of mesons at sea level, but this is by no means an unalterable conclusion if strong contrary evidence should be presented. Other evidence presented in later chapters favors a spin of $\frac{1}{2}$.

* A further qualification should be mentioned with respect to the experimental data. Not only do the burst frequencies exhibit an altitude dependence which cannot easily be reconciled with production by mesons alone at all altitudes, but, to quote Schein and Gill: "Different (ionization) meters, even though located at the same place, record different burst rates, and hence a comparison of their absolute burst rates cannot give more than the right order of magnitude of the burst-rate ratio. . . . " Since the conclusions on meson spin are, in fact, based on absolute burst rates, it is evident that the comparison of theory with experiment cannot be made too precise.

5. SUMMARY

The characteristics of the mesons observed at sea level are summarized in Table 5.

TABLE 5. CHARACTERISTICS OF NORMAL MESONS OBSERVED AT SEA LEVEL

Mass	$215 \pm 4m_e$
Charge	$1.00 \pm 0.02e$
Spin	0 or $\frac{1}{2}$ (probably)
Magnetic moment	No definite information

REFERENCES

1. Hughes, D. J., *Phys. Rev.*, *69*, 371 (1946).
2. Corson, D. R., and R. B. Brode, *Phys. Rev.*, *53*, 773 (1938).
3. Street, J. C., and E. C. Stevenson, *Phys. Rev.*, *52*, 1003 (1937).
4. Neddermeyer, S. H., and C. D. Anderson, *Phys. Rev.*, *54*, 88 (1938).
5. Leprince-Ringuet, L., S. Gorodetzky, E. Nageotte, and R. Richard-Foy, *Compt. rend.*, *211*, 382 (1940).
6. Wheeler, J. A., and R. Ladenburg, *Phys. Rev.*, *60*, 754 (1941).
7. Bethe, H. A., *Phys. Rev.*, *70*, 821 (1946).
8. Fretter, W. B., *Phys. Rev.*, *70*, 625 (1946).
9. Street, J. C., *J. Franklin Inst.*, *227*, 765 (1939).
10. Brode, R. B., *Phys. Rev.*, *75*, 904 (1949).
11. Retallack, J. G., and R. B. Brode, *Phys. Rev.*, *75*, 1716 (1949).
12. Merkle, T. C. Jr., E. L. Goldwasser, and R. B. Brode, *Phys. Rev.*, *79*, 926 (1950).
13. Brode, R. B., *Revs. Modern Phys.*, *21*, 37 (1949).
14. Neddermeyer, S. H., and C. D. Anderson, *Revs. Modern Phys.*, *11*, 191 (1939).
15. Hazen, W. E., *Phys. Rev.*, *67*, 269 (1945).
16. Frost, R. H., Thesis, University of California, 1947, quoted by R. B. Brode, *Revs. Modern Phys.*, *21*, 37 (1949).
17. Christy, R. F., and S. Kusaka, *Phys. Rev.*, *59*, 414 (1941).
18. Bhabha, H. J., H. Carmichael, and C. N. Chou, *Proc. Indian Acad. Sci.*, *10*, No. 4, 221 (1939).
19. Schein, M., and P. S. Gill, *Revs. Modern Phys.*, *11*, 267 (1939).
20. Chakrabarty, S. K., *Indian J. Phys.*, *16*, 377 (1942).
21. Chakrabarty, S. K., and R. C. Majumdar, *Phys. Rev.*, *65*, 206 (1944).
22. Lapp, R. E., *Phys. Rev.*, *69*, 321 (1946).

CHAPTER 3

NEW TYPES OF MESONS

1. THE DISCOVERY OF THE PARTICLE PREDICTED BY YUKAWA

The mass measurements of Fretter, which were described in Chap. 2, were undertaken to find out whether mesons of different masses existed. Under the conditions of his experiments all mesons appeared to have the same mass. At the end of 1946, there was no definite experimental evidence that more than one kind of meson was to be found.

Some theoretical work had, however, already suggested that such might be the case. Mixed meson theories had been proposed by a number of authors in which two different meson fields were postulated with properties chosen so that some of the undesirable infinite values were made finite. Sakata and Inoue [1] suggested that the cosmic-ray meson was not to be considered responsible for nuclear forces, but that "the meson is an elementary particle which has close correlations to the Yukawa particle, but it should be considered as an elementary particle of a different sort." They estimated that if the mass of the Yukawa particle (or nuclear-force meson) was taken to fit the range of the nuclear forces, its mass would actually be about twice that of the cosmic-ray meson. The Yukawa particle would then, according to their prediction, decay into a meson and neutral particle with a lifetime of the order of 10^{-21} sec. A similar hypothesis was made independently by Marshak and Bethe [2]. They based their argument largely on the fact that the theoretical Yukawa particle must interact strongly with nuclei, whereas observations on cosmic-ray mesons indicated that they did not. (This question is discussed more fully in Chap. 6.) At the same time Powell and coworkers at the University of Bristol brought forward quite clear-cut proof that there were, in fact, mesons whose mass was different from that of the normal cosmic-ray meson and that they were fairly common under certain conditions at high altitude [3]. Before describing their measurements in detail, a brief digression on experimental technique is in order.

The experiments of Powell's group were made using special photographic emulsions devised for nuclear research. When a charged particle passes through such a photographic emulsion, the ions formed cause the grains in the emulsion to become developable. After development the silver grains produced show the track of the ionizing particle. For an emulsion to be useful as a detector of ionizing particles, its background of grains which are produced by purely chemical action must be sufficiently slight that tracks can be clearly recognizable. A relatively thick layer of emulsion is desirable if one is to observe more than short segments of track crossing it, but the background tends, of course, to become worse the thicker the emulsion. In recent years emulsions and methods of developing them have become available which provide an extremely useful tool for the study of ionizing particles. General discussions of emulsions and their uses in nuclear research have been given by Powell and Occhialini [4] and by Yagoda [5].

Early emulsions were able to detect only those particles which produced a high density of ionization. In cosmic-ray research they were used to detect "stars" which contained heavily ionizing protons and alpha particles. More and more sensitive emulsions were made, however, and types are now available which will detect relativistic particles of minimum ionization.

It is possible to obtain a measure of the density of ionization of the particle from the number of photographic grains per unit length produced along its track, called "grain density." The method requires extreme care, however. Variations exist even in emulsions of the same kind, so that identical particles with identical velocities may produce different grain densities in different (apparently identical) photographic plates, or even in different regions of the same plate. For meaningful measurements, the emulsion sensitivity must be determined from the grain density of tracks of known ionization. In addition, fading takes place so that tracks produced at different times have different grain densities even though the ionizations are the same.

These difficulties are by no means prohibitive, however, and improvements in the emulsions themselves and in their processing have made them much less important than they were in 1947 and 1948. Emulsions have many advantages. Their simplicity is obvious. They are continuously sensitive and therefore compare favorably with cloud chambers for the detection of rare events. They provide data on the actual tracks of the particles concerned, the density of ionization along the tracks, and, for particles that stop in the emulsion, the range. In addition the observed small-angle scattering of the particles can be interpreted to give an estimate of energy analogous to the momentum measurement with a magnetic field in a cloud chamber.

So much for emulsion technique; the points discussed will be amplified in connection with the actual experiments. At the time of the first emulsion experiments concerning mesons, it was not possible to observe tracks of minimum ionization, so that singly charged particles could be observed only near the end of their range where their density of ionization was sufficiently great. It was possible to detect mesons of energies up to about 10 Mev and protons of energies up to about 100 Mev. Meson tracks were characterized by a considerable scattering, whereas proton

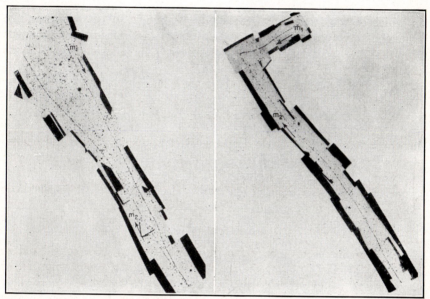

FIG. 1. Primary meson m_1 and secondary m_2, from Lattes, Muirhead, Occhialini, and Powell [3]. In the second example the arrow for m_2 should be reversed.

tracks were straight, and by a rapid change of grain density, since the mesons were slowed down much more by a given energy loss than were the heavier protons. When a track a few hundred microns long was observed, it was not difficult to tell whether it was a meson.

Powell and coworkers found that in nuclear emulsions exposed at mountain altitudes mesons can cause nuclear disruptions and are some-times ejected from disintegrating nuclei, subjects which will be dis-cussed in later chapters. In addition, they reported events in which a meson stopped (as indicated by the rapid increase in grain density) and a meson then left the same spot with an energy of a few Mev. In their first report [3] they had found two such events among 65 mesons which came to the end of their range in the emulsion, which are shown in

Fig. 1. It was hardly possible that the meson had stopped, and then received some sort of impulse giving it that much energy. They say:

"We have attempted to interpret these two events in terms of an interaction of the primary meson with a nucleus of the emulsion which leads to the ejection of a second meson of the same mass as the first. Any reaction of the type represented by the equations

$$A_z{}^N + \mu_{-1}{}^0 \rightarrow B_{z-2}{}^N + \mu_{+1}{}^0 \qquad \text{or} \qquad A_z{}^N + \mu_{+1}{}^0 \rightarrow C_{z+2}{}^N + \mu_{-1}{}^0$$

in which A represents any stable nucleus known to be present in the emulsion, involves an absorption of energy in contradiction with the fact that the secondary meson is observed to have an energy of about 2 Mev.

"A second process, represented by the equation

$$\text{Ag}_{47} + \mu_{-1}{}^0 \rightarrow X_z + Y_{45-z} + \mu_{+1}{}^0$$

in which X and Y represent two nuclei of approximately equal charge number may be energetically possible, but the chance of it occurring in conditions where the total energy of the two recoiling nuclei is of the order of only a few million electron volts is remote. It is therefore possible that our photographs indicate the existence of mesons of different mass."

Possible sources of energy for the second meson were considered in detail by Frank [6]. He confirmed that no nuclear transformation or degradation could provide the required energy. The only possibility appeared to be a series of reactions in which a negative meson became attached to a hydrogen nucleus in the emulsion, forming an excited neutron which then would add to another nucleus reemitting the meson. The statistical probability of such a process was too low to make it a satisfactory explanation.

The conclusion was that the second meson must be lighter than the first, produced from it in a decay process. It was not long before a sufficient number of cases were available to permit the ratio between the masses of the two mesons to be established with some reliability by grain counting.

A few months after their first paper Lattes, Occhialini, and Powell gave results based on 644 meson tracks ending in the emulsion [7]. There were 40 secondary mesons. In eleven cases the second meson stopped in the emulsion, but in only two of these cases was the track of the first meson long enough that the ratio of their masses could be determined.

The procedure which they followed was to count the number of grains starting at the end of the track where the particle stopped. The number of grains counted was plotted against range from the end of the track (residual range), as in Fig. 2. Logarithmic scales were used. The heavier the particle, the higher its curve lies on such a plot. When the eleven cases in which the secondary mesons stopped in the emulsion were so plotted, it was found that the line representing the observations on the primary meson lay above that for the secondary meson in each case,

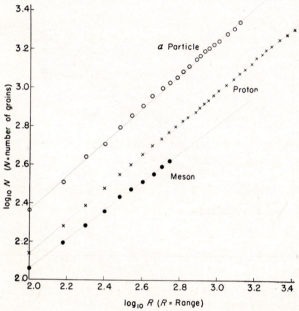

FIG. 2. Plot of grain count N vs. residual range R of particle tracks in emulsions as used by Powell and coworkers for mass determinations [7].

indicating that the primary was heavier than the secondary. In the two cases where long tracks were obtained for both primary and secondary mesons the ratios of their masses were estimated to be 2.0 and 1.8. The difference in mass was quite clearly established.

In describing these events Powell's group gave them the name of mu decays. The first (heavier) meson was called the pi meson, the second (lighter) one the mu meson. It was generally considered likely that the mu meson was to be identified with the previously studied cosmic-ray meson, the pi meson with the heavy meson just predicted theoretically.

By 1948, 31 mu decays had been found which gave grain counts suitable for mass determination [8]. Average grain counts as a function of residual range are given in Fig. 3. In determining the mass ratio m_{pi}/m_{mu} by grain counts, they used the fact that if N is the number of grains in the track of range R, under reasonable assumptions,

$$N = mF(R/m) \tag{1}$$

where $F(\ )$ is an experimentally determined function and m is the mass of the particle.

The necessary assumptions are that the energy loss be a function of the velocity only, while the energy itself is equal to the rest mass times some

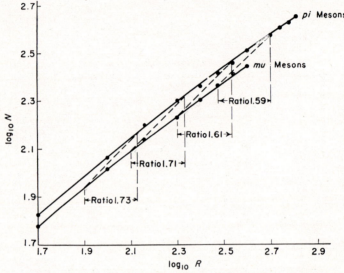

FIG. 3.   Plots of log $N_{mu}(R)$ and log $N_{pi}(R)$ against R, illustrating calculation of ratio of mass of pi meson to that of mu meson [8].

function of velocity, and that the grain density be a function of the energy loss only. To show the validity of Eq. (1), we consider a particle of velocity v; the distance it will travel for a given change in velocity is proportional to m, since the energy loss is a function of v only. Correspondingly, the total range is equal to some function of v, say $f(v)$, multiplied by the mass.

$$R = mf(v) \qquad \text{or} \qquad \frac{R}{m} = f(v) \tag{2}$$

Since the grain density dN/dR is a function of energy loss, it is a function of velocity, and therefore of R/m, as indicated in Eq. (3).

$$\frac{dN}{dR} = g(R/m) \tag{3}$$

Since the range is proportional to m, integrating introduces a factor m, so that the total grain count is given by Eq. (1) above.

To determine the mass ratio, one first plots N_{mu} as a function of R for mu mesons, considering the mass of the mu meson to be unity. One now considers m to be increased, with R increased proportionately to keep $F(R/m)$ constant. Then N also increases proportionately to m. That is, the locus of these points is a straight line drawn at 45°. Figure 3 shows the curves obtained by Lattes, Occhialini, and Powell for the grain counts of pi and mu mesons. From the intercepts of the diagonals (lines of constant R/m) they obtained a mass ratio of

$$\frac{m_{pi}}{m_{mu}} = 1.64 \pm 0.12$$

The error indicated includes statistical uncertainties only. The actual deviation from the true value was somewhat larger because of systematic experimental errors.

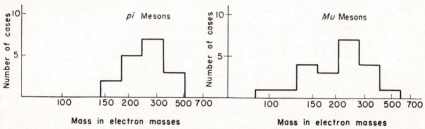

FIG. 4. Distribution of meson masses inferred from multiple scattering of tracks by Goldschmidt-Clermont, King, Muirhead, and Ritson [10].

More recent experiments have further reduced the errors [9]. Fading was reduced by the use of shorter exposures and an improved method of development employed which was more uniform. The latest result is

$$\frac{m_{pi}}{m_{mu}} = 1.33 \pm 0.05$$

As a check on the mass ratios obtained by grain counting an investigation of the scattering of mesons in photographic plates was also undertaken at Bristol [10]. The observed scattering was compared with the theory of Williams and Moliere, with the mass of the particle taken as an adjustable parameter. The results are not very precise, but they are not subject to error due to nonuniformities in fading or development. The data summarized in Fig. 4 lead to values of

$$m_{pi} = 260 \pm 30 m_e$$
$$m_{mu} = 205 \pm 20 m_e$$
$$\frac{m_{pi}}{m_{mu}} = 1.27 \pm 0.20$$

This is in good agreement with the final value arrived at by grain counting.

Since pi mesons, by definition, decay into mu mesons when they stop in an emulsion, it has generally been assumed that they are positively charged, so that they are repelled by nuclei and do not react with them. If these mesons are nuclear force mesons, one would expect that such a negatively charged meson would be attracted to a nucleus and absorbed, giving up its mass energy to the nucleons. This would cause a nuclear reaction involving an energy of 100 to 150 Mev, *i.e.*, a small "star." Powell and coworkers did, in fact, find that a substantial

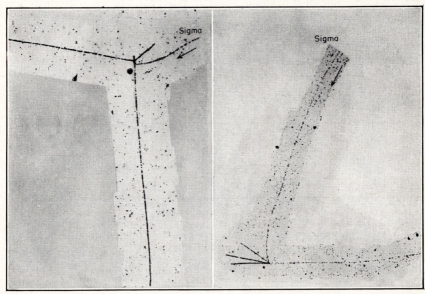

FIG. 5a. Typical sigma mesons stopping and producing a star. Observed by Powell and coworkers.

fraction of the mesons observed to stop caused such events. These they called sigma mesons, while mesons stopping uneventfully were called rho mesons. An example is shown in Fig. 5. In a total of 644 stopped mesons 105 sigma mesons were actually observed whereas only 40 pi-mu decays were observed [11]. From the geometrical considerations involved they concluded that pi and sigma mesons occurred with equal frequency, since pi-mu decays were not definitely recognized as such unless the tracks stayed in the emulsion for distances that were fairly long compared with the emulsion thickness. Actually a correction had to be made to the observed numbers for any type of event to take account of this inefficiency of observation. The correction was small for sigma mesons whose stars are easily recognized, but quite large for pi-mu

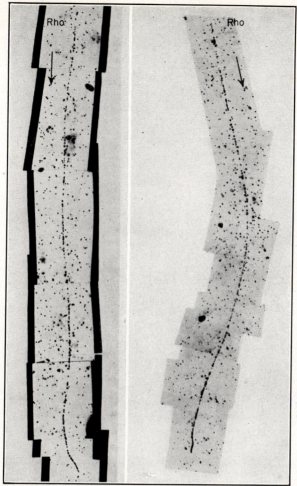

Fig. 5b. Typical rho mesons stopping uneventfully, observed by Powell and coworkers.

decays. When the proper correction was made for this inefficiency, the results were as given in Table 1.

TABLE 1. FREQUENCIES OF OCCURRENCE OF PI AND SIGMA MESONS ACCORDING TO LATTES, OCCHIALINI, AND POWELL [11]

	Observed	Adjusted true frequency
pi mesons	40	117 ± 20
sigma mesons	105	122 ± 20

It was not possible to conclude from Powell's work that pi and sigma mesons were unquestionably positive and negative mesons, although it seemed very probable. One cannot determine whether a particle is positive or negative from its track in an emulsion. At first it was not even certain that the sigma mesons were heavier than mu mesons, since grain counting could not give an absolute mass measurement of great accuracy and there were no mu mesons for comparison in the stars by which sigma mesons were identified.

Measurements of the mass of sigma mesons had to be made by scattering. The results of Goldschmidt-Clermont, King, Muirhead, and Ritson

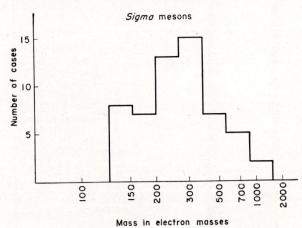

FIG. 6. Distributions of masses of mesons causing stars, inferred from multiple scattering of tracks by Goldschmidt-Clermont, King, Muirhead, and Ritson [10].

are shown in Fig. 6. The over-all average was $275 \pm 15m_e$, in agreement with the mass of the pi meson. A similar result was obtained by Lattimore [12]. As a result of these measurements it seemed to be quite certain that the masses of pi and sigma mesons were at least approximately, and probably exactly, the same.

As a matter of fact the most recent mass determinations by grain counting have, thanks to improved techniques, been made as absolute mass determinations [9]. No difference between pi and sigma mesons was observed and they were actually lumped together.

The correctness of this picture has been confirmed by Barbour [13] and Franzinetti [14], using magnetic deflection. In their experiments two nuclear emulsions are placed face to face with a small air gap between them in a magnetic field. If a meson (or other particle) stops in one of the emulsions after passing through the other emulsion and the air gap, its mass can be determined from the range in the emulsion and the change in angle produced by the magnetic field. The sign of the charge is, of course, also determined. Barbour's data were obtained by balloon flights and Franzinetti's at mountain altitudes, but the procedures were otherwise closely similar. In both cases it was found that all pi mesons and mu mesons had positive charge, while all sigma mesons had negative. The results on meson masses are summarized in Table 2. The more accurate measurements of Franzinetti show especially good agreement

TABLE 2. MASSES OF MESONS FOUND BY MAGNETIC DEFLECTION [13,14]

	Barbour	Franzinetti
pi mesons	$250 \pm 25 m_e$	$281 \pm 10 m_e$
mu mesons	$229 \pm 21 m_e$	$217 \pm 4 m_e$
sigma mesons	$302 \pm 39 m_e$	$288 \pm 13 m_e$

with the assumption that mu mesons are to be identified with the normal cosmic-ray mesons, while pi and sigma mesons are, respectively, positive and negative mesons of greater mass.

Further very definite confirmation of these results has been obtained from experiments on mesons produced artificially in the Berkeley cyclotron, which will be discussed in Chap. 4.

The existence of mesons with mass 250 to $300 m_e$ is thus clearly established by experiments using nuclear emissions. It is of interest to inquire whether cloud-chamber results involving deflection in a magnetic field have given any indication of such mesons. It is quite clear that the measurements of Fretter and Brode described in Chap. 2 rule out the possibility that any large fraction of the mesons observed in their experiment could have mass 250 to $300 m_e$, although the data of Merkle, Goldwasser, and Brode suggest the existence of a small number with this mass. One can conclude from these results that pi and sigma mesons are not often found at sea level, but only at the higher altitudes where the nuclear emulsions were exposed. At sea level, pi and sigma mesons cannot make up more than a few per cent of the total number of mesons, and probably actually make up only a small fraction of a per cent.

Some mass measurements have, however, been made at higher altitudes, using magnetic deflection techniques similar to those of Fretter and Brode, and evidence has been claimed for the existence of such mesons. Peyrou and Lagarrigue measured in a magnet cloud chamber the momentum of particles appearing to stop in absorbers beneath the chamber, as evidenced by discharges in counter trays [15,16]. The work was done at an elevation of 1000 m. While preliminary results appeared

to indicate the presence of mesons with masses of 250 to 300m_e, the final
conclusion was to the opposite effect.   They obtained a meson mass of
212 $\pm$ 5m_e.

A more extensive set of measurements at high altitude was made by
Alichanian, Alichanow, and Weissenberg [17,18].   At an altitude of
3250 m an apparatus shown in Fig. 7 was used.   Counters in the first
four groups were individually connected to neon tubes so that the path
of a particle could be followed through them and it could be determined
whether or not the particle stopped in the absorbers.   Information on
range and curvature were thus avail-
able to determine the mass.   The
basic observation was that there were
some particles which appeared to stop
which were not curved as much by
the magnetic field as one would
expect for mesons of mass 200m_e.
Therefore they concluded that
heavier particles were present.   A
typical experimental curve is given in
Fig. 8.   The data plotted are number
of particles observed with a given
deflection in the magnetic field.
Theoretical mass values are plotted
on the abscissa.   The resolution of
the instrument is such that particles
of unique mass would be observed
experimentally as a distribution
spread out by a factor of about 2 and
is thus much inferior to that of
Brode's apparatus.   We may conclude that the data suggest the presence of protons and very likely heavy
mesons, but that not a great deal can
be said about the latter.   Several
points are uncertain in the interpretation of the experiment.   It is possible
that a considerable fraction of the

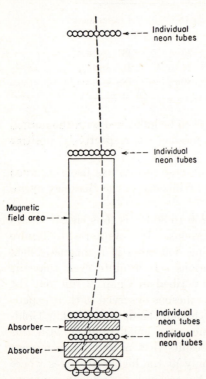

Individual
neon tubes

Individual
neon tubes

Magnetic
field area

Individual
neon tubes
Absorber
Individual
neon tubes
Absorber

FIG. 7.   Counter apparatus of Alichanian, Alichanow, *et al.* for mass measurements made at mountain altitude [17].
(Not to scale.)

particles which appear to stop are, in fact, scattered in the lead absorbers
and pass out the sides.   This effect is known to be important in studies
of slow mesons [19].   It would cause mesons to appear to be particles
of higher mass.   In addition protons and heavy mesons can lose energy
by nuclear collisions as well as by ionization, but the mass determinations

depend on a range-energy relationship based on ionization only. In this way also fallaciously high masses might be obtained. The experimental distributions are affected by an instrumental bias in favor of small deflections for which the effective aperture of the apparatus is largest. While the results are interesting they do not appear to be in any way conclusive.

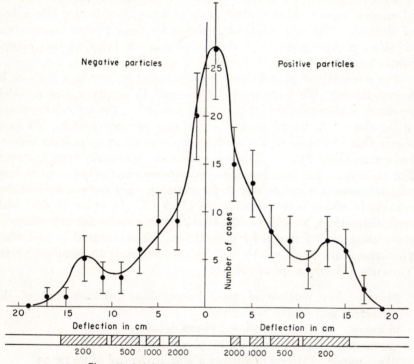

FIG. 8. Number of particles of range between 2.4 and 5.4 cm of lead having various deflections in apparatus of Alichanian, Alichanow, and Weissenberg, with corresponding mass scale. The spread in deflection for a given mass takes into account the thickness of the absorber, but not the finite size of the counters used to determine the deflection [17].

From the curves shown in Fig. 8, Alichanian, Alichanow, et al. concluded that particles of mass 500, 1000, and 2000m_e and both positive and negative charges were present, which they called varitrons. In a subsequent paper they elaborated their analysis to indicate masses of 200, 250, 300, 350, 450, 550, 680, 850, 1000, 1300, 2500, 3800, 9000, 25,000m_e, but there is no obvious justification for such conclusions. The emulsion work of Powell and coworkers provides the best evidence for the existence of mesons with different masses and leaves no doubts concerning the matter.*

As a matter of fact, the pi and sigma mesons which have been discussed are not the only form of mesons with masses of 250 to $300m_e$. Neutral mesons have also been shown to exist. This is not surprising since neutral mesons would be expected theoretically if these are indeed the mesons responsible for nuclear forces. These neutral mesons, like the pi mesons, have a characteristic mode of decay, in this case into a pair of photons. The first clear-cut evidence for these neutral mesons was obtained in experiments with the cyclotron at Berkeley, so that experiments having to do with them will be discussed in Chap. 4.

The discovery of pi and sigma mesons has given rise to a problem in nomenclature. We have used "pi meson" to signify a meson which produces a pi-mu decay, while a "mu meson" is the secondary meson of the event. A "sigma meson" is one that produces a star. We have shown that pi and sigma mesons have mass about $280m_e$ and mu mesons have mass about $215m_e$. The converse is not necessarily true, however. For example, some negative mass 280 mesons may be observed to stop without causing a visible star if, for example, they cause a nuclear disruption in which only neutrons are given off. In order to deal with such distinctions, we will use the Greek letter π meson for any meson of mass $280m_e$, and μ meson for mass $215m_e$, without regard to just what phenomena are produced by it. This corresponds to common usage. Thus our definitions are as follows:

Meson. Any particle of mass intermediate between that of the electron and proton

pi meson. Meson producing a pi-mu decay

mu-meson. Meson produced by pi-mu decay

sigma meson. Meson producing a star at the end of its range

rho meson. Meson stopping without producing any event

π meson. Meson of mass about $280m_e$, as discovered by Powell

μ meson. Meson of mass about $215m_e$, the normal cosmic-ray meson

The first group of definitions are phenomenological, whereas the latter

---

* Prior discovery has been claimed by the Russian group [*Nature*, *163*, 701 (1949)]. While the question of priority does not seem very important, it appears that the first evidence was presented by Sakata and Inoue several years in advance of their publication in 1946.

The author regrets that it has not been possible to include a complete account of Russian investigations on mesons in this work. The question of varitrons seemed to be of especial interest and has therefore been discussed on the basis of information at his disposal. For other aspects of Russian work, omission appeared preferable to incomplete discussion and inadequate evaluation.

are based on an a priori concept of properties.* The a priori definitions are mainly used in the following chapters. The phenomenological terms are applicable only to mesons observed to stop in nuclear emulsions.

The information which has been presented concerning the π meson is summarized in Table 3. The remainder of this chapter is concerned with evidence concerning other types of mesons whose existence is uncertain.

TABLE 3. EXPERIMENTAL PROPERTIES OF π MESONS

Mass	$m_{\pi^+} = 277.4 \pm 1.1m_e$, $m_{\pi^-} = 276.1 \pm 1.3m_e$ [according to Barkas, Smith, and Gardner (20)]
Charge	$\pm e$
Spin	Probably 0 or 1 (see Chaps. 4, 5, and 6 for details)
Interactions	π^+ meson, when stopped, decays to give μ^+ meson
	π^- meson, when stopped, interacts with a nucleus causing its disruption

2. THE λ-MESON HYPOTHESIS

In 1948, a meson of mass intermediate between that of the electron and μ meson was proposed by Auger, Daudin, Freon, and Maze [21]. The mass of this "λ meson" was not determined with any accuracy, since its presence was inferred indirectly from the properties of the extensive air showers,† but it was thought that it might be in the range 3 to $10m_e$. While some evidence supporting the hypothesis has been found, the λ meson does not now seem necessary to explain the behavior of the air showers, and it therefore seems unlikely at present that such λ mesons really exist. Nevertheless, it is worth while to give a brief review of the data bearing on this hypothesis.

The extensive air showers consist of large showers formed in the atmosphere. They contain a large number of particles, thousands or

* This distinction has been made clearly by Powell and coworkers, whose terms correspond in the following way:

This Book	Powell et al.
pi meson	π meson
mu meson	μ meson
sigma meson	σ meson
rho meson	ρ meson
π meson	π particle
μ meson	μ particle

Most authors, however, use π and μ meson in the same a priori sense as in this work. Powell's system is not in general use. Care must be taken to avoid confusion with respect to these terms.

† Often called Auger showers after their discoverer.

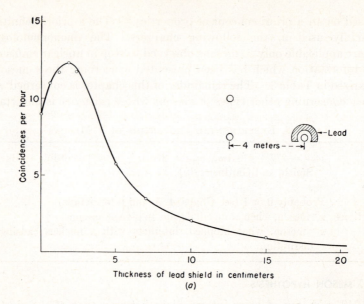

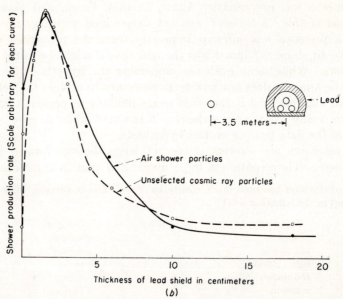

Fig. 9. Penetration and shower production by particles in extensive showers compared with normal unselected cosmic-ray particles by Auger, Maze, Ehrenfest, and Freon [25].

millions in some cases, and extend over wide areas having lateral dimensions of tens or even hundreds of meters.   Detailed descriptions of these showers have been given by Heisenberg [22], Janossy [23], Montgomery [24], and others.   The λ-meson hypothesis arose from the attempt to identify the particles present in them.   One might expect them to be cascade showers made up of electrons and photons.   To determine the nature of the air-shower particles, Auger and collaborators measured their penetration and shower production [25,26].   Typical data appear in Fig. 9.   Figure 9a shows the rate of coincidences between an unshielded counter telescope and a shielded counter 4 m away as a function of shielding thickness.   The first few centimeters of lead give an increase

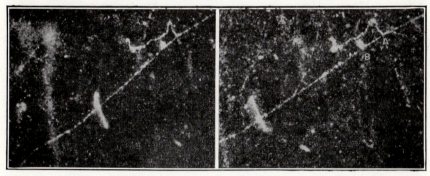

Scale: 1 cm

Fig. 10.   Photograph of particle which is scattered in forming low-energy knock-on electrons.   Mass estimated to be $\approx 10m_e$ by Cowan [27].

such as would occur due to the multiplication of electrons and photons If all the particles were electrons and photons, additional lead would reduce the rate very rapidly, but the data show only a gradual decrease after 5 cm of lead.   These particles are absorbed more rapidly than μ mesons of the hard component but less rapidly than the soft component.   In a similar way Fig. 9b shows that showers are produced more frequently than by the hard component, though less than by the soft.   To explain this result, the λ-meson hypothesis was introduced, assuming that some particles of mass intermediate between electron and μ meson were present.   A particle of intermediate mass would have penetration and multiplication intermediate between hard and soft components, and would offer a qualitative explanation of the observed phenomena.

Quite a different sort of evidence for a low-mass meson was found by Cowan [27] in a cloud-chamber photograph taken at 8850 m, reproduced in Fig. 10.   The straight track produces two knock-on electrons of low energy at A and B and suffers appreciable scattering in each case.   From the first collision the mass ratio is calculated to be 11.4, from the second only an upper limit of 30 can be obtained.   If only the scattering at A were present, one could either assume that production of the knock-on had coincided by chance with a nuclear scattering or that the event was actually a three-pronged star, but the occurrence of the second event at B makes these explanations unlikely.   If the straight track is actually that of an electron, the apparent angle at which the knock-on is emitted at A must be wrong, and Cowan's estimate that the densities of ionization of the two tracks are similar, while the knock-on is much the more scattered, must be in error.   This explanation does not seem very likely either, so that we are left with the original interpretation in terms of a λ meson of mass $11m_e$.

The evidence for the λ-meson hypothesis was never very strong.   The cloud-chamber track of Cowan is the only direct argument for a particle of mass $\approx 10m_e$.   The other arguments depend upon the observation of phenomena which the investigators were not able to explain by the known behavior of electrons, photons, and μ mesons.   An explanation has, however, been produced by Greisen, who has shown that cascade showers of electrons and photons should actually produce some particles having the penetration which had previously been ascribed to λ mesons.   Both experimental and theoretical evidence was found to support Greisen's conclusion.

The experimental evidence is based on an investigation of particles in air showers capable of penetrating up to 500 g/cm² of absorber carried out by Cocconi, Tongiorgi, and Greisen [28].   Their data, plotted in Fig. 11, show that there are two quite distinct regions of the absorption curve, a very flat curve for large thicknesses and a steep one for thinner layers.   For an all lead absorber, the dividing line is just about 20 cm of lead, so that the data of Auger, Maze, Ehrenfest, and Freon are limited to the steep part only.   The particles responsible for the flat part of the curve are very penetrating, and it seems fairly certain that they are μ mesons like those in the normal hard component.   What particles, then, are responsible for the steep initial part of the curve?   The most interesting fact shown by Fig. 11 is that lead is considerably more effective than iron in stopping these particles, which suggests that they may be electrons and photons.   If one makes such an assumption, the particles should have the same penetration in iron and lead, provided thicknesses are measured in radiation units.   In Fig. 12 the part not due to μ mesons is plotted in these terms, and points for "absorber all lead" and "absorber lead and iron" are in quite good agreement.   This indicates that the particles are actually electrons and photons, not λ mesons.

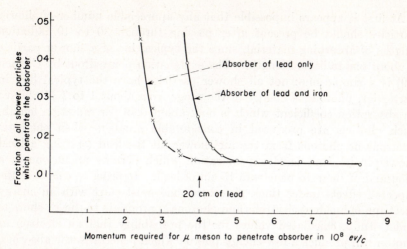

FIG. 11.   Penetration of particles in air showers for large thicknesses of iron and lead absorbers, from Cocconi, Tongiorgi, and Greisen [28].

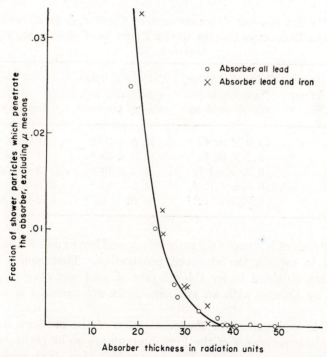

FIG. 12.   Penetration of air-shower particles other than μ mesons, from Cocconi, Tongiorgi, and Greisen [28].

At first it appears impossible that any appreciable number of shower particles should be present after passing through 30 to 40 radiation lengths of absorbing material, since the typical life of a shower particle is about one radiation length. The explanation pointed out by Greisen [29] is a simple one: not all shower particles have the typical life; in particular, photons of energy in the range from about 1 to 7 Mev have an absorption coefficient which is only about 0.19 per radiation length. Such photons are produced in considerable numbers when energetic electrons or photons from the air shower hit the lead (starting a local shower in it), and have a penetration which permits about one in a thousand of them to penetrate 15 cm of lead. In order to calculate the expected effects under thick absorbers, one must start with an energy spectrum of incident electrons and photons appropriate to the air showers under study, calculated values for the probability that an electron or photon will produce a low-energy photon which penetrates the absorber, and a value for the probability that the low-energy photon will produce a Compton electron in the counter to be counted. Greisen's results from such a calculation are given in Table 4.

TABLE 4. VALUES FOR THE FRACTION OF SOFT COMPONENT IN EXTENSIVE AIR SHOWERS PRODUCING COUNTS UNDER THICK LEAD ABSORBERS, FROM GREISEN [29]

Lead thickness, in.	Calculated value, ignoring low-energy photons	Calculated value, considering low-energy photons	Experimental
4	14.0×10^{-3}	31.5×10^{-3}	31–33×10^{-3}
5	2.2×10^{-3}	11.0×10^{-3}	9–13×10^{-3}
6	0.30×10^{-3}	4.2×10^{-3}	3–4.5×10^{-3}
7	0.036×10^{-3}	1.7×10^{-3}	0.5–2.0×10^{-3}
8	0.0036×10^{-3}	0.68×10^{-3}	0.0–0.5×10^{-3}

The agreement is completely satisfactory and leaves no need to invoke λ mesons to explain the observed penetration. That counts due to photons are obtained under thick layers of lead was checked experimentally by Daudin with an anticoincidence arrangement of counters [30].

With this explanation for the penetration of the particles in Auger showers, the experiments of the French group are no longer to be interpreted in terms of λ mesons. We can conclude then, that evidence for the λ-meson hypothesis is reduced to the event observed by Cowan.

While such particles may exist, much more evidence will be required before their existence can be considered proved, or even very probable. If they do exist, they are certainly rare.

3. HEAVY MESONS

We have seen that there are certainly two different kinds of mesons, π and μ. A number of investigators have found evidence indicating that there are also mesons with greater mass. Most estimates of their mass fall in the range 700 to $1300m_e$. It is fairly certain that such particles exist, but it is not possible to determine, as this is written, what different types exist, or how they are related to each other and to other known particles. In the following section a provisional summary is given of the experimental evidence for such heavy mesons. A more detailed account of the field has been given by Butler [55].

The first report of a particle in this mass range was made by Leprince-Ringuet and Lheritier in 1944 [31]. They were carrying on an experiment to measure the masses of particles in the penetrating component of cosmic radiation from cloud-chamber pictures showing knock-on electrons occurring in the cloud-chamber gas. Such a measurement does not depend on assumptions concerning the energy loss of the particle, but does require the assumption that the collision with the electron is an elastic one. Such events are, unfortunately, rare. Ten thousand countercontrolled cloud-chamber pictures were taken and ten knock-on events found. In six of them the curvature of the penetrating particle was too small to measure, so that no mass determination could be made. Three gave masses consistent with that of the μ meson, but the accuracy of the measurements was poor. The final one resulted in a mass of $990 \pm 120m_e$. The determination was felt to be a reliable one, with the errors indicated representing maximum expected errors. Bethe has shown that the particle could be a proton with spurious curvature due to scattering, but the probability that a proton would actually cause the observed event is ~ 0.01, so that such an explanation is not completely satisfactory [32]. Having only one event, statistical arguments are not very meaningful, so that we can only conclude that the result does suggest the existence of a particle with mass about $1000m_e$.

Leprince-Ringuet, Lheritier, and Richard-Foy have interpreted results on the curvature and ionization of tracks in the cloud chamber as confirming the existence of particles with a mass intermediate between mesons and protons [33]. Since estimates of density of ionization are not highly reliable, there seems to be less necessity to invoke a particle of mass 1000 to explain these observations than the previous one. A large number of protons were observed. The curve of ionization vs. curvature for a particle of mass 1000 lies close enough to that for protons that the observed particles might well have been protons.

As mentioned in Chap. 2, the very careful mass measurements of Brode have shown some indication of masses in the range 500 to $800m_e$ which might be considered as evidence for heavy mesons [34,35]. Brode, however, considers that the data are not conclusive, although they would be consistent with the hypothesis that heavy mesons do exist, but are considerably less frequent than protons or μ mesons. Other systematic measurements have been made by Franzinetti, using the curvature

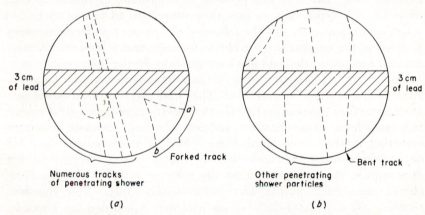

(a) (b)

Fig. 13. (a) Forked track occurring in the gas of the cloud chamber, thought to represent disintegration of a neutral particle of mass $\approx 1000m_e$. (b) Bent track thought to represent decay of the corresponding charged particle, from Rochester and Butler [38].

caused by a magnetic field in the air gap between two emulsions [14], and by Bastin, Becker, Chanson, Nageotte, and Treille, using the curvature in a cloud chamber and range determined by counter trays [36]. They obtained upper limits for the proportion of mesons heavier than π mesons as 3 per cent and 5 per cent, respectively. In neither case was there any evidence of them.

If, however, cloud-chamber photographs are taken with counter control arranged to select penetrating showers (*i.e.*, events in which two or more simultaneous particles penetrate substantial amounts of absorbing material), then events are found which may involve heavy mesons. The first such results were presented by Rochester and Butler [37]. The two events which they observed are shown in Fig. 13. In event A, two fork prongs a and b are thought to be produced by the disintegration of a neutral particle. Track a has momentum $3.4 \pm 1.0 \times 10^8$ ev/c, +

charge, approximately minimum ionization; track b has momentum $3.5 \pm 1.5 \times 10^8$, $-$ charge, and approximately minimum ionization. They argue that the event must represent a decay process rather than a collision or interaction, because in the latter case virtually all such events should occur in the lead plate, whereas actually very few events at all similar were observed in the lead plate. The fork cannot be an electron-positron pair because the angle between tracks would be only 0.1° for electrons of such high energy, instead of the actual 67°. In addition, the photon would certainly have produced many electrons in the lead plate. The fork cannot represent a star in the gas because the tracks would be fairly heavily ionizing if they were caused by protons. Hence the conclusion that a spontaneous disintegration is involved.

The event cannot be a π-μ decay or a μ meson decaying into an electron* because the particles have opposite electric charge and the energies involved are too high. Rochester and Butler used the balance of energy and momentum to calculate what the mass of the original particle must have been for assumed masses of the secondary particle of 0, $200m_e$, and $400m_e$, since it seemed most probable that the secondaries were mesons. To secure an energy and momentum balance, it was necessary to assume a primary mass between $700m_e$ and $1600m_e$, whatever secondary mass was assumed up to $400m_e$.

Similar arguments apply to the event shown in B. The momenta are $6 \pm 3 \times 10^8$ ev/c for the upper track and $7.7 \pm 1.0 \times 10^8$ ev/c for the lower, and both are positive. They are too lightly ionizing to be star prongs, nor is it likely that the event is a large-angle scattering because there is no evidence of any recoil particle. Rochester and Butler concluded that the simplest explanation was the decay of a charged particle of mass about $1000m_e$ into charged and neutral particles.

These observations were made at sea level. Additional events were subsequently recorded by the Manchester group at mountain elevation. The neutral particles appeared to be the more numerous, since 36 events similar to event A were observed and only 7 similar to event B [38]. Because of the V-shaped track produced, the particles causing them have been called neutral and charged V particles.

These results have been confirmed by Anderson and coworkers, who found a total of 30 neutral and 4 charged V-particle events in a cloud chamber triggered for penetrating showers [39]. Similar observations have been made by Bridge and Annis [46], Thompson, Cohn, and Flum [47], and by Fretter [48].

---

* The μ meson does decay with the formation of electron or positron. The half-life is about 2×10^{-6} sec., and the electrons have energies up to about 50 Mev. Discussion of this decay process is given in Chap. 5.

In most cases the tracks observed are of minimum ionization, and it is not possible to identify the particles causing them. The number of neutral V-particle decays that have been observed is now quite great, however, and some of the particles produced have been identified as either π or μ mesons. On the other hand some have been identified as protons [39,47,49,50]. Armenteros, Barker, Butler, and Cachon found nine tracks that were denser than minimum ionization produced by 70 neutral V-particle decays [50]. Five were protons and four were negative π or μ mesons. There were also cases in which the positive particle was lighter than a proton and presumably was a meson. The mesons produced are thought to be π mesons rather than μ mesons because instances appearing to involve π-μ decay in flight and nuclear interactions have been observed [50]. Thus it appears that either there are two types of neutral V particles decaying according to the schemes

$$V_1{}^0 \rightarrow p + \pi^- \quad\text{and}\quad V_2{}^0 \rightarrow \pi^+ + \pi^-$$

or there are two modes of three particle decay

$$V^0 \rightarrow p + \pi^- + \pi^0 \quad\text{and}\quad V^0 \rightarrow n + \pi^+ + \pi^-$$

(Here π^0 represents a neutral π meson.) If the former of these two alternatives is correct, the mass of the $V_2{}^0$ particle is about $800m_e$, and it can be considered a heavy meson. The other decay schemes, of course, involve a mass for the V^0 which is greater than the proton mass, and it is perhaps more appropriate in such a case to consider the V^0 particle as a metastable excited state of the nucleon.

Other evidence of heavy mesons has also been obtained from cloud-chamber photographs triggered by penetrating showers. With a magnet cloud chamber, Butler, Rosser, and Barker obtained three examples of tracks whose momentum and ionization indicated masses of 900 to 1140, 650 to 900, and 800 to 1020 electron masses [40]. Two were positive, one negative. All were produced in stars observed in the cloud chamber. None was observed to decay.

The work of the Russian group has also led to results which could be interpreted in terms of meson masses of about $1000m_e$. The masses listed [18] are 680, 850, 1000 and $1300m_e$. Such results cannot, of course, be accepted without further confirmation.

Tracks have also been found in nuclear emulsions by a number of investigators which appear to have been caused by particles of mass about $1000m_e$. One type, first found by Powell and coworkers in an electron-sensitive emulsion [9], is reproduced in Fig. 14. Two events occur at A and B, and it is considered unlikely that their juxtaposition is due to chance. Change in grain density and scattering indicate that particle k approaches point A and is near the end of its range. An estimate of its mass based on grain counting gave $1080 \pm 160 m_e$. The mass estimated by scattering was somewhat higher. The over-all conclusion is that "the true value of m_k lies between 700 and $1800 m_e$, and we think it highly probable that it is substantially less than that of a proton."

It was also concluded that the event occurring at A was a disintegration rather than an interaction. The particle t linking the two events is a slow one, presumably a π^- meson. Particles a and b produce tracks whose grain density is about twice minimum and fairly constant so that they must be mesons or protons. Their energy is high enough that they would not be expected to occur in a star without the presence of many other low-energy prongs. If event A is to be interpreted as a disintegration, all tracks should lie in a plane. They do, and a good momentum balance is obtained on such an assumption. Powell and coworkers concluded that the stopped particle, which they called a tau meson, had disintegrated into three other mesons. Subsequently two similar events were found which could be given the same interpretation [52]. In each case a good momentum balance was obtained if the three decay particles

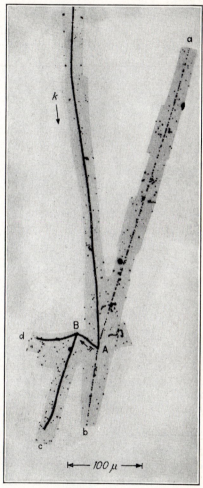

FIG. 14. Double star in which the particle k appears to have a mass of approximately $1000 m_e$, after Powell et al. [9].

were all considered to be π mesons. On this basis the mass of the tau meson was estimated to be $966 \pm 8 m_e$.

Two additional events have been observed by Harding [41]. In one case the event could not be analyzed in detail. In the other the three emitted tracks could be shown to be coplanar, with a momentum balance. Assuming them to be π mesons, he calculated the mass of the initiating particle to be $1040m_e$. Another similar case has been reported by Hodgson [53].

Still another decay process of a heavy meson has been reported by O'Ceallaigh [54]. In the first example a charged particle stopped, producing a single lightly ionizing decay particle whose multiple scattering

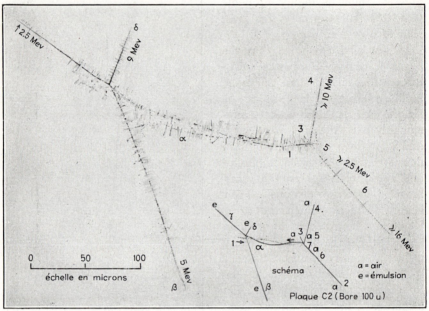

FIG. 15. Double star in which the initiating particle, 1, produces a star in which a meson, marked a, is emitted, which produces a second star, observed by Leprince-Ringuet and coworkers [42,43].

was much too small for it to be an electron produced by the decay of a μ meson (as discussed in Chap. 5). The mass of the incoming particle could be estimated from grain density and scattering to be about $1200m_e$. Three additional events were found in which a particle of similar mass decayed to give a single charged decay product. These particles have been called kappa mesons.

Leprince-Ringuet has also presented evidence for heavy mesons in the form of a double star linked by a sigma meson, the first star of which appears to be caused by a particle at the end of its range [42,43]. It is shown in Fig. 15. Several typical low-energy prongs come from the first star. It was estimated that if the energy of the star prongs was supplied by the rest mass of the stopping particle its mass was greater than $700m_e$. Here the heavy meson apparently is absorbed by a nucleus causing its disruption, a different type of event from the other endings reported. A similar case has been observed by Forster [44]. A star appears to be caused by a stopped (or very slow) particle, but a meson is emitted in the star. To supply the energy required for the meson and star prongs, the originating particle must have had a mass at least $500m_e$, and more probably in the range 700 to $800m_e$.

In emulsions flown at 90,000 to 100,000 ft altitude, Wagner and Cooper [45] found three tracks whose grain counts indicated a mass of $725 \pm 40m_e$. All appeared to reach the end of their range in the emulsion, two stopping without effect while one caused a star with two heavy prongs.

Thus quite a number of phenomena have been observed which indicate, with various degrees of certainty, that there are heavy mesons with masses in the range 700 to $1300m_e$. One can hardly doubt that such mesons do exist. The results available by early 1952 do not, however, determine clearly how many different mesons there are, what their various decay processes are, and how these serve to explain the observed events.

REFERENCES

1. Sakata, S., and T. Inoue, *Progress Theor. Phys.*, *1*, 143 (1946).
2. Marshak, R. E., and H. A. Bethe, *Phys. Rev.*, *72*, 506 (1947).
3. Lattes, C. M. G., H. Muirhead, G. P. S. Occhialini, and C. F. Powell, *Nature*, *159*, 694 (1947).
4. Powell, C. F., and G. P. S. Occhialini, "Nuclear Physics in Photographs," Oxford University Press, New York, 1947.
5. Yagoda, H. J., "Radioactive Measurements with Nuclear Emulsions," John Wiley & Sons, Inc., New York, 1949.
6. Frank, F. C., *Nature, 160*, 525 (1947).
7. Lattes, C. M. G., G. P. S. Occhialini, and C. F. Powell, *Nature, 160*, 453 (1947).
8. Lattes, C. M. G., G. P. S. Occhialini, and C. F. Powell, *Proc. Phys. Soc. (London)*, (A)*61*, 173 (1948).
9. Brown, R., U. Camerini, P. H. Fowler, H. Muirhead, C. F. Powell, and D. M. Ritson, *Nature, 163*, 82 (1949).
10. Goldschmidt-Clermont, Y., D. T. King, H. Muirhead, and D. M. Ritson, *Proc. Phys. Soc. (London)*, (A)*61*, 183 (1948).
11. Lattes, C. M. G., G. P. S. Occhialini, and C. F. Powell, *Nature, 160*, 486 (1947).
12. Lattimore, S., *Nature, 161*, 518 (1948).
13. Barbour, I., *Phys. Rev.*, *76*, 320 (1949); *78*, 518 (1950).
14. Franzinetti, C., *Phil. Mag.*, *41*, 86 (1950).

15. Peyrou, C., and A. Lagarrigue, *Compt. rend.*, *228*, 312 (1949).
16. Peyrou, C., A. Lagarrigue, and F. Bousser, *Compt. rend.*, *230*, 1058 (1950).
17. Alichanian, A. I., A. I. Alichanow, and A. Wiessenberg, *J. Phys.* (*U.S.S.R.*), *11*, 97 (1947); *J. Exp. Theoret. Phys.* (*U.S.S.R*)., *18*, 301 (1948).
18. Alichanian, A. I., A. I. Alichanow, V. M. Morosow, and A. V. Khrimjan, *Doklady Akad. Nauk S.S.S.R.*, *61*, 35 (1948).
19. Kraushaar, W. L., *Phys. Rev.*, *76*, 1045 (1949).
20. Barkas, W. H., F. M. Smith, and E. Gardner, *Phys. Rev.*, *82*, 102 (1951).
21. Auger, P., J. Daudin, A. Freon, and R. Maze, *Compt. rend.*, *226*, 169 (1948).
22. Heisenberg, W., "Cosmic Radiation," Chap. 3, Dover Publications, New York, 1946.
23. Janossy, L., "Cosmic Rays," 2d ed., Oxford University Press, New York, 1950.
24. Montgomery, D. J. X., "Cosmic Ray Physics," Princeton University Press, Princeton, N.J., 1949.
25. Auger, P., R. Maze, P. Ehrenfest, Jr., and A. Freon, *J. Phys. radium*, *10*, 39 (1939).
26. Daudin, J., *Ann. phys.*, *20*, 563 (1945).
27. Cowan, E. W., *Science*, *108*, 534 (1948).
28. Cocconi, G., V. Cocconi-Tongiorgi, and K. Greisen, *Phys. Rev.*, *75*, 1063 (1949).
29. Greisen, K., *Phys. Rev.*, *75*, 1071 (1949).
30. Daudin, J., *Compt. rend.*, *228*, 1286 (1949).
31. Leprince-Ringuet, L., and M. Lheritier, *Compt. rend.*, *219*, 618 (1944); *J. Phys. radium*, *7*, 65 (1946).
32. Bethe, H. A., *Phys. Rev.*, *70*, 821 (1946).
33. Leprince-Ringuet, L., M. Lheritier, and R. Richard-Foy, *Compt. rend.*, *221*, 465 (1945); *J. Phys. radium*, *7*, 69 (1946).
34. Brode, R. B., *Revs. Modern Phys.*, *21*, 37 (1949).
35. Retallack, J. G., and R. B. Brode, *Phys. Rev.*, *75*, 1716 (1949).
36. Bastin, E., J. Becker, P. Chanson, E. Nageotte, and P. Treille, *J. Phys. radium*, *11*, 273 (1950).
37. Rochester, G. D., and C. C. Butler, *Nature*, *160*, 855 (1947).
38. Armenteros, R., K. H. Barker, C. C. Butler, A. Cachon, and A. H. Chapman, *Nature*, *167*, 501 (1951).
39. Seriff, A. J., R. B. Leighton, C. Hsiao, E. W. Cowan, and C. D. Anderson, *Phys. Rev.*, *78*, 290 (1950).
40. Butler, C. C., W. G. V. Rosser, and K. H. Barker, *Proc. Phys. Soc.* (*London*), (A)*63*, 145 (1950).
41. Harding, J. B., *Phil. Mag.*, *41*, 405 (1950).
42. Leprince-Ringuet, L., Hoang Tchang-Fong, L. Jauneau, and D. Morellet, *Compt. rend.*, *226*, 1897 (1948).
43. Leprince-Ringuet, L., *Revs. Modern Phys.*, *21*, 42 (1949).
44. Forster, H. H., *Phys. Rev.*, *77*, 733 (1950).
45. Wagner, N., and D. Cooper, *Phys. Rev.*, *76*, 449 (1949).
46. Bridge, H. S., and M. Annis, *Phys. Rev.*, *82*, 445 (1951).

47. Thompson, R. W., H. O. Cohn, and R. S. Flum, *Phys. Rev.*, *83*, 175 (1951).
48. Fretter, W. B., *Phys. Rev.*, *83*, 1053 (1951).
49. Leighton, R. B., S. D. Wanlass, and W. L. Alford, *Phys. Rev.*, *83*, 843 (1951).
50. Armenteros, R., K. H. Barker, C. C. Butler, and A. Cachon, *Phil. Mag.*, *42*, 1113 (1951).
51. Bridge, H., H. Courant, and B. Rossi, *Phys. Rev.*, *85*, 159 (1952).
52. Fowler, P. H., M. G. K. Menon, C. F. Powell, and O. Rochat, *Phil. Mag.*, *42*, 1040 (1951).
53. Hodgson, P. E., *Phil. Mag.*, *42*, 1060 (1951).
54. O'Ceallaigh, C., *Phil. Mag.*, *42*, 1032 (1951).
55. Butler, C. C., "Progress in Cosmic Ray Physics," Chap. II, Interscience Publishers, Inc., New York, 1952.

CHAPTER 4

ARTIFICIALLY PRODUCED MESONS

According to the ideas originating with Yukawa, free mesons might be produced when a nucleon (which is the source of a meson field) is vigorously accelerated, in somewhat the same way that a photon is produced when an electrically charged particle is accelerated. The acceleration required is so large that it can be achieved only by a collision with another nucleon of high relative velocity or by a similar process. The energy required to form a π meson is about 140 Mev.* To produce π mesons artificially, an accelerator must be able to bombard a target with particles having such an energy in the center of mass system. Several high-energy accelerators now exist which are capable of achieving these energies, but the majority of the experiments here described were performed at the University of California Radiation Laboratory at Berkeley, California.

1. EVIDENCE FOR ARTIFICIAL PRODUCTION

The first evidence of the artificial production of mesons was obtained with the 184-in. cyclotron at Berkeley. Nuclear emulsion plates had been exposed directly to the 380-Mev α-particle beam and a search made for mesons. Many disintegrations were found, but in an inspection of about 5000 α-particle induced stars no mesons were found [1]. The emulsions used at that time were sensitive only to fairly heavily ionizing particles, so that only slow mesons could be observed. These are only rarely emitted from stars, so that the negative result was not unexpected. In order to separate the mesons from the large number of protons, α particles, and other disintegration products, the scheme shown in Fig. 1 was employed. The α-particle beam circulating in the cyclotron vacuum tank struck the target (most frequently carbon). The plate was shielded from the target so that only negative particles could reach it without penetrating the shielding. The entire assembly was inside the

---

* Since π mesons, rather than μ mesons, are the mesons associated with nuclear forces, they would be expected to be produced directly, but μ mesons would not.

vacuum tank, and the cyclotron's magnetic field bent negative mesons of a few Mev so as to strike the plate where their characteristic tracks could be observed. With this arrangement the background was much reduced and a large number of meson tracks observed, which showed typical scattering and grain density [2]. In good exposures it was possible to achieve a meson to background ratio of about 1 to 50. A 10-min exposure of a plate tipped at a 5° angle provided about 4000 meson tracks.

With the geometry shown, only negative mesons should be able to reach the plate. It was found that about two-thirds of the mesons

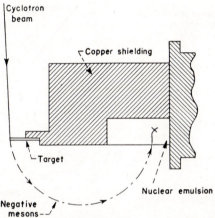

Fig. 1. Arrangement used for the detection of negative mesons produced in the Berkeley cyclotron by Gardner and Lattes [2].

produced stars at the end of their range, so that they could be identified with the mesons which Powell had called sigma mesons and considered to be negatively charged. The meson masses could be estimated from range in the emulsion and magnetic curvature, and proved to be about $300m_e$. So far the results proved to be consistent with the inferences drawn from the cosmic-ray work.

The detection of positively charged mesons was somewhat more difficult because the meson charge was of the same sign as that of the other particles present in the cyclotron. Consequently the magnetic field did not separate mesons from background as effectively. Positive mesons were, however, detected successfully [3], using the arrangements shown in Fig. 2. The scheme shown in Fig. 2a detected positive mesons ejected backward from the target; that shown in Fig. 2b accepted forward mesons, but avoided interference with the circulating α-particle beam by having the detectors and shielding placed below it. Tracks were found having the scattering and grain density characteristic of mesons. They did not form stars. Masses of about 300 and 200m_e were both present. Those of mass 300m_e usually produced a secondary meson by pi-mu decay at the end of their range. The mass 200m_e cases did not (the decay electron was not observed because the emulsions were not sensitive to tracks of minimum ionization). It seemed probable that the mass 200m_e mesons were actually all secondaries of mass 300m_e mesons and were not produced directly in the target.

Thus these observations on positive mesons were also completely consistent with the cosmic-ray data. There is no reason to doubt that the

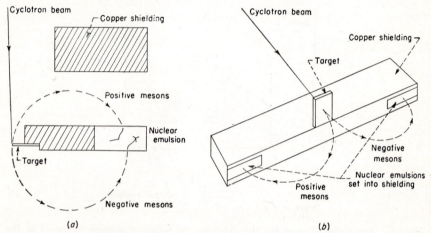

Fig. 2. Arrangements used for the detection of positive mesons produced in the cyclotron, by Burfening, Gardner, and Lattes [3].

artificially produced mesons are identical with those occurring in cosmic rays.

π mesons* have been produced by several other bombarding particles besides α particles. The 345-Mev proton beam of the Berkeley cyclotron is also an effective meson producer. Essentially the same methods have been employed for detecting the mesons, but the background tends to be higher because the protons and also the neutrons and other secondaries produced by them are more penetrating than is the case with the α-particle beam. More recently, however, an external proton beam has been obtained. Mesons produced when this beam hits a target can be separated magnetically and background very greatly reduced. With

* In view of the evidence presented, we will henceforth consider the artificially produced mesons to be π mesons identical with those observed in cosmic radiation. There seems to be no reason to question this identification.

the arrangement shown in Fig. 3, Richman, Skinner, Merritt, and Youtz [4] were able to produce a π^+-meson beam with an intensity of about 5000 mesons per sec with energies in a 48- to 60-Mev band!

π mesons have also been produced by high-energy neutrons, but in smaller numbers. When an internal target is bombarded by the proton beam, high-energy neutrons are produced which pass out through the

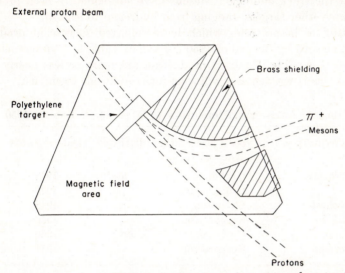

FIG. 3. Arrangement for producing π^+-meson beam from external proton beam of Berkeley cyclotron, used by Richman, Skinner, Merritt, and Youtz [4].

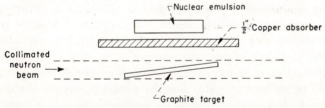

FIG. 4. Schematic arrangement used for detecting π mesons produced by 270-Mev neutrons on a carbon target, by Bradner, O'Connel, and Rankin [7].

cyclotron wall. Mesons have been observed in a cloud chamber placed in this neutron beam [5]. In emulsions similarly placed, several stars were found in which mesons were emitted from a total sample of about 50,000 stars [6]. By keeping the emulsions which were used to detect the mesons out of the neutron beam, as shown in Fig. 4, Bradner, O'Connel, and Rankin detected several hundred mesons produced by 270-Mev neutron bombardment of carbon [7].

Artificial π mesons have also been produced by photons (or X rays), as reported by McMillan, Peterson, and White [8]. Photons (X rays) produced by bombarding a platinum target with electrons of 335 Mev strike a carbon target and plates are stacked nearby. With suitable exposure about 100 meson track endings were found per square centimeter of 100-micron emulsion. The typical stars and pi-mu decays are found at the track endings. Mesons have subsequently been produced from many other targets, ranging from hydrogen to lead [9].

A listing of laboratories which have reported success in producing artificial mesons by the end of 1950 is given in Table 1. Numerous other accelerators capable of meson production are more or less nearly completed as this is written and will soon form additions to the list.

TABLE 1. ARTIFICIAL PRODUCTION OF MESONS BY END OF 1950

Laboratory	Type of accelerator	Particle	Date reported
Berkeley	Cyclotron	α	1948
	Synchrotron	γ	1949
Rochester	Cyclotron	p	1949
M.I.T.	Synchrotron	γ	1950
Columbia	Cyclotron	p	1950
Cornell	Synchrotron	γ	1951

2. DESCRIPTION OF THE PRODUCTION PROCESS

One can imagine an attempt to give a complete description of the artificial production of mesons which would cover all possible combinations of circumstances. That is, for each target nucleus, each bombarding particle, and each energy, the number of mesons produced would be given as a function of energy, angle, charge, and possibly other variables. This would be an impracticably lengthy program, even if the data were known, which they are not, except for scattered items. A more reasonable approach would be to try to describe meson production in simple two-particle collisions such as p-p, γ-p, n-p, and so on, and to neglect, for example, α particles on carbon.

There are, however, as this is written, many gaps in the information on these simple events, and some, such as n-n collisions, will probably not be studied directly (a pure neutron target being difficult to assemble) for a long time. In addition there are interesting things about the more complicated processes. For these two reasons it seems wiser not to introduce such a restriction. The following two sections give a rather undiscriminating catalogue of results known about artificial production based on information published at the time of writing.

3. PRODUCTION AS A FUNCTION OF BOMBARDING PARTICLE AND ENERGY

The excitation curves giving relative yield of negative π mesons from a carbon target bombarded with α particles and protons of various energies have been measured by Jones and White [10]. Their data are plotted in Fig. 5, with the yields normalized to 100 for α-particle energy

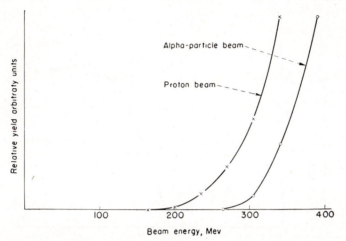

FIG. 5.   Relative production of 2 to 10 Mev mesons from carbon as a function of bombarding energy of protons and α particles, according to Jones and White [10]. Proton and α-particle curves are drawn to different scales.

of 390 Mev and proton energy of 345 Mev. It is evident that some production of mesons takes place at α-particle energies considerably below the maximum which the cyclotron can produce. Comparable data have not yet been published for positive π mesons.

Information on meson production by neutrons as a function of neutron energy has not yet been published. Such data would be difficult to obtain because the energy and intensity of the neutron beam are not known with accuracy comparable to that of the proton beam. In addition the intensity of the beam is less, so that fewer mesons are produced.

Similar difficulties arise in measuring the excitation curve for meson production by photons. Photons are produced by electrons of definite energy, but the bremsstrahlung photons are produced with a distribution of energies from zero up to the full electron energy. The number of photons with energy E is approximately proportional to $1/E$. Measurements of the energy spectrum of the photons produced by the Berkeley synchrotron have been made by Powell, Hartsough, and Hill [11].

The difficulty involved in this energy spread has been overcome by Bishop, Steinberger, and Cook in the case of photon bombardment of liquid hydrogen [12]. They measured the meson production as a function of angle and energy and were able to calculate the energy of the photon responsible from conservation of energy and momentum. Since the number of photons as a function of energy was known, this gave them the meson production rate as a function of photon energy. The results are given in Fig. 6.

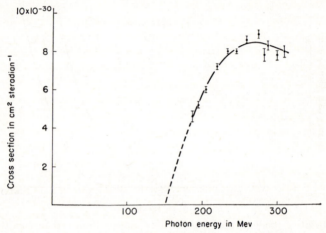

Fig. 6. Absolute cross sections for the production of π mesons by the reaction $\gamma + p \rightarrow n + \pi^+$ as a function of photon energy, according to Bishop, Steinberger, and Cook [12].

It is in some respects surprising that mesons can be produced by protons and α particles of energy as low as is shown by Fig. 5. It is simplest to picture the formation of a meson as occurring in a collision between two nucleons, which must supply an energy of about 140 Mev. In the case of a 380-Mev α particle, each of the four nucleons has, on the average, a kinetic energy of 95 Mev in the laboratory system. In the center-of-mass system of the two colliding nucleons (one in the α particle, the other in the nucleus) the kinetic energy would be only half as great, however, and only this energy is available for meson creation. On this argument one would not expect mesons to be produced by α particles of 380 Mev. The explanation for the observed threshold apparently lies in the internal motion of the nucleons in the α particle and the bombarded nucleus. This motion has a kinetic energy of about 25 Mev and therefore makes a substantial contribution [2,13]. In the most favorable case the three velocities add so that the kinetic energy available for meson formation (in the center of mass system of the two colliding nucleons) is

$$\text{Available energy} = \tfrac{1}{2}(\sqrt{95} + \sqrt{25} + \sqrt{25})^2 = 195 \text{ Mev}$$

This is indeed adequate to produce a meson.

An alternative picture has been employed by Barkas in which no assumption is made concerning the collision responsible for meson formation [14]. The threshold for meson production is calculated from the masses of the reacting and product particles in a manner analogous to that employed for other nuclear reactions, the product particles having zero kinetic energy in the center-of-mass system. This procedure gives the absolute threshold below which meson formation is impossible consistent with conservation of energy and momentum. If a suitable mechanism does not exist for achieving this transformation of the energy of the reacting particles into a meson, the experimentally observed threshold will be higher. Some typical absolute thresholds are given in Table 2. The absolute thresholds for the reactions whose excitation curves are given in Fig. 5 are somewhat lower than the experimentally observed thresholds, but the difference is not very great.

TABLE 2. ABSOLUTE THRESHOLDS FOR TYPICAL MESON PRODUCTION REACTIONS, ACCORDING TO BARKAS [14]

Beam	Target	Products	Threshold, Mev
γ	p	$\pi^+ + n$	159
γ	C^{12}	$\pi^+ + B^{12}$	161
γ	C^{12}	$\pi^- + N^{12}$	165
p	p	$\pi^+ + D$	301
p	C^{12}	$\pi^+ + C^{13}$	155
p	C^{12}	$\pi^- + N^{12} + p$	178
α	C^{12}	$\pi^- + F^{16}$	207
α	C^{12}	$\pi^+ + N^{16}$	202

One very important conclusion can be drawn from these observations on the threshold for π-meson production: *π mesons can be produced singly rather than in pairs.* As a consequence of this it appears virtually certain that the *π meson has integral spin, probably 0 or 1.* Otherwise spin would not be conserved in the formation of π mesons. One can see this by considering the reaction

$$\underset{\text{spin } \frac{1}{2}}{p} + \underset{\text{spin } \frac{1}{2}}{p} \rightarrow \underset{\text{spin } \frac{1}{2}}{p} + \underset{\text{spin } \frac{1}{2}}{n} + \underset{\text{spin ?}}{\pi^+}$$

The two spins on the left-hand side of the equation add to give either 0 or 1. If the π meson has spin 0 or 1, the right-hand side can add to the same value, but if the π-meson spin is $\frac{1}{2}$, it can only add up to $\frac{1}{2}$, or $\frac{3}{2}$, so that spin would not be conserved, a situation that would be contrary to our basic ideas about elementary particles.

4. PRODUCTION AS A FUNCTION OF MESON CHARGE, ENERGY, AND ANGLE

A considerable number of measurements have been made giving energy spectra, angular distribution, and + to − ratio for various bombarding particles and targets. The targets generally used have been carbon and hydrogen. α particles, protons, neutrons, and γ rays have been used for bombardment. The following discussion outlines the data available in each case.

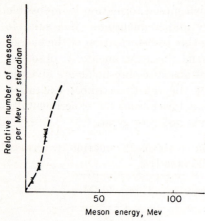

FIG. 7. Energy spectrum of π mesons in forward direction from $\alpha + C$ reaction, according to Jones and White [16].

The α-article beam was used in the earliest experiments, but has not been used recently. The information available is quite incomplete. Barkas [1,15] showed that for mesons of 2 to 5 Mev energy from carbon the + to − ratio was about 0.19. This is understandable because positive particles of such low energy tend to be eliminated by the Coulomb barrier. The energy distribution at low energies was measured by Jones and White [16] for π^- mesons. They obtained the points shown in Fig. 7 from the position of tracks on plates exposed with an arrangement similar to that of Fig. 1. An estimate by Peterson [1,17] places the absolute cross section for the production of mesons in the energy range of 2 to 5 Mev at $3.0 \pm 0.8 \times 10^{-32}$ cm^2 Mev^{-1} sterad^{-1} per carbon nucleus. Data on α bombardment of hydrogen seems to be lacking. These data were obtained working inside the cyclotron vacuum chamber where such measurements were very difficult.

For production by the proton beam, more complete information is available. Richman and Wilcox have measured the absolute cross section for the production of π^+ and π^- mesons by 345-Mev protons in the external beam on carbon at 90° to the beam [18]. The mesons were detected at the end of their range in nuclear emulsions embedded in absorbers.   The energy with which the mesons were produced was measured from the amount of absorber penetrated.   The energy distributions are shown in Fig. 8.   The integral of the π^- curve is 4.0 $\pm$ 1.6 $\times$ 10^{-29} cm² sterad^{-1} nucleus^{-1} while that for π^+ is 2.0 $\pm$ 0.5 $\times$ 10^{-28} cm² sterad^{-1} nucleus^{-1}.   The positive to negative ratio is thus about 5, just the opposite of the Coulomb barrier effect observed for low-energy mesons.   Somewhat higher cross sections have been reported by Block, Passman, and Havens for 381-Mev protons [34].

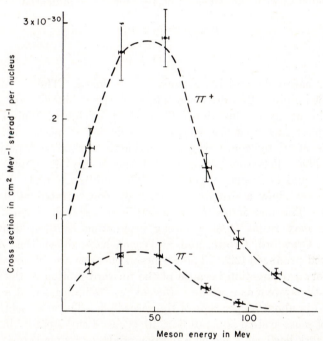

FIG. 8.   Energy spectra of π mesons from $p + C$ reaction for 345-Mev protons, at 90° to beam, according to Richman and Wilcox [18].

In this case the positive to negative ratio depends on the bombarding particle and target nucleus.   The main consideration is a statistical one.   Consider, for example, a proton incident on a carbon nucleus.   If the incoming proton interacts with a proton, either may change into a neutron and a π^+ meson, a total of twelve possibilities.   If the incoming proton interacts with a neutron, either the proton may change to a neutron emitting a π^+ meson or the neutron to a proton emitting a π^- meson.   There are six possibilities for each, so that the odds are 3 to 1 in favor of positive π mesons.   In addition, formation of a π^+ meson results in a $6p + 7n$ nucleus, whereas formation of a π^- meson gives $8p + 5n$, which would be more difficult in view of the exclusion principle, since only cells of relatively high energy would be available in phase space for the eighth proton [19]. The observed ratio of 5 for carbon seems reasonable in view of these considerations.

Information is not yet available concerning the angular distribution of mesons from proton bombardment of carbon.

Meson production by proton bombardment of hydrogen (that is, p-p collisions) is of special interest. One of the protons is transformed into a neutron with the emission of a π^+ meson as indicated

$$p + p \rightarrow n + p + \pi^+$$

or

$$\rightarrow D + \pi^+$$

in either case only positive mesons are produced. The $+$ to $-$ ratio should be infinite. If a deuteron is formed, the π^+ should have a definite energy in any given direction. Cartwright, Richman, Whitehead, and Wilcox have measured the energy spectrum for π^+ mesons produced at an angle of $0°$ by comparing production in carbon and polyethylene targets [20]. Peterson has measured the energy distribution at $30°$ using a liquid hydrogen target [21]. The results are plotted in Fig. 9. Both curves show a distribution strongly concentrated at its highest energies. This may indicate that a deuteron is actually formed in many cases or may result from a strong interaction between neutron and proton. Crawford, Crowe, and Stevenson have shown that deuterons are indeed produced [22]. The π^+-meson energies are, of course, higher in the forward direction because of the forward motion of the center of mass of the system as a whole. Recent results indicate that a deuteron is formed in about 50 per cent of the cases [32]. The cross section in the center of mass system is about $3 \times 10^{-29} \cos^2 \theta$ cm^2 sterad^{-1} [33].

Less work has been done on π mesons produced by neutrons. An estimate of the $+$ to $-$ ratio has, however, been made by Bradner, O'Connel, and Rankin for carbon bombarded with 270-Mev neutrons [23]. They observed 34 pi-mu decays and 307 sigma mesons producing stars. Other experiments indicated that practically every π^+ meson produces a recognizable pi-mu decay, whereas about 73 per cent of the π^- mesons are sigma mesons giving observable stars. Using these figures, the actual $+$ to $-$ ratio is about $\frac{1}{13}$. The explanation is the same as in the case of proton bombardment of carbon except that now statistics and exclusion principle both favor the formation of negative rather than positive π mesons. No results are yet available on the energy and angular distributions of the π mesons or on production in neutron bombardment of hydrogen.

Fairly complete data are available on the production of π mesons by photons. Using the synchrotron beam with maximum energy of about 330 Mev bombarding a carbon target, McMillan, Peterson and White [24] obtained a + to − ratio of 1/1.7. More detailed measurements by Peterson, Gilbert, and White [25] gave a ratio of about 1/1.3. The figure is based on the number of pi-mu decays observed compared with

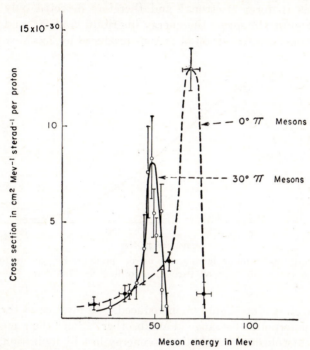

FIG. 9. Energy spectra of π^+ mesons produced by 345-Mev protons on protons at 0 and 30° to the beam, according to Cartwright, Richman, Whitehead, and Wilcox, and Peterson [20,21].

the number of stars. The processes involved are presumably

$$\gamma + p \rightarrow n + \pi^+$$

and

$$\gamma + n \rightarrow p + \pi^-$$

The higher frequency of the second is apparently due to the fact that the π^- meson is accompanied by a recoil proton while the π^+ meson has a recoil neutron [26]. The former combination is better coupled to the electromagnetic field and is therefore produced in greater abundance. The theoretical ratio calculated on this basis is in general agreement with experiment. The energy distribution for sigma and pi mesons taken together is shown in Fig. 10. There were no large departures from spherical symmetry of meson emission.

When π mesons are produced by photons on hydrogen, only positive mesons would be expected. Measurements of energy and angular distribution have been made by Bishop, Steinberger, and Cook (27,28). They used counters in delayed coincidence to detect the resulting decay of μ mesons to form electrons* and therefore detected only positive mesons. Figure 11a shows the energy distribution at 90° and Fig. 11b shows the angular distribution of mesons produced by 250-Mev photons.

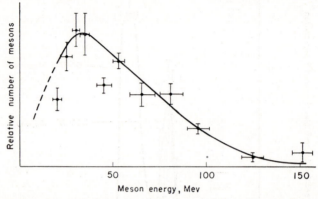

FIG. 10. Energy spectrum of sigma and pi mesons produced by synchrotron beam of maximum energy ≈335 Mev on carbon, according to McMillan, Peterson, and White [24].

One note of caution should be introduced. In most cases the energies have been determined by range in an absorber. Since the π mesons also suffer nuclear collisions in addition to energy lost by ionization, some of them may be removed thereby, which will make the number of π mesons recorded tend to be consistently too low by a small amount. No corrections have been made for this effect.

5. MASSES OF ARTIFICIALLY PRODUCED MESONS

The observations made on mesons produced in the cyclotron can yield an accurate measurement of the meson mass through a simultaneous measurement of the curvature in the magnetic field of the cyclotron and range in the emulsion. A plate holder such as that shown in Fig. 12 was first used [1]. In order to measure curvature accurately the target was made very small and an accurate fiducial mark placed in the plate. The magnetic field was mapped carefully. The main sources of error were

* See Chap. 5 for details on μ meson decay and delayed-coincidence counting.

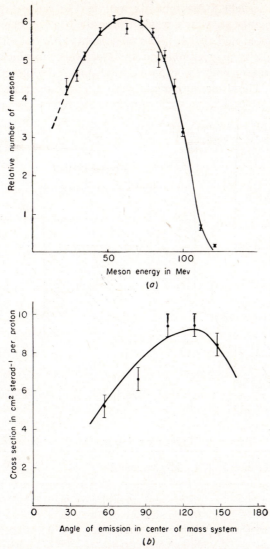

FIG. 11. Distribution of π^+ mesons produced by photons on hydrogen. (a) Energy
distribution at 90° to beam from 330-Mev synchrotron; (b) angular distribution in
center-of-mass system of π^+ mesons produced in hydrogen by 250-Mev photons
(energy in lab system) (Bishop, Steinberger, and Cook [28]).

in the magnetic-field measurements and in the range-energy relation used for the emulsion, which was an empirical one. The mass values obtained are listed in Table 4. The uncertainty due to the range-energy relationship was largely eliminated in later work in which ranges and curvatures of mesons were compared with those of protons of the same velocity [29]. These measurements gave a π^+-meson mass of (277.4 $\pm$

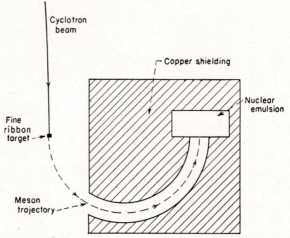

Fig. 12. Experimental arrangement for measuring negative meson masses in cyclotron [1].

1.1)m_e and a π^--meson mass of (276.1 $\pm$ 1.3)m_e, which are the final values listed in Table 3.

TABLE 3. MASSES OF ARTIFICIAL MESONS

Type of meson	Measurement	Mass
π^-	Range and curvature	$(280.5 \pm 6)m_e$
π^+	Range and curvature	$(278 \pm 8)m_e$
π^+	Range and curvature	$(276 \pm 6)m_e$
μ^+	Range and curvature	$(212 \pm 6)m_e$
π^+	Proton comparison	$(277.4 \pm 1.1)m_e$
π^-	Proton comparison	$(276.1 \pm 1.3)m_e$

These mass values have been checked using the grain count vs. residual range method of Lattes, Occhialini, and Powell. Three independent measurements gave $264^{+26}_{-22}m_e$, $305m_e$, and $280 \pm 15m_e$ for the π^- mass. The value obtained for μ^- was $202m_e$. This method is, however, less accurate than that based on magnetic curvature and range or direct comparison with protons.

These results are all in good agreement with corresponding measurements on cosmic-ray mesons and of comparable accuracy. The final π-meson mass measurements are much the most accurate that have been made.

6. BEHAVIOR OF ARTIFICIAL MESONS

As has been mentioned, artificially produced negative mesons of mass $\approx 280 m_e$ usually produce stars at the end of their range. This interaction has been studied in some detail, but the results will be presented in Chap. 6 rather than here. Similarly artificially produced positive mesons of mass $\approx 280 m_e$ usually produce pi-mu decays. Accordingly, these are identified as negative and positive π mesons, respectively. It has been possible to show that both π^+ and π^- mesons decay in flight, because the number of mesons observed decreases with increasing source-to-detector distance more rapidly than would be the case from geometrical divergence alone. A discussion of these measurements of the lifetime is given in Chap. 5.

7. EVIDENCE FOR NEUTRAL MESONS

As mentioned in Chap. 3, there is reason to believe that neutral mesons exist as well as charged ones and that neutral nuclear force mesons decay into two photons. The original evidence for this neutral meson hypothesis (from cosmic-ray observations) was the production of cascade showers in nuclear events which also produced charged mesons. The neutral mesons provide a mechanism for the origin of the soft component.* Very convincing confirmation of this hypothesis has been obtained from high-energy photons observed when (charged) mesons were being produced artificially.

High-energy photons were observed by Bjorklund, Crandall, Moyer, and York when various targets were bombarded by protons of 180 Mev or more [30]. They measured the energy of the photons by means of a pair spectrometer. The general arrangement is shown in Fig. 13. It was possible to select photons at either 0 or 180° to the bombarding proton beam by reversing the direction of rotation of the beam. They found that the yield of photons of 30 Mev or more began at a proton energy of about 180 Mev and rose rapidly with energy, in somewhat

---

* These phenomena are discussed in Chap. 7 since they are a part of the complicated observations on meson production in cosmic radiation.

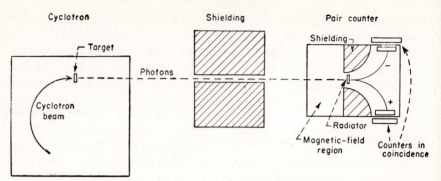

FIG. 13.   Arrangement for detecting high-energy photons produced in the cyclotron used by Bjorklund, Crandall, Moyer, and York [30].   (Not to scale.)

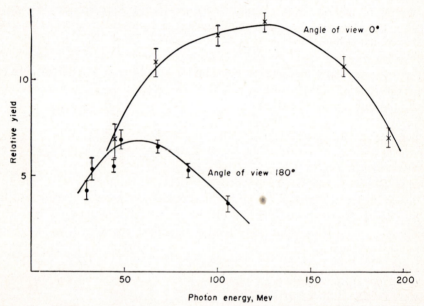

FIG. 14.   Photon energy spectra at 0° and 180° to the direction of the bombarding protons (350 Mev) with 2-in. Be target, according to Bjorklund, Crandall, Moyer, and York [30].

the same fashion as the meson yield.   The energy spectra of the photons in forward and backward directions are shown in Fig. 14, for bombardment with 350-Mev protons on beryllium.   The striking feature of these curves is the higher energy of the photons at 0°.   The difference between 0 and 180° is most naturally interpreted as a Doppler shift due to emission from a moving source having a velocity of 0.32 c.   When corrected for such a source velocity, the two curves coincide.

Several possibilities might be considered for the origin of the photons: (1) Excitation of the nucleus as a whole.   This is ruled out by the Doppler shift, since the nucleus could not have such a high velocity.   (2) Bremsstrahlung by the proton.   This would be expected to be much weaker than is observed and to have an energy spectrum decreasing with increasing energy rather than showing a maximum.   (3) Highly excited nucleons. A possible but unlikely explanation.   (4) Excited π mesons.   Also possible but unlikely.   (5) Neutral mesons.   This hypothesis seems to fit the observed data quite well.   If the meson had mass $280m_e$ and decayed to two photons, each should have energy ≈ 70 Mev in the coor-

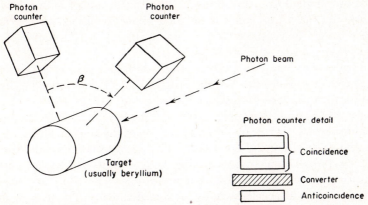

FIG. 15.   Experimental arrangement for counting photon coincidences due to neutral meson decays, used by Steinberger, Panofsky, and Steller [31].

dinate system in which the meson is at rest, and the curves of Fig. 14 do indeed have their maximum at about 80 Mev when reduced to a system with $v = 0.32$ c.   This velocity is just about that of the center of mass of the 350-Mev proton and a struck nucleon and should, therefore, be the mean component of the meson velocity in the forward direction.   The spread of actual neutral meson velocities could account for the breadth of the energy spectra.   On the whole, therefore, these data give strong support to the neutral meson picture.

Further quite conclusive evidence has been obtained by Steinberger, Panofsky, and Steller [31].   They were able to count coincidences between two photons which were almost certainly the result of the decay of a neutral meson.   Their experiment is shown schematically in Fig. 15. The two photon counters each consist of three scintillation counters, the first in anticoincidence and the next two in coincidence.   A converter (normally $\frac{1}{4}$ in. of lead) is placed between the first and second so that an incident photon, converted in the lead, counts in the last two, but not in the first.   Two such photon detectors register coincidences.

By studying counting rate for various converters with various absorbers in the path of photon or electron, it was shown that the particles registered were quite surely photons producing electrons of about 50 Mev, so that the photons had an energy of about 100 Mev, as would be produced by the decay of a moving neutral meson.   The yield increased by a factor of at least 50 as beam maximum energy was increased from 175 to 330 Mev, corresponding approximately to the increase in meson yield.   (Recent measurements by Silverman and Stearns [35] indicate that the yield of neutral mesons actually increases much more rapidly with increasing photon energy than the yield of charged mesons shown in Fig. 6.)   Comparison of the yield from a lead target with that from beryllium showed a cross section for a lead nucleus only six times as big as for beryllium, whereas the ordinary shower cross section increases by a factor of 400. Thus the photons have a nuclear origin.

The angular correlation of the photons provides a further check on the neutral-meson hypothesis.   If we assume that the meson decaying at rest emits two photons in opposite directions, the angle between the two photons will be less than 180° for a meson decaying while in motion. The counting rate was measured as a function of the angle β, and a marked maximum was obtained at 80 to 90°.   This means that the usual particle producing the photons was traveling with velocity ≈ 0.8 c.   Such a velocity is plausible for a meson, but would not be possible for a nucleon or heavier particle accelerated by bombardment with a photon beam of maximum energy 330 Mev.

Thus these recent experiments provide very convincing evidence for the existence of neutral mesons decaying into two photons.   It seems likely that the mass of the neutral mesons is about the same as that of charged π mesons.   By an ingenious argument, described in Chap. 5, it has been possible to estimate that the $\pi°$-meson (neutral π meson) mass is about $10m_e$ lower than the π^--meson mass.   The lifetime of the $\pi°$ meson must be short.   In Chap. 5 evidence will be described which sets an upper limit of 5×10^{-14} sec on the lifetime.

8. ARTIFICIAL PRODUCTION OF HEAVY MESONS

Investigations dealing with the production of mesons by accelerators are just beginning, and a great development of this field is to be expected in the next few years, unless scientific research is brought to a halt by war or other catastrophe.   A possibility of especially great interest is that of producing heavy mesons or other unsuspected particles with the large accelerating machines now under construction at Brookhaven and

Berkeley, which should achieve proton energies as high as 3000 and 6000 Mev.

REFERENCES

1. Bradner, H., "Review of Work on Artificially Produced Mesons," *University of California Radiation Laboratory Report* 486, Oct. 19, 1949.
2. Gardner, E., and C. M. G. Lattes, *Science, 107*, 270 (1948).
3. Burfening, J., E. Gardner, and C. M. G. Lattes, *Phys. Rev., 75*, 382 (1949).
4. Richman, C., M. Skinner, J. Merritt, and B. Youtz, *Phys. Rev., 80*, 900 (1950).
5. Hartsough, W., E. Hayward, and W. M. Powell, *Phys. Rev., 75*, 905 (1949).
6. Smith, F. M., E. Gardner, and H. Bradner, *Phys. Rev., 77*, 562 (1950).
7. Bradner, H., D. J. O'Connel, and B. Rankin, *Phys. Rev., 79*, 720 (1950).
8. McMillan, E. M., J. M. Peterson, and R. S. White, *Science, 110*, 579 (1949).
9. Mozley, R. F., *Phys. Rev., 80*, 493 (1950).
10. Jones, S. B., and R. S. White, *Phys. Rev., 78*, 12 (1950).
11. Powell, W. M., W. Hartsough, and M. Hill, *Phys. Rev., 81*, 213 (1951).
12. Bishop, A. S., J. Steinberger, and L. J. Cook, *Phys. Rev., 80*, 291 (1950).
13. McMillan, W. G., and E. Teller, *Phys. Rev., 72*, 1 (1947).
14. Barkas, W. H., *Phys. Rev., 75*, 1109 (1949).
15. Barkas, W. H., *Phys. Rev., 75*, 1467(A) (1949).
16. Jones, S. B., and R. S. White, *Phys. Rev., 82*, 374 (1951).
17. Peterson, V., *Phys. Rev., 75*, 1469(A) (1949).
18. Richman, C., and H. A. Wilcox, *Phys. Rev., 78*, 496 (1950).
19. Chew, G. F., and J. L. Steinberger, *Phys. Rev., 78*, 497 (1950).
20. Cartwright, W. F., C. Richman, M. N. Whitehead, and H. A. Wilcox, *Phys. Rev., 78*, 823 (1950).
21. Peterson, V. Z., *Phys. Rev., 79*, 407 (1950).
22. Crawford, F. S., Jr., K. M. Crowe, and M. L. Stevenson, *Phys. Rev., 82*, 97 (1951).
23. Bradner, H., D. J. O'Connel, and B. Rankin, *Phys. Rev., 79*, 720 (1950).
24. McMillan, E. M., J. M. Peterson, and R. S. White, *Science, 110*, 579 (1949).
25. Peterson, J. M., W. S. Gilbert, and R. S. White, *Phys. Rev., 81*, 1003 (1951).
26. Brueckner, K. A., and M. L. Goldberger, *Phys. Rev., 76*, 1725 (1949).
27. Steinberger, J., and A. S. Bishop, *Phys. Rev., 78*, 494 (1950).
28. Bishop, A. S., J. Steinberger, and L. J. Cook, *Phys. Rev., 80*, 291 (1950).
29. Barkas, W. H., F. M. Smith, and E. Gardner, *Phys. Rev., 82*, 102 (1951).
30. Bjorklund, R., W. E. Crandall, B. J. Moyer, and H. F. York, *Phys. Rev., 77*, 213 (1950).
31. Steinberger, J., W. K. H. Panofsky, and J. Steller, *Phys. Rev., 78*, 802 (1950).
32. Peterson, V., E. Iloff, and D. Sherman, *Phys. Rev., 84*, 372 (1951).
33. Whitehead, M. N., and C. Richman, *Phys. Rev., 83*, 855 (1951).
34. Block, M. M., S. Passman, and W. W. Havens, Jr., *Phys. Rev., 83*, 167 (1951).
35. Silverman, A., and M. Stearns, *Phys. Rev., 83*, 853 (1951).

CHAPTER 5

DECAY OF MESONS

It is a characteristic property of mesons that they are unstable and undergo spontaneous disintegration—or decay—in a rather short time with the formation of other particles.   Until about 1947 it was thought that the phenomenon of meson decay was a fairly simple one.   Yukawa had postulated that the free meson would decay, forming an electron, in order to give an explanation for the β decay of nuclei.   Convincing evidence had been obtained that such a process did, in fact, take place, which will be outlined in the following discussion.   At that time, however, the π-μ decay process was discovered, and it now appears likely that heavy mesons decay to form other types of mesons, though the details of the process are uncertain.   Hence the phenomena are really quite complicated.

The π meson is now associated with the nuclear force field as pictured by Yukawa.   It does undergo decay, but with the formation of a μ meson rather than an electron.   The μ meson, on the other hand, decays into an electron.   One possible scheme for nuclear β decay thus involves two intermediate mesons $\pi \rightarrow \mu \rightarrow e$.   Whether such a scheme is adequate to provide a satisfactory meson theory of nuclear forces and β decay is not clear at present.   For free mesons, however, the existence of this two-stage decay process is quite definite.   Information on the π-μ and μ-e decays will be discussed in some detail in this chapter.   Concerning the heavy meson much less is known.

Not only does each kind of meson have its own decay process, but, in addition, the behavior of mesons with respect to decay depends, in some cases, on the sign of the meson's electric charge.   This is true for mesons which decay in solid or liquid matter.   The qualitative argument is the following: When the meson has high energy, it is traveling at very nearly the velocity of light and the relativistic time dilatation tends to increase the apparent lifetime so that it is unlikely to decay. Less than a meter of dense material is enough to slow it from such speeds to a virtual stop, but to traverse a meter takes only $\sim 10^{-8}$ sec, so that decay in this period is unlikely unless the lifetime is very short indeed.

In solid or liquid matter a large fraction of the mesons decay only after they are stopped. A negative meson which has been stopped will be attracted by the Coulomb force to a nucleus and, after reaching its lowest Bohr orbit, may interact with the nucleus and be absorbed without decay. A positive meson, on the contrary, will be repelled and have no chance to interact, but must decay [1]. In a vacuum, of course, no interaction would be possible and mesons of both signs would decay. We will find that both π and μ mesons have sufficiently short lifetimes that in a gas of low density, such as the upper atmosphere, most mesons of both signs decay before they stop.

All these matters will be discussed further in the following chapters. They are mentioned by way of an introduction and as a demonstration that it is necessary to distinguish clearly between the types and signs of mesons in discussing decay and interaction processes.

1. EVIDENCE FOR DECAY OF THE μ MESON

The first experimental indication of the instability of the μ meson was obtained indirectly from the so-called absorption anomaly of the hard component of the cosmic radiation, which was observed by several investigators prior to 1938. At that time, of course, no other type of meson had been discovered and μ mesons were expected to have the properties predicted by Yukawa. The qualitative observations were the following: To a first approximation solid absorbers of different materials caused the same reduction in μ-meson intensity if they had the same mass (grams per square centimeter), but the absorption in a given layer of air was considerably greater than in a solid absorber having the same mass per unit area. The absorption of the μ mesons apparently depended both on the mass of the absorber and the space occupied by it. The explanation was simply that the time required for a μ meson to traverse the layer of air involved was comparable with its lifetime, so that an appreciable fraction of the μ mesons were lost by decay without having to be stopped by ionization losses in the absorber. For a solid absorber, however, the transit time was short compared with the lifetime, so that only μ mesons which were stopped by ionization losses failed to penetrate the absorber. Hence the over-all absorption was greater in air than in solid (or liquid) absorbers.

Calculations based on this argument were first made by Euler and Heisenberg in 1938 to estimate the average lifetime of the μ mesons [2]. They obtained a value of 2.7×10^{-6} sec. The exact meaning of the term "lifetime" is as follows: The average lifetime, τ_μ of a μ meson at rest, determines $N(t)$, the number of μ mesons present at time t, by Eq. (1),

$$N(t) = N(0) \exp \frac{-t}{\tau_\mu} \qquad (1)$$

if the μ mesons are at rest. When $t = \tau_\mu$, the fraction of them remaining is $1/2.718$. The half-life is the time at which the fraction remaining is $\frac{1}{2}$ and is given by $\tau_\mu \log_e 2$. These are the conventional definitions used for all decay processes. If the μ meson has appreciable velocity relative to the observer, the apparent lifetime τ_μ' is longer than the rest lifetime because of the relativistic time dilatation.

$$\tau_\mu' = \tau_\mu \frac{1}{\sqrt{1 - v^2/c^2}} = \tau_\mu \frac{W}{m_\mu c^2} \qquad (2)$$

where W is the total energy of the μ meson.

In the next few years a large number of indirect measurements of the μ-meson lifetime were made by various investigators. The results were not, in general, of very great accuracy, one of the main uncertainties being in the application of the theory of ionization losses to absorbers as different as air and lead. While the absorption anomaly gave good qualitative evidence for μ-meson decay, the quantitative values obtained for the lifetime are no longer of sufficient interest to merit detailed discussion. A fairly complete listing of the results is given in Table 1.

TABLE 1. μ-MESON LIFETIMES ESTIMATED FROM ABSORPTION ANOMALY

Reference	Rest lifetime, microsec
H. Euler and W. Heisenberg, *Ergeb. exakt. Naturw.*, *17*, 1 (1938)	2.7
P. Ehrenfest and A. Freon, *J. phys. radium*, *9*, 529 (1938)	4 ± 2
B. Rossi, *Nature*, *142*, 993 (1938)	2
T. H. Johnson and M. A. Pomerantz, *Phys. Rev.*, *55*, 104 (1939)	2–3
M. A. Pomerantz, *Phys. Rev.*, *57*, 3 (1940)	3.9 ± 0.3
J. Clay, *Proc. Acad. Sci. Amsterdam*, *43*, 664 (1940)	2.6
B. Rossi, N. Hilberry, and J. B. Hoag, *Phys. Rev.*, *57*, 461 (1940)	2
M. Ageno, G. Bernardini, N. B. Cacciapuoti, B. Ferretti, and G. C. Wick, *Phys. Rev.*, *57*, 945 (1940)	4–5
H. V. Neher and H. G. Stever, *Phys. Rev.*, *58*, 766 (1940)	2.8
A. Ehmert, *Z. Physik*, *115*, 333 (1940)	3.7 ± 1
B. Rossi and D. B. Hall, *Phys. Rev.*, *59*, 223 (1941)	2.4
W. M. Nielsen, C. M. Ryerson, L. W. Nordheim, and K. Z. Morgan, *Phys. Rev.*, *59*, 547 (1941)	1.25 ± 0.3
B. Rossi, K. Greisen, J. C. Stearns, D. K. Froman, and P. G. Koontz, *Phys. Rev.*, *61*, 675 (1942)	2.8 ± 0.3
G. Bernardini, *Z. Physik*, *120*, 413 (1942)	3

Descriptions of these experiments have been given by Janossy and Mont-gomery [3,4]. For a complete discussion, the original articles must be consulted. The results clearly indicate that the meson *does* decay and that the lifetime is about 2 to 3 microsec.

In addition to the indirect evidence a few cloud-chamber pictures were obtained at about the same time which showed a μ meson decaying with the formation of an electron. The first of these was obtained by Williams and Roberts [5] in 1940. A diagram of it is shown in Fig. 1. The dense track AB was quite certainly that of a meson. The radius of curvature of the track AB near A was about 70 cm, the magnetic field 1180 gauss. The remaining range corre-sponded to 41 cm of air. This led to an estimated mass of $250 \pm 70m_e$, so that the particle could not be electron or proton. (It is presumably a μ meson rather than π meson since the latter are very infrequent at sea level.) Scattering and δ tracks along AB were consistent with the conclusion that the particle had such a mass. The track BC was lightly ionizing and therefore represented a relativistic particle, presumably an electron. Its radius of curvature was ≈ 200 cm which led to an energy of 70 Mev $\pm$ 50 per cent. This would be consistent with a decay of a μ meson to an electron, with the electron taking a major fraction of the rest energy of the μ meson.

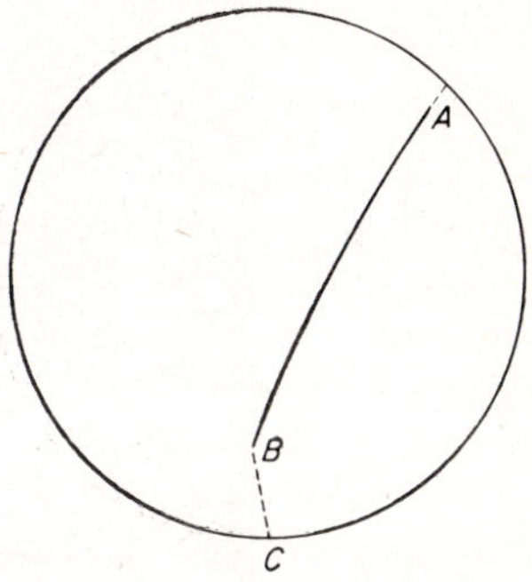

Magnetic field 1180 gauss

FIG. 1. Diagram showing a μ meson which stops, produc-ing a particle of minimum ion-ization, presumably an elec-tron, from cloud-chamber photograph by Williams and Roberts [5].

Another cloud-chamber photograph show-ing what appeared to be the decay of a μ meson was obtained by Williams and Evans [6] in a high-pressure cloud chamber which was operated at 80 atm to increase the probability of seeing a meson stop in the chamber. The quality was not as good as that of the first picture and the identification of the event not quite as certain. A somewhat clearer photograph of a decay event in a high pressure cloud chamber was obtained by Shutt, DeBene-detti, and Johnson [7]. In recent years a large number of cloud-chamber photographs of μ-meson decays have been obtained, so that there is no doubt remaining concerning the occurrence of such decays. A typical example is shown in Fig. 2.

The existence of μ-meson decay has been used to explain many facts concerning cosmic-ray phenomena, among them the following:

1. The observed distribution of electrons in the lower part of the atmosphere can be accounted for by assuming that the electrons arise

partly from knock-on electrons of μ mesons and partly from electrons produced by the decay of μ mesons in the atmosphere. (The remainder come from the transmission of the soft component from the upper atmosphere.)

2. The ratio of electrons to μ mesons under absorbing materials is less than in the atmosphere. The reason is that the contribution due to μ-meson decay is present in the atmosphere but largely absent under the

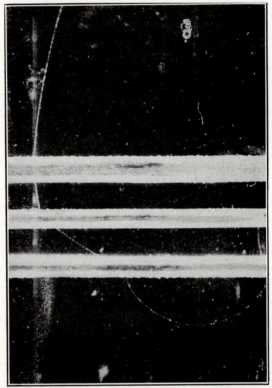

FIG. 2. Typical μ-meson decay observed in a cloud chamber by Lagarrigue and Peyrou. The heavy track is a μ meson which stops in the middle graphite plate, producing a decay electron.

absorbers, because the μ mesons pass through the absorber in too short a time to produce many decay electrons.

3. The intensity of cosmic rays at sea level decreases with increasing temperature. This can be explained on the basis that an increase of temperature means an expansion of the atmosphere. μ mesons are produced at a higher level and have more time to decay before reaching sea level, and accordingly the intensity is decreased.

These effects will be referred to again in Chap. 8. For a more detailed discussion of them, the reader should consult books dealing with cosmic rays as such. Indirect arguments of this sort were among the first indications of μ-meson decay, and were introduced before the discovery of direct evidence, which began with the cloud-chamber photograph of Williams and Roberts. For the present discussion, however, they are of historical interest only.

2. DIRECT MEASUREMENT OF μ-MESON LIFETIME

There are three main problems in making direct measurements of meson lifetimes. The first is that the number of mesons available for measurement is always small; one cannot get a piece of material containing a lot of mesons as one does with radioactive nuclei. The second is that the times involved are quite short—a few microseconds for μ mesons—so that their measurement has been a difficult problem in the past, although the electronic techniques for doing so are now quite well developed. The third is that direct measurements can hardly be made on mesons of the energy typical of those in the cosmic radiation which may travel thousands of meters before disintegrating. Direct measurements can be made only on very slow mesons, those that are "stopped" as far as cosmic-ray processes go.

The first successful measurement of this type was made by Rasetti [8]. He measured coincidences between μ mesons stopping in an absorber and their decay electrons, using coincidence circuits of several resolving times. Since the decay process takes appreciable time, some of the decays were missed by the circuits with short resolving time. The details of the experimental arrangement are shown in Fig. 3. The fourfold coincidence system $ABCD$ selects a beam of μ mesons which passes through 15 cm of lead. Anticoincidence counters G reduce the counts due to showers, and the anticoincidence counters F select μ mesons which are stopped in the absorber or scattered out of the beam by it. Unit a selects all $ABCDE$ coincidences with a resolving time of 15 microsec. To be recorded on Recorder 1, anticoincidences with F and G are required. Such an event is presumably a μ meson which decays in the absorber or is scattered by it. To be recorded in Recorder 2, however, the more stringent requirement of ADE coincidence in Unit b with a resolving time of only 1.95 microsec is added. Similarly Recorder 3 requires a DE coincidence in Unit b with 0.95 microsec resolving time.

These results give the lifetime directly because $N(15) - N(1.95)$ is a measure of the number of μ mesons decaying after 1.95 microsec, and $N(15) - N(0.95)$ of the number after 0.95 microsec. But since virtually

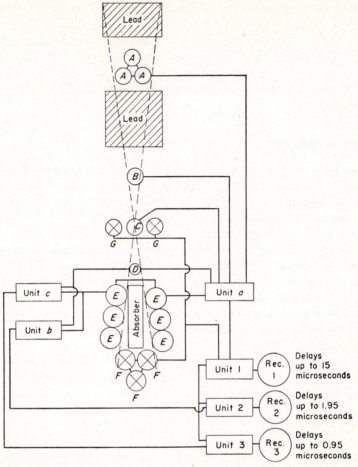

Fig. 3.   Counter coincidence scheme of Rasetti for measuring the delay in emission of electrons in μ-meson decay [8].

all μ mesons decay before 15 microsec, these numbers can be used as the numbers of μ mesons present after 1.95 and 0.95 microsec, namely, $N(0) \exp(-1.95/\tau_\mu)$ and $N(0) \exp(-0.95/\tau_\mu)$.   Then τ_μ is obtained from Eq. (3).

$$\frac{N(15) - N(1.95)}{N(15) - N(0.95)} = \frac{N(0) \exp(-1.95/\tau_\mu)}{N(0) \exp(-0.95/\tau_\mu)} = \exp\frac{-1.00}{\tau_\mu} \qquad (3)$$

The actual data are tabulated in Table 2.   They lead to a value of 1.5 ± 0.3 microsec for the lifetime.

Measurements made by Maze, Chaminade, et al. employed a different approach [9 to 12].   The pulses from the counters recording the incident

TABLE 2. COINCIDENCE RATES AND μ-MESON LIFETIMES OF RASETTI [8]

Absorber	Coincidences after 0.95 microsec, $N(15) - N(0.95)$*	Coincidences after 1.95 microsec, $N(15) - N(1.95)$	Lifetime, τ_μ, microsec
Fe	113 ± 11	56 ± 8	1.4 ± 0.3
Al	63 ± 8	30 ± 6	1.6 ± 0.4

*For aluminum data, replace 0.95 microsec by 0.75 microsec.

μ meson were delayed artificially so that a coincidence would be recorded only for a decay electron occurring after the same delay. Coincidences were obtained for delays up to about 5 microsec which led to a lifetime of 2.2 ± 0.2 microsec.

More accurate measurements were made by Rossi and Nereson [13] who employed an electronic timing circuit to measure the actual delays between pulses produced by μ mesons and decay electrons. Their apparatus is shown in Fig. 4. The "coincidence circuit" requires a coincidence LA_1A_2B with anti-coincidence in M and has a resolving time large compared with the μ-meson lifetime. The "timing circuit" provides a pulse whose height measures the time interval between A_1A_2 and the pulse from B. The time lags of the counters were shown to be only a few tenths of a microsecond, so that the observed times should give an accurate measurement of the lifetime. The experimental data which they obtained are plotted in Fig. 5.

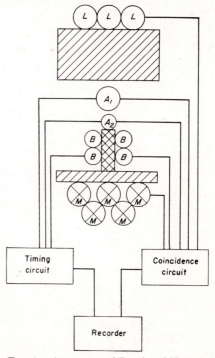

FIG. 4. Apparatus of Rossi and Nereson for measuring delays of electrons from μ-meson decay [13].

Except for the points below 1 microsec, which show deviations due to delays in the counters, the points in each case fall approximately on straight lines with identical slopes. The aluminum and "no absorber" curves have the largest statistical fluctuations. Since the "no absorber"

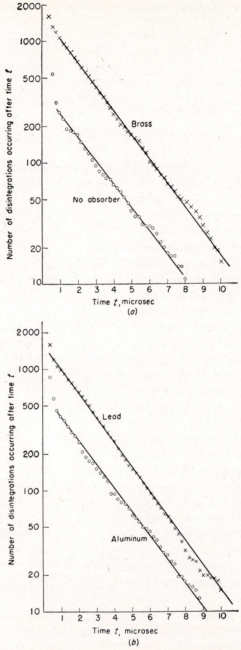

FIG. 5.   Integral disintegration curves for μ mesons in various absorbers obtained by Rossi and Nereson [13].

curve has the same slope, most of the events in this case are really μ-meson decays. By combining the results with lead, brass, and aluminum they obtained the value

$$\tau_\mu = 2.15 \pm 0.07 \text{ microsec}$$

This is in good agreement with the values given in Table 1 from indirect measurements, but is considerably more accurate than previous determinations.

Independent measurements were made by Conversi and Piccioni [14]. (Their experiments were performed in 1941 to 1943 without knowledge of the work of Rossi and Nereson because of the wartime interruption of communications.) They used a delayed coincidence system similar, in principle, to that of Auger, Maze, and Chaminade. For μ mesons stopping in an iron absorber, they found delayed coincidences whose rate dropped off exponentially with time corresponding to a lifetime $\tau_\mu = 2.33 \pm 0.15$ microsec. The most recent measurements of Bell and Hincks lead to a value of 2.22 ± 0.02 microsec [48].

Further confirmation of this value for the lifetime has been obtained from other experiments whose main purpose has been to investigate the difference between positive and negative μ mesons with respect to decay. The significance of these experiments can be understood only in terms of their historical background. The first of them were made at a time when π mesons had not yet been discovered. The cosmic-ray mesons then being studied were μ mesons, but it was thought that they should interact strongly with nucleons. According to the ideas of Tomonaga and Araki, negative mesons which stop should be attracted to the nucleus and interact with it before having an appreciable chance to decay, whereas positive mesons would be repelled from the nucleus and decay without interaction. It was originally thought that this argument would apply to cosmic-ray μ mesons, in which case only the positives would be expected to produce decay electrons. It was not possible to obtain an accurate estimate of the fraction of mesons producing decay electrons from the experiments intended to measure lifetime because it was not known to what extent the decay electrons would themselves be stopped in the absorber without being counted or escape counting due to the geometry of the apparatus. A considerable number of experiments have been performed in recent years in which a magnetic separation of positive and negative mesons has been accomplished, which has permitted them to be studied separately.

The first such experiment was reported by Conversi, Pancini, and Piccioni [15]. Their method of selecting particles of a known sign involved a magnetic selector shown in Fig. 6a. Two blocks of iron are placed as the absorber in a twofold counter telescope, with coils so that they have magnetizations parallel to the counters but in opposite directions. Then particles of one sign will tend to be bent in and converged, the opposite sign bent out and diverged. Since the experiment is concerned with μ mesons which will then stop in an absorber, their momentum is not very high and a considerable bending is possible. With magnetic induction of 15,000 gauss, the separation should be complete. To select μ mesons of the opposite sign, it is only necessary to reverse the current magnetizing the magnetic selectors. The μ mesons

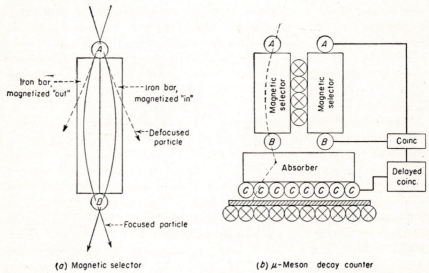

(a) Magnetic selector   (b) μ-Meson decay counter

FIG. 6. Apparatus of Conversi, Pancini, and Piccioni for measuring decay electrons from positive and negative μ mesons stopping in different absorbers [15].

of known sign are then stopped in an absorber and decay electrons are detected by coincidences which involve a delay of 1 to 4.5 microsec.

With an iron absorber the expected result was obtained, i.e., decay electrons from positive μ mesons, but virtually none when negative μ mesons were selected. With a carbon absorber, however, both positive and negative μ mesons gave decay electrons. The results are given in Table 3. It appeared that in a material of low atomic number such as carbon μ mesons were able to undergo decay before being absorbed by the nucleus.

This observation was of great importance because it showed quite directly that μ mesons did not have the strong interaction with nuclei expected of the nuclear force particle predicted by Yukawa, and was actually the first experiment to show this in a completely unambiguous fashion. At that time the π meson had not been observed, and the lack

TABLE 3. FREQUENCY OF DECAY ELECTRONS FROM POSITIVE AND NEGATIVE μ MESONS, FROM CONVERSI, PANCINI, AND PICCIONI [15]

Sign	Absorber	Decays per 100 hr
+	5 cm Fe	67 ± 6.5
−	5 cm Fe	3
+	4 cm C	36 ± 4.5
−	4 cm C + 5 cm Fe*	27 ± 3.5

* The 5 cm of Fe was to guard against scattering of very low-energy μ mesons which might destroy the magnetic selection. Of course the decays cannot come from the Fe, but must come from the C.

of nuclear interaction of the μ meson seemed to be in contradiction to the basic ideas of meson theory. With the information now available, this result adds an additional confirmation of the conclusion that the π meson is a nuclear force meson while the μ meson is not.

This result of Conversi, Pancini, and Piccioni was confirmed by Valley in a similar experiment [16]. He used a cloud chamber with magnetic field to determine the sign of the incident μ meson. A counter telescope selected particles passing through the chamber and giving a delayed coincidence (1 to 10 microsec delay) in a group of counters surrounding an absorber. This delayed coincidence then triggered the cloud chamber. With absorbers of steel and brass, only positive particles gave decays, but with carbon, water, and beryllium, it appeared that both positive and negative did so, as indicated by the data in Table 4. In determining the

TABLE 4. FREQUENCIES OF DECAY ELECTRONS FROM POSITIVE AND NEGATIVE μ MESONS STOPPED IN VARIOUS MATERIALS, OBSERVED BY VALLEY [16]

Absorber	Observed no. of μ^+	Observed no. of μ^-	Calculated fraction of μ^- decaying
Stainless steel	59	0	0
Brass	21	0	0
Water	54	18	0.7 ± 0.2
Carbon	79	56	1.2 ± 0.2*
Beryllium	25	17	1.8 ± 0.6

* In this value a special adjustment is required due to a misalignment of the telescope.

fraction of negative μ mesons that decay (last column in Table 4), two corrections were applied: one for the fact that about 20 per cent more positive μ mesons than negative are incident on the apparatus, and the other for the fact that some decays come from counter walls and other material outside the absorbing sample involved. These measurements by Valley provided an additional check upon the interpretation of the data because the curvatures observed in the cloud chamber taken with the thicknesses of the absorber gave a measure of the mass of the particle decaying. The results indicated a mass of about $200m_e$, showing that the incident particle was indeed a μ meson.

It appears, therefore, that negative μ mesons may sometimes decay, and sometimes be absorbed by nuclei when stopped in an absorber. In elements of high atomic number, absorption predominates; in those of low atomic number, decay is the more probable. It seems likely that a transition region exists where decay and absorption have comparable probabilities and that interesting effects should be observable there. Let $N^+(t)$ be the number of positive μ mesons present a time t and $N^-(t)$ the number of negative ones. If dN^- is the number of negative μ mesons disappearing in time dt, λ the probability per unit time for disintegration, and Λ that for absorption, Eq. (4) gives the rate of disappearance of μ mesons.

$$-dN^- = (\lambda + \Lambda)N^- \, dt \tag{4}$$

Equation (5) gives the number still existing at time t.

$$N^-(t) = N^-(0) \exp\left[-(\lambda + \Lambda)t\right] \tag{5}$$

Here all the quantities refer to μ mesons with velocities $\ll c$. The numbers that decay and interact per unit time at t, respectively, are given in Eq. (6).

$$
\begin{aligned}
& N^-(t) = \lambda N^-(0) \exp\left[-(\lambda + \Lambda)t\right] \\
& \text{decay} \\
& N^-(t) = \Lambda N^-(0) \exp\left[-(\lambda + \Lambda)t\right] \\
& \text{interact}
\end{aligned}
\tag{6}
$$

Both processes follow an exponential curve with time which is characterized by a lifetime $\tau_{\mu^-} = 1/(\lambda + \Lambda)$, whereas $\tau_{\mu^+} = 1/\lambda$. The lifetime is reduced by the contribution of the interaction. A fraction $\lambda/(\lambda + \Lambda)$ of the negative μ mesons undergo decay. If the ratio of negative to positive μ mesons incident upon an apparatus to detect decays is ϵ (which is observed to be equal to about 0.82), then the total number of negative μ mesons observed to decay should be given by Eq. (7).

$$
\begin{aligned}
& N_{\text{obs}}^- = \epsilon \, \frac{\lambda}{\lambda + \Lambda} \, N_{\text{obs}}^+ \\
& \epsilon \, \frac{N_{\text{obs}}^+}{N_{\text{obs}}^-} = \frac{\lambda + \Lambda}{\lambda} = \frac{\tau_{\mu^+}}{\tau_{\mu^-}}
\end{aligned}
\tag{7}
$$

Thus a change might be expected both in the relative frequencies of decay electrons from positive and negative μ mesons and in the lifetimes of positive and negative μ mesons for absorbers whose atomic number is in the transition region.

Ticho has shown that observations on both numbers of decays and lifetimes fit the above scheme fairly well [17]. He used a magnetic selector and delayed coincidence scheme similar to that of Conversi, Pancini, and Piccioni to measure the lifetime of positive and negative μ mesons and the frequency of decays in various absorbers. The results are tabulated in Table 5. There is indeed a marked change in the lifetimes of the

TABLE 5. FREQUENCIES OF DECAY ELECTRONS AND LIFETIMES FOR DECAY OF μ MESONS, OBSERVED BY TICHO [17]

Absorber	Atomic number	Charge of μ mesons	Mean life τ_μ, micro-sec	$\tau_{\mu^+}/\tau_{\mu^-}$	Relative frequency of + and − decays, corrected for positive excess, $\epsilon N_{obs}{}^+/N_{obs}{}^-$
H_2O	8	+	2.19 ± 0.30	1.14 ± 0.09	1.20 ± 0.12
		−	1.89 ± 0.15		
NaF	10.1(av)	+	2.14 ± 0.27	1.68 ± 0.17	1.66 ± 0.17
		−	1.28 ± 0.12		
Mg	12	+	2.14 ± 0.21	2.24 ± 0.16	1.79 ± 0.14
		−	0.96 ± 0.06		
Al	13	+	2.04 ± 0.18	2.9 ± 0.3	2.5 ± 0.2
		−	0.75 ± 0.07		
S	16	+	2.13 ± 0.25	4.0 ± 0.7	3.5 ± 0.4
		−	0.54 ± 0.12		

negative μ mesons and a marked change in the ratio of positive to negative decay events. As indicated by the foregoing explanation, the last two columns in Table 5 should be equal, and they are quite closely so.

Results similar to those described above have been obtained by other investigators. Valley and Rossi [18] have measured the mean life of negative μ mesons in aluminum, obtaining $\tau_{\mu^-} = 0.74 \pm 0.17$ microsec, in agreement with Ticho. Nereson has checked the relative frequencies of μ^+ and μ^- decays in boron, carbon, aluminum, and iron, finding negative decays appreciable only in boron and carbon [19]. Kissinger and Cooper report that μ^+ and μ^- mesons have the same lifetime in carbon, as would be expected since absorption is unimportant [20]. Sigurgeirsson and Yamakawa have made a careful investigation of the number of decay electrons from μ mesons stopped in various materials without distinction as to sign [21]. The relative numbers of decay electrons per stopped meson for various absorbers were Be, 0.91 ± 0.06; B_4C, 1.03 ± 0.08; C, 1.0 ± 0.07; Teflon, C_2F_4, 0.68 ± 0.05; NaF, 0.60 ± 0.05; Mg, 0.53 ± 0.05; S, 0.54 ± 0.03. Again there is evidence of a change in behavior for elements such as carbon or lighter on the one hand and magnesium or heavier on the other, with a transition for the few intermediate elements.

It would be natural at this stage to go on to consider the absorption of negative μ mesons in more detail. We might ask, for example, what products are formed by the absorption. This subject will, however, be deferred until the following chapter, which deals specifically with meson interactions. Several aspects of meson decay remain to be discussed, and these will be taken up next. In the following section information on the products of μ-meson decay will be presented.

To summarize the information on the μ-meson lifetime we can list the following points:

1. Free μ mesons decay with a rest lifetime of 2.22 microsec. This applies to fast μ mesons and to positive μ mesons brought to rest in an absorber.

2. Stopped negative μ mesons do substantially the same in materials of atomic number 6 or less.

3. Stopped negative μ mesons disappear more rapidly in materials of higher atomic number because they are also absorbed by the nuclei. For atomic number 16, the apparent lifetime is 0.5 microsec, and it becomes very small for larger atomic weights. In such absorbers most negative μ mesons interact rather than decay.

3. PRODUCTS OF μ-MESON DECAY

As long as it was thought that the cosmic-ray μ meson was to be identified with Yukawa's nuclear force particle, it seemed quite clear that the products of its decay were an electron ($+$ or $-$) and a neutrino, since these were the particles occurring in nuclear β decay. Now that the π meson is considered to be the nuclear force particle the reasoning is less clear-cut. Nuclear β decay may be a three-step process in which nucleon $\rightarrow \pi$ meson $\rightarrow \mu$ meson $\rightarrow$ electron, in which case it would remain necessary for the μ meson decay product to be an electron, but it is not known definitely that nuclear β decay follows that sequence. The main reason for considering the decay particle to be an electron is simply that the decay particle must be lighter than the μ meson, and the electron (including the positron in the generic term) is the only lighter particle known.   It would be unscientific to assume a totally new particle to be involved, if it can be considered to be an electron.   An indirect argument confirming the identification of the electron as one of the decay products is based on the fact that the soft component of the cosmic radiation at sea level would not be expected to be as abundant as it is unless decay particles from μ mesons contributed to it.   Since the charged particles in the soft component are considered to be electrons, the μ-meson decay products must be also.

Numerous cloud-chamber photographs of meson decay processes have been obtained which are consistent with the assumption that the decay particle is an electron, as, for example, that shown in Fig. 2.   The typical μ-meson track is quite heavily ionized and somewhat scattered, being either stopped or very slow when it decays, whereas the decay track is lightly ionized, indicating a relativistic particle.   This means that its mass cannot possibly be greater than about $50m_e$ and is quite consistent with the identification as an electron.   A similar conclusion can be drawn from the μ-meson decay tracks seen in nuclear emulsions.   These observations would, however, also be consistent with a particle of mass a few times that of the electron, if there were any reason to believe such to be the case.

The identification of the decay particle as an electron is generally accepted, and there seems to be no reason to question it.   The truth of the matter is, however, that, while experiments on the absorption of the charged particle (which are discussed later) show that its mass cannot be much greater than that of an electron, if any, no experiments have specifically proved that the decay particle is identical with the electrons found in atoms.*

Conservation of momentum requires that some other decay particle be produced when an electron is emitted by a stopped meson, in order that its momentum may balance that of the electron.   Cloud-chamber photographs show that only one charged particle is produced, so that the other must be neutral, and it was thought most reasonable that it should be a neutrino.   Another possibility was that a photon might be involved, and one could also imagine that two or more neutral particles might be produced.   Evidence bearing on these various possibilities will now be presented.

For a decay process in which two particles are produced by a stopped meson, conservation of energy and momentum lead to Eqs. (8) to (10).

---

* For nuclear β decay, the existence of K capture in which an orbital electron is captured instead of a β^+ particle emitted shows that the β rays and orbital electrons are identical.   Such a proof has not yet been demonstrated for μ meson decay.

μ-meson decays occurring in solid or liquid absorbers are almost entirely by stopped (or very slow) mesons, so that these equations apply.

$$P_e = P_r \tag{8}$$

$$W_e + W_r = m_\mu c^2 \tag{9}$$

$$W_e = \sqrt{(cP_e)^2 + (m_e c^2)^2} \qquad W_r = \sqrt{(cP_r)^2 + (m_r c^2)^2} \tag{10}$$

Here P_e is the momentum of the electron, P_r is the momentum of recoil, W_e and W_r are their total energies, m_e and m_r their rest masses, and m_μ the rest mass of the μ meson. Since $m_\mu c^2$ is about 100 Mev, the rest energies of the decay particles are small compared with their total energies (or zero), which are, approximately,

$$W_e \approx W_r \approx 50 \text{ Mev}$$

Experiments designed to check the possible occurrence of photons as products of μ-meson decay, therefore, involve an attempt to detect photons of about 50 Mev. Such an experiment was carried out by Hincks and Pontecorvo [22]. An absorber and counter telescope selected μ mesons stopping in the graphite absorber shown in Fig. 7a. A decay electron gives a delayed count in counter tray B or C. If a photon is given off, it may produce an electron pair and be counted; the probability of a count is about 15 per cent. They looked for coincidences between B and C in which one tray would count the electron, the other the photon. The rate of single delayed counts was 13.07 ± 0.62 per hr from μ mesons stopping in the graphite and lead. If photons were produced, the expected BC delayed-coincidence rate would be about 1 per hr. They observed 0.21 ± 0.05, and estimated a chance coincidence rate of 0.22 ± 0.02. They concluded that photons were not produced in any appreciable numbers.

Similar experiments have been performed by Sard and Althaus [23] and Piccioni [24]. The former detected delayed photons by counting electrons formed in a lead screen when no count was registered in the anticoincidence tray, directly below the brass in which μ mesons stopped (see Fig. 7b). To count decay electrons, the lead screen and anticoincidence tray were removed. The result was an electron counting rate of 0.57 ± 0.03 per hr, but the apparent photon counting rate was only 0.019 ± 0.006, which was comparable with the chance coincidence rate. In Piccioni's experiment a group of counters were arranged to indicate which one or ones fired. This hodoscope set, shown in Fig. 7c, was sensitive for about 2 microsec after a μ meson stopped in the lead. A decay photon would give discharges in three properly aligned counters to the left of the lead screen with no counts to the right. Four such events were obtained where 46 should have been if μ mesons produced 50 Mev decay photons, and these 4 events probably were not actually associated with μ mesons in any way. The possibility that photons might be the neutral particle produced can therefore be ruled out.*

The original presumption of a decay to form an electron and neutrino would appear to be justified since the photon has been eliminated. There

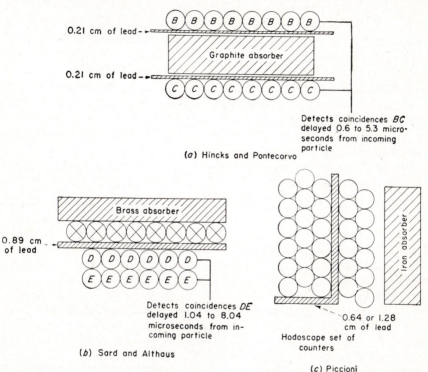

(a) Hincks and Pontecorvo

(b) Sard and Althaus

(c) Piccioni

FIG. 7. Photon detectors used in search for photons from μ-meson decay. Counters used to select the incoming particles are not shown [22 to 24].

remains, however, one very important check to be made upon such a supposition, namely, to consider the energy distribution of the decay electrons. We would expect a definite energy of 50 Mev for the electron if a single neutrino is the other product. If a different energy is observed, a different mass must be assumed for the neutral particle, while a dis-

* These results do not, of course, prove that no electromagnetic radiation is given off. Since the change from a stationary μ meson to a rapidly moving electron involves an acceleration of charge, some radiation of energy should result. Feer [*Phys. Rev.*, 75, 731 (1949)] has shown that a minor fraction of the energy involved in the decay process should go into radiation of this sort. There are, however, no appreciable number of high-energy photons.

tribution of electron energies would imply the existence of more than one neutral decay particle. The measurement of the energy of the decay electron is, therefore, a crucial experiment for the understanding of the decay process.

Two main methods have been used to measure the energy of the decay electron. The most direct method involves measurement of the curvature of the electron track in a cloud chamber with a magnetic field. The other involves a measurement of the range of the delayed decay electron with a countercoincidence scheme. The main difficulty with the cloud-chamber measurement is that a decay is an extremely rare event so that it is difficult to accumulate adequate statistics. The main difficulty with the counter measurement is that to obtain an adequate number of counts poor geometrical resolution is required and the range is not well defined. We will consider cloud-chamber measurements first.

The first cloud-chamber measurements were made on isolated instances of μ-meson decay tracks. The resulting data are given in Table 6.

TABLE 6. μ-MESON DECAY ELECTRON ENERGIES FROM CLOUD-CHAMBER MEASUREMENTS

Reference	Energy, Mev
E. J. Williams and G. E. Roberts, *Nature*, *145*, 102 (1940)	70 ± 35
R. P. Shutt, S. DeBenedetti, and T. H. Johnson, *Phys. Rev.*, *62*, 552 (1942)	> 30
C. D. Anderson, R. V. Adams, P. E. Lloyd, and R. R. Rau, *Phys. Rev.*, *72*, 724 (1947)	24
R. V. Adams, C. D. Anderson, P. E. Lloyd, R. R. Rau, and R. C. Saxena, *Revs. Modern Phys.*, *20*, 334 (1948)	25

By using a delayed coincidence scheme to trigger his cloud chamber, Thompson succeeded in obtaining a number of photographs of decay electrons [25]. The countercontrol system, however, may have introduced a slight bias against electrons of low energies. Thompson's data are given in Table 7. He concluded that his measurements were consistent with a unique energy in the range 40 to 50 Mev, though this did not fit the values 24 and 25 Mev obtained by Anderson's group.

At about the same time an energy of 15 ± 3 Mev was reported by Fowler, Cool, and Street [26], based on scattering observed in a number of thin aluminum foils. Zar, Hershkowitz, and Berezin [27] found values of 13 ± 3, 18 ± 4, and 50^{+15}_{-10} Mev for tracks in a chamber triggered by an anticoincidence scheme, but it is less certain that they were actually

TABLE 7. μ-MESON DECAY ELECTRON ENERGIES BY THOMPSON [25]

Place of disintegration	Sign	Energy, Mev
Al plate	+	20–50
Al plate	+	42 ± 12
Glass	−	70
Glass	+	53 ± 15
Gas	+	20–50
Al plate	+	43 ± 9
Al plate	+	40 ± 8
Glass	+	40 ± 12
Al plate	+	48 ± 10
Al plate	+	42 ± 8

decay electrons. It was not clear whether the discrepancies were due to the different conditions of experiment or actually represented a spread in decay electron energies.

This question was answered conclusively by the results of Leighton, Anderson, and Seriff [28]. They obtained 75 examples of μ-meson decay electrons from a total of 15,000 photographs. Their apparatus is shown schematically in Fig. 8. The chamber was triggered by a coincidence C_1C_2 in anticoincidence with C_3, that is, by a particle stopping in the chamber. Accordingly, there should not be much bias exerted on the decay-electron spectrum. The magnetic field of 7250 gauss permitted accurate curvature measurements, so that the decay-electron energy was given with an error of from 1 to 5 Mev. A typical photograph of a decay event in their cloud chamber is shown in Fig. 9. The result was an unmistakable distribution of energies, as shown in Fig. 10, which has been checked by Lagarrigue and Peyrou [49].

This result leaves one with a choice of three assumptions by way of explanation: (1) that the laws of conservation of energy and momentum have, in fact, broken down completely, (2) that one or more of the particles involved has a variable mass, or (3) that the μ meson disintegrates into three (or possibly even more) particles rather than two. Of these possibilities the last seems the most likely. Before discussing its implications, some other experiments should be mentioned which confirm the basic result.

Two of these experiments involve measurements of the range of the decay electron, one by Steinberger [29] and the other by Hincks and Pontecorvo [30]. The third experiment, based on multiple scattering in nuclear emulsions, was performed by Davies, Lock, and Muirhead [31]. Similar results have been obtained by Bramson and Havens [50].

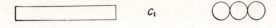

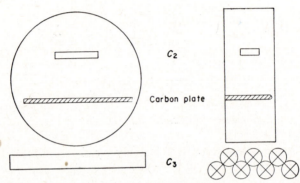

FIG. 8.   Schematic diagram of counter-controlled cloud chamber used by Leighton, Anderson, and Seriff for measurement of decay electron energies [28].   Cloud chamber is in magnetic field of 7250 gauss.

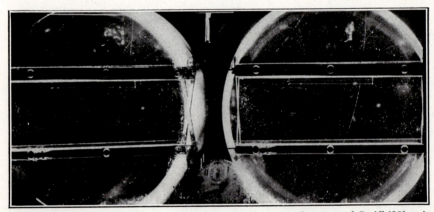

FIG. 9.   Typical μ-meson decay observed by Leighton, Anderson, and Seriff [28].   A positive μ meson passes through the counter, enters the carbon plate with momentum 72 Mev/c, stops, and produces an upward-directed decay positron with momentum 37 $\pm$ 1.5 Mev/c.

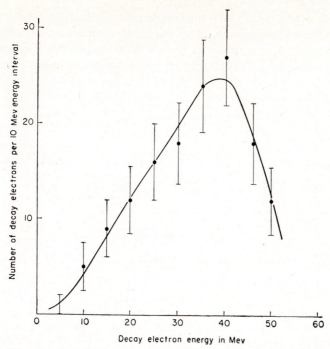

FIG. 10.   Energy spectrum of μ-meson decay electrons from measurements of Leighton, Anderson, and Seriff [28].

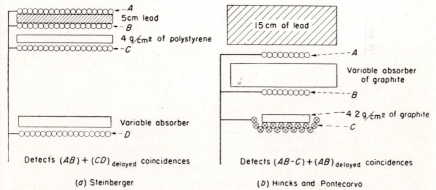

FIG. 11.   Counter telescopes for measuring range of decay electrons from μ mesons [29,30].

Steinberger's apparatus is shown in Fig. 11a. The events counted had a coincidence AB indicating an incident μ meson followed 0.7 to 4.4 microsec later by a coincidence CD indicating a decay electron. The frequency of such events was obtained as a function of the thickness of the variable absorber. Now electrons of a perfectly definite energy would not penetrate a perfectly definite thickness of variable absorber for two reasons: straggling due to bremsstrahlung and scattering, and finite geometrical resolution due to various points of origin of the decay electron in the 4 g/cm² polystyrene source and various angles of emission.

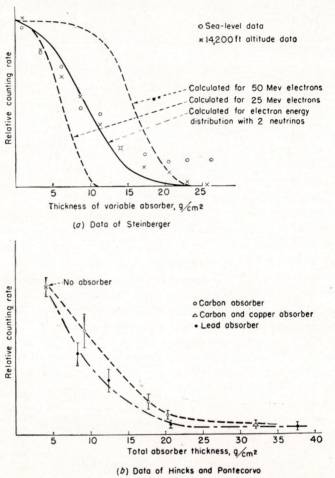

FIG. 12.   Data on range of decay electrons from μ mesons [29,30].

It was necessary, therefore, to calculate expected penetration curves for electrons of various energies such as those shown in Fig. 12a for comparison with the experimental data.   As can readily be seen from Fig. 12a the experimental data do not fit well with a unique energy of either 25 Mev or 50 Mev, but do seem to be quite consistent with a distribution of energies as calculated from a three-particle decay process.

Hincks and Pontecorvo's apparatus, shown in Fig. 11b, was similar in principle. The main difference is that the anticoincidence tray C required the μ meson to stop and trays A and B were reused to count delayed electrons from the 4.2 g/cm^2 carbon block. Their results, shown in Fig. 12b, are much the same as those of Steinberger, again indicating a distribution of electron energies. Their curve has a tail for penetration of thick layers which is due to the bremsstrahlung photons produced by the decay electrons. This fact was shown by introducing an anticoincidence photon detector. From a detailed study of these photons they showed that the charged decay particle (presumed to be an electron) must have a mass $< 2m_e$ to account for the observed bremsstrahlung photons. This is the best *direct* evidence so far that an electron actually *is* the decay particle though there is of course very strong indirect evidence supporting the presumption.

The measurements of Davies, Lock, and Muirhead also indicate a distribution of decay-electron energies. They measured the small-angle scattering of decay-electron tracks in nuclear emulsions. If the electrons all had energies of 50 Mev, a certain distribution of scattering measurements would be expected due to the statistical nature of the process. The observed distribution of scattering measurements had a considerably greater spread, which was interpreted as showing that the electron energy was not unique. The results do not, however, give much evidence concerning the nature of the electron-energy distribution. The data of Leighton, Anderson, and Seriff, on the other hand, provide a definite energy distribution, though the statistical accuracy is not very good.

It would be desirable to measure the energy spectrum of the electrons much more accurately, since an accurate spectrum might serve to determine the nature of the coupling between μ meson and electron [32]. A start on such measurements has been made by Sagane, Gardner, and Hubbard [33]. They used the external proton beam of the Berkeley cyclotron with pulsed operation to produce mesons, and detected decay electrons a few microseconds later. The electrons followed spiral orbits in a magnetic field, and those which approximated a stable circular orbit were detected with high efficiency by a scintillation counter telescope. The spectrum obtained was consistent with that of Leighton, Anderson, and Seriff, but had better statistical accuracy at the high-energy end. The spectrum appeared to drop off smoothly to zero at a maximum energy of 53 ± 2 Mev, corresponding to a μ-meson mass of $212 \pm 5m_e$, in agreement with previous mass measurements.

Our present knowledge concerning the products of μ-meson decay can be summarized as follows:

1. One charged particle results, which has a small mass and almost certainly is an electron.

2. More than one neutral particle is produced; the simplest assumption is that *two* neutral particles result. They have small mass.

3. There are no photons of any appreciable energy resulting from the decay process.

4. Presumably a neutrino is one of the neutral particles, while the other might be a neutrino or neutral meson of low mass. If the particles are both neutrinos, then the maximum energy of the electron should be very nearly half the rest mass of the μ meson, whereas, if a neutral meson of appreciable mass is involved, the maximum electron energy should be correspondingly lower. From the results of Sagane, Gardner, and Hubbard it is evident that there is no surplus to provide for a very massive neutral meson. The simplest assumption seems to be that the process consists of

$$\mu \rightarrow e + 2\nu$$

Since both electron and neutrino are particles with spin $\frac{1}{2}$, the above process indicates that the μ *meson probably has a spin of $\frac{1}{2}$ rather than* 0, these being the two possibilities arrived at in Chap. 2. If the two neutral particles are both neutrinos of spin $\frac{1}{2}$, then the μ-meson spin must be $\frac{1}{2}$ (or possibly $\frac{3}{2}$ if the results of Chap. 2 are discarded). An integral spin for the μ meson would require the introduction of a light neutral meson, which seems like a good thing to avoid, if possible, since there is no experimental evidence for the existence of such a particle.

4. DECAY OF π MESONS

The decay of π mesons has already been discussed in Chap. 3, since the first experimental evidence for this new type of meson was the discovery of the pi-mu decay process by Lattes, Muirhead, Occhialini, and Powell [34]. At first it was not certain what the identities of the pi meson or mu meson were except that they were both lighter than protons because their tracks in the emulsion showed noticeable scattering. Since it was fairly certain that the cosmic-ray μ meson decayed forming an electron, rather than another meson, it was natural to assume that the mu meson could be identified with the μ meson* and that the pi meson was a heavier meson of a new type. Its mass appeared to be the same as that of star-forming sigma mesons which obviously had strong nuclear

* The distinction between the terms mu meson and μ meson is made in Chap. 3. The mu meson is simply defined as the emitted particle observed in pi-mu decay events. The μ meson is defined as a particle of mass about $215m_e$, with a 2.22 microsec decay time and low nuclear interaction, *i.e.*, the conventional cosmic-ray meson. As has been pointed out before, the two are believed to be identical. The evidence for this conclusion is summarized again in this section.

interactions, so they were both identified with Yukawa's nuclear force meson. This nuclear force meson is called the π meson. (Nuclear interactions are discussed further in Chap. 6.)

Two subsequent observations have shown fairly definitely that mu mesons and cosmic-ray μ mesons are in fact the same particle. In the first place the absolute mass determinations for mu mesons give a mass close to the value of $215m_e$ determined for cosmic-ray μ mesons. Goldschmidt-Clermont, King, Muirhead, and Ritson [35] obtained $205 \pm 20m_e$ from the scattering of mu mesons in emulsions. Barbour [36], using range in emulsion and deflection in a magnetic field, obtained $229 \pm 21m_e$ and Franzinetti [37] obtained $217 \pm 4m_e$. In the second place "electron-sensitive" emulsions have shown that mu mesons themselves produce decay particles which may be identified with the electrons resulting from μ-meson decay [38,31]. A complete π-μ-e decay sequence is shown in Fig. 13. It has even been possible to show, from measurements on scattering, that the electrons have energies in the range 20 to 50 Mev, so that there seems to be no question that the mu meson and μ meson have the same decay process and are, therefore, identical.

We conclude that when a π meson decays, a μ meson is formed. Some other particle must be involved in order to conserve momentum, and since no other recoil tracks have been observed in the emulsions the recoil must be uncharged. From information on the energy distribution of the μ mesons, however, it is possible to determine a good deal concerning the nature of the recoil particle. While we have seen that the decay electrons from μ meson decay have a wide distribution of energies, the μ mesons from π meson decay seem to have a unique energy. Early observations on pi-mu decays showed that the range of the mu meson was constant [39]. The values obtained were 613, 565, 621, 591, 638, 595, 616, 610, 666, 637, and 590 microns, with an average 614 ± 8. The corresponding kinetic energy was 4.2 Mev. Since

FIG. 13. Complete π-meson–μ-meson–electron decay sequence observed by Powell and coworkers in an "electron-sensitive" emulsion.

this energy is unique, there is only one recoil particle. Its energy and momentum are determined, from which data an approximate mass can be inferred.*

The conservation of momentum and energy require equations corresponding to Eqs. (8) to (10).

$$P_\mu = P_r \tag{8a}$$

$$W_\mu + W_r = m_\pi c^2 \tag{9a}$$

$$W_\mu = \sqrt{(cP_\mu)^2 + (m_\mu c^2)^2} \qquad W_r = \sqrt{(cP_r)^2 + (m_r c^2)^2} \tag{10a}$$

where P_μ is the momentum of the μ meson, P_r is the momentum of recoil, W_μ and W_r are their total energies, m_μ and m_r their rest masses, and m_π the rest mass of the π meson. The currently accepted values are

$$m_\pi = 277m_e \qquad m_\mu = 215m_e$$

Since $m_e c^2 = 0.51$ Mev, we have

$$W_r = m_\pi c^2 - W_\mu = 0.51 \times 277 - (0.51 \times 215 + 4.2) \text{ Mev}$$
$$= 28 \pm 4 \text{ Mev}$$
$$cP_r = cP_\mu = \sqrt{W_\mu{}^2 - (m_\mu c^2)^2} = \sqrt{2 \times 0.51 \times 215 \times 4.2 + 4.2^2} \text{ Mev}$$
$$= 30 \text{ Mev}$$

Then

$$m_r c^2 = \sqrt{W_r{}^2 - (cP_r)^2} = \sqrt{-116}$$

This imaginary result indicates that the data are most consistent with a recoil mass of zero. Unfortunately, this method is based on taking the difference of two large and nearly equal numbers and is therefore not an accurate method of calculating the mass of the recoil particle. Small changes in π-μ mass difference or in the μ meson energy change the apparent recoil mass considerably. We can only conclude that the recoil particle is much lighter than a μ meson and probably has zero mass, which hypothesis would be in good agreement with the observations.

Thus the neutral decay particle is probably a single photon or neutrino. There is not very much experimental data on which to base a decision between the two possibilities. As in the case of μ mesons, the existence of a recoil photon should lead to observable electrons, whereas the

---

* Practically all positive π mesons do in fact decay in this way. One might expect that an electron might sometimes be produced instead of a μ meson. Smith [*Phys. Rev., 81*, 897 (1951)] estimated that at least 99 per cent give normal π-μ decays. Friedman and Rainwater [*Phys. Rev., 84*, 684 (1951)] found one apparent π-e decay in 1419 cases, but the meson may well have really been a μ meson which could not be distinguished from the π mesons. Fry [*Phys. Rev., 83*, 1268 (1951)] has reported four anomalously short μ tracks in 3018 π-μ decays, but Primakoff [*Phys. Rev., 84*, 1255 (1951)] has shown that a very few such cases would be expected because of energy radiated at the instant of decay. On the whole the constancy of the π-μ decay process is remarkable.

neutrino would be quite undetectable. O'Ceallaigh has made a search for such electrons with negative results [40]. A total of 253 pi-mu decays occurring in nuclear emulsions were selected in which the mu track and hence the opposed neutral recoil were in the plane of the emulsion. The area traversed by the recoils was searched for electron pairs that could have originated from the hypothetical photons. If the neutral decay particle was assumed to be a photon, 5.8 electron pairs would have been expected. None were observed. It was concluded that the neutral decay particle was not a photon, but presumably was a neutrino.

Such a conclusion fits well with the conservation of angular momentum, since the π meson presumably has integral spin (because π mesons are produced singly) and the μ-meson half integral (because of its decay products). Thus the neutral recoil should have half-integral spin as does the neutrino rather than spin 1 as would be the case for the photon. Thus the decay processes appear to be

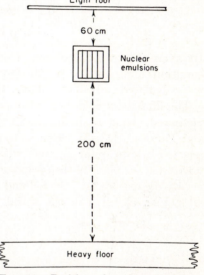

$$\pi \to \mu + \nu$$
$$\mu \to e + 2\nu$$

The lifetime of the π meson has been measured with approximately the same accuracy as that of the μ meson. It is easy to see that the π-meson lifetime should be considerably the shorter of the two. It is believed that π mesons are formed in the upper atmosphere and then decay into μ mesons. If the π-meson lifetime were comparable to that of the μ meson, the former

Fig. 14. Position of nuclear emulsions in which locally produced mesons were observed by Camerini, Muirhead, Powell, and Ritson [41].

would be a common constituent of cosmic rays at sea level. Since they are not numerous, they must decay quickly.

A first rough estimate of the π-meson lifetime was made by Camerini, Muirhead, Powell, and Ritson [41]. The results are not in agreement with later measurements, but the method is of interest. In a group of nuclear emulsions placed as shown in Fig. 14, they observed mesons traveling upward which apparently were produced locally in the floor underneath the emulsions (or in material farther below). They estimated that about 10 per cent of the mesons were π mesons and 90 per cent μ mesons. From the energy required to penetrate to the middle of the stack of plates they obtained the velocity with which a typical meson crossed the air, which turned out to be about 2×10^{10} cm/sec. Therefore the time of flight was about 10^{-8} sec, and the lifetime could be calculated from Eq. (11), assuming that π mesons were produced and decayed to μ mesons in crossing the air.

$$N(t) = N(0) \exp \frac{-t}{\tau_\pi} \tag{11}$$

Since it was estimated that 10 per cent of the π mesons had not decayed when the emulsion position was reached,

$$0.1 \approx \exp \frac{-10^{-8}}{\tau_\pi}$$
$$\tau_\pi \approx 0.5 \times 10^{-8} \text{ sec}$$

By averaging over the observed points at which mesons stopped in the emulsions and points at which they could have been created, the lifetime was calculated to be $0.6 \pm 0.3 \times 10^{-8}$ sec.

The lifetime of π mesons produced in the Berkeley cyclotron has been measured, using a similar method, by Richardson and by Martinelli and Panofsky [42,43]. π mesons produced in the cyclotron target are selected by two spiral channels which diverge slightly upward and downward from the plane of the cyclotron beam. In Richardson's experiment, negative π mesons are selected and emulsions placed so as to detect them after $\frac{1}{2}$ or $1\frac{1}{2}$ turns of the spiral. Figure 15 shows the meson paths

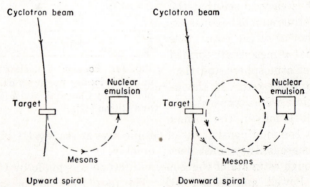

FIG. 15. Geometrical scheme for measuring π^--meson lifetime with cyclotron used by Richardson [42].

schematically. Meson-produced stars were counted in the emulsions. The number observed after $1\frac{1}{2}$ turns was less than that after $\frac{1}{2}$ turn because of geometrical divergence on the one hand and π-meson decay on the other. The divergence effect was determined experimentally by counting alpha particles from a source. When it was taken into account, the expected number of stopped π^- mesons in the emulsions at $1\frac{1}{2}$ turns was 92, whereas 48 were observed. The time for a π meson to make one revolution was 7.2×10^{-9} sec, and the resulting value for the lifetime was $1.1 \pm 0.3 \times 10^{-8}$ sec. The same general procedure was followed by Martinelli and Panofsky except that the channels were arranged for positive π mesons, pi-mu decays were counted, and an additional position was added which detected them after $2\frac{1}{2}$ turns. The value which they obtained for the lifetime was $1.97^{+0.14}_{-0.17} \times 10^{-8}$ sec. The lifetime for negative π mesons has been determined by Lederman, Booth, Byfield, and Kessler from the number of decays observed when a π-meson beam passes through a cloud chamber [51]. They obtained a lifetime of $2.9 \pm 0.3 \times 10^{-8}$ sec.

While these lifetimes are very short, direct measurements of the lifetime of positive π mesons have been made successfully, using scintillation crystal counters. Artificially produced π mesons were incident on a pair of scintillation crystals. In some cases the π meson would pass through one crystal and stop in the second, then produce a delayed μ-meson pulse, and finally a further delayed electron pulse, showing a complete $\pi \rightarrow \mu \rightarrow e$ decay chain. From the delays between the first two pulses the π-μ lifetime would be determined. In this way Kraushaar, Thomas, and Henri [44] obtained a lifetime of $1.65 \pm 0.33 \times 10^{-8}$ sec, while Chamberlain, Mozley, Steinberger, and Wiegand [45] found a value of $2.59 \pm 0.12 \times 10^{-8}$ sec. (An alternative calculation gave $2.65 \pm 0.12 \times 10^{-8}$.) Similarly Jakobson, Schulz, and Steinberger [46] obtained $2.54 \pm 0.11 \times 10^{-8}$ sec.

The agreement between these values is not especially good. In all probability the final values are the most accurate, since they are direct measurements and have the best statistical accuracy. While Richardson's value is considerably lower, it does not seem likely that there is a different lifetime for negative π mesons. The best value for the π-meson lifetime is probably

$$\tau_{\pi^+} = \tau_{\pi^-} = 2.6 \times 10^{-8} \text{ sec}$$

The decay process of the neutral π meson is quite different from the charged case. As stated in Chap. 4, the existence of the neutral π meson (π^0 meson) is actually inferred from observations on photons which are thought to be its decay products. The behavior of the photons can be most satisfactorily explained if they are assumed to be formed from the decay of a neutral meson. It appears plausible theoretically that such a decay process should take place for a neutral meson which is strongly coupled to nucleons, since such a meson would be accompanied by virtual nucleon-antinucleon pairs in somewhat the same way that nucleons are accompanied by virtual mesons. A nucleon-antinucleon pair can annihilate producing two high-energy photons, and photons of this type are, in fact, observed experimentally. Of course the observations are somewhat indirect, since neither photons nor neutral meson are ionizing particles which can be detected directly. Nevertheless, it seems fairly certain that the $\pi^0 \rightarrow 2\gamma$ process really does take place.

A very ingenious estimate of the lifetime of the π^0 meson has been made by Carlson, Hooper, and King [47]. They observed electron pairs

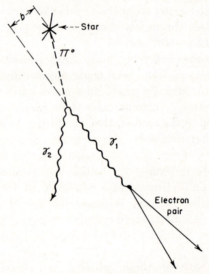

Fig. 16. Schematic diagram of electron pair due to γ ray from π° meson produced in star.

near stars in nuclear emulsions exposed at balloon altitudes. The directions of the electron pairs were such as to line up rather closely with a star in which the π^0 meson might have been formed. A schematic diagram is given in Fig. 16, which shows an intervening π^0-γ link. Now neither the π^0 meson nor the γ ray can be observed; but the distance b is obviously a rough measure of the lifetime of the π^0 meson, and for any assumed lifetime it is possible to calculate an expected distribution of values for b. Carlson, Hooper, and King measured the perpendicular distance, b, for 15 electron pairs and obtained a distribution corresponding to a lifetime of 5×10^{-14} sec. The distances were actually so small as to be at the limit of accuracy of their measurements, so that the figure of 5×10^{-14} sec is really only an upper limit to the lifetime. It might quite possibly be shorter yet.

5. DECAY OF HEAVY MESONS

There is not much detailed information yet about the decay of heavy mesons with masses between those of π meson and proton. The results concerning the identification of the various heavy mesons and their decay products were summarized in Chap. 3.

There are no precise data on the lifetimes of these mesons, but from the distribution of the positions of neutral V-particle decay events the lifetime of the neutral V particle has been estimated to be about 10^{-10} sec [52].

6. SUMMARY

According to present information, the decay processes of mesons seem to have the characteristics given in Table 8.

TABLE 8. SUMMARY OF RESULTS ON MESON DECAY

Meson	Decay process	Lifetime, sec
μ^+	$\mu^+ \to e^+ + 2\nu$	2.22×10^{-6}
μ^-	$\mu^- \to e^- + 2\nu$	2.22×10^{-6}, except for apparent shorter life in heavy materials due to capture
π^+	$\pi^+ \to \mu^+ + \nu$	2.6×10^{-8}
π^-	$\pi^- \to \mu^- + \nu$ (decays only in flight, absorbed if stopped)	Probably 2.6×10^{-8}
π^0	$\pi^0 \to 2\gamma$	Upper limit is 5×10^{-14}
tau	Produces 3π	
kappa	Produces μ plus neutral particle or particles	
V_2^0	May produce 2π	About 10^{-10}

REFERENCES

1. Tomonaga, S., and G. Araki, *Phys. Rev.*, *58*, 90 (1940).
2. Euler, H., and W. Heisenberg, *Ergeb. exakt. Naturw.*, *17*, 1 (1938).
3. Janossy, L., "Cosmic Rays," Oxford University Press, New York, 1948.
4. Montgomery, D. J. X., "Cosmic Ray Physics," Princeton University Press, Princeton, N.J., 1949.

5. Williams, E. J., and G. E. Roberts, *Nature*, *145*, 102 (1940).
6. Williams, E. J., and G. R. Evans, *Nature*, *145*, 818 (1940).
7. Shutt, R. P., S. DeBenedetti, and T. H. Johnson, *Phys. Rev.*, *62*, 552 (1942).
8. Rasetti, F., *Phys. Rev.*, *60*, 1948 (1941).
9. Auger, P., R. Maze, and R. Chaminade, *Phys. Rev.*, *62*, 307 (1942).
10. Auger, P., and R. Maze, *Compt. rend.*, *213*, 381 (1941).
11. Maze, R., and R. Chaminade, *Compt. rend.*, *214*, 266 (1942).
12. Chaminade, R., A. Freon, and R. Maze, *Compt. rend.*, *218*, 402 (1944).
13. Rossi, B., and N. Nereson, *Phys. Rev.*, *62*, 417 (1942); *64*, 199 (1943); *Rev. Sci. Instruments*, *17*, 65 (1946).
14. Conversi, M., and O. Piccioni, *Nuovo cimento*, *2*, 40 (1944); *Phys. Rev.*, *70*, 859 (1946).
15. Conversi, M., E. Pancini, and O. Piccioni, *Phys. Rev.*, *68*, 232 (1945); *71*, 209 (1947).
16. Valley, G. E., *Phys. Rev.*, *72*, 772 (1947).
17. Ticho, H. K., *Phys. Rev.*, *74*, 1337 (1948).
18. Valley, G. E., and B. Rossi, *Phys. Rev.*, *73*, 177 (1948).
19. Nereson, N., *Phys. Rev.*, *73*, 565 (1948).
20. Kissinger, C. W., and D. Cooper, *Phys. Rev.*, *74*, 349 (1948).
21. Sigurgeirsson, T., and K. A. Yamakawa, *Revs. Modern Phys.*, *21*, 124 (1949).
22. Hincks, E. P., and B. Pontecorvo, *Phys. Rev.*, *73*, 257 (1948).
23. Sard, R. D., and E. J. Althaus, *Phys. Rev.*, *74*, 1364 (1948).
24. Piccioni, O., *Phys. Rev.*, *74*, 1754 (1948).
25. Thompson, R. W., *Phys. Rev.*, *74*, 490 (1948).
26. Fowler, E. C., R. L. Cool, and J. C. Street, *Phys. Rev.*, *74*, 101 (1948).
27. Zar, J. L., J. Hershkowitz, and E. Berezin, *Phys. Rev.*, *74*, 111 (1948).
28. Leighton, R. B., C. D. Anderson, and A. J. Seriff, *Phys. Rev.*, *75*, 1432 (1949).
29. Steinberger, J., *Phys. Rev.*, *74*, 500 (1948); *75*, 1136 (1949).
30. Hincks, E. P., and B. Pontecorvo, *Phys. Rev.*, *74*, 697 (1948); *75*, 698 (1949); *77*, 102 (1950).
31. Davies, J. H., W. O. Lock, and H. Muirhead, *Phil. Mag.*, *40*, 1250 (1950).
32. Tiomno, J., J. A. Wheeler, and R. R. Rau, *Revs. Modern Phys.*, *21*, 144 (1949).
33. Sagane, R., W. L. Gardner, and H. W. Hubbard, *Phys. Rev.*, *82*, 557 (1951).
34. Lattes, C. M. G., H. Muirhead, G. P. S. Occhialini, and C. F. Powell, *Nature*, *159*, 694 (1947).
35. Goldschmidt-Clermont, Y., D. T. King, H. Muirhead, and D. M. Ritson, *Proc. Phys. Soc. (London)*, (A)*61*, 183 (1948).
36. Barbour, I., *Phys. Rev.*, *76*, 320 (1949); *78*, 518 (1950).
37. Franzinetti, C., *Phil. Mag.*, *41*, 86 (1950).
38. Brown, R., U. Camerini, P. H. Fowler, H. Muirhead, C. F. Powell, and D. M. Ritson, *Nature*, *163*, 47 (1949).
39. Lattes, C. M. G., G. P. S. Occhialini, and C. F. Powell, *Nature*, *160*, 453 (1947).
40. O'Ceallaigh, C., *Phil. Mag.*, *41*, 838 (1950).
41. Camerini, U., H. Muirhead, C. F. Powell, and D. M. Ritson, *Nature*, *162*, 433 (1948).

42. Richardson, J. R., *Phys. Rev.*, *74*, 1720 (1948).
43. Martinelli, E. A., and W. K. H. Panofsky, *Phys. Rev.*, *77*, 465 (1950).
44. Kraushaar, W. L., J. E. Thomas, and V. P. Henri, *Phys. Rev.*, *78*, 486 (1950).
45. Chamberlain, O., R. F. Mozley, J. Steinberger, and C. Wiegand, *Phys. Rev.*, *79*, 394 (1950).
45a. Wiegand, C. E., *Phys. Rev.*, *83*, 1085 (1951).
46. Jakobson, M., A. Schulz, and J. Steinberger, *Phys. Rev.*, *81*, 894 (1951).
47. Carlson, A. G., J. E. Hooper, and D. T. King, *Phil. Mag.*, *41*, 701 (1950).
48. Bell, W. E., and E. P. Hincks, *Phys. Rev.*, *84*, 1243 (1951).
49. Lagarrigue, A., and C. Peyrou, *Compt. rend.*, *233*, 478 (1951).
50. Bramson, H., and W. W. Havens, Jr., *Phys. Rev.*, *83*, 861 (1951).
51. Lederman, L. M., E. T. Booth, H. Byfield, and J. Kessler, *Phys. Rev.*, *83*, 685 (1951).
52. Seriff, A. J., R. B. Leighton, C. Hsiao, E. W. Cowan, and C. D. Anderson, *Phys. Rev.*, *78*, 290 (1950).

CHAPTER 6

INTERACTION OF MESONS WITH MATTER

In empty space all mesons end their lives by decay in accordance with the processes discussed in the previous chapter. In the presence of matter there is another possibility: the meson may interact with some other particle and disappear in the process. If the meson is considered to be a quantized manifestation of a nuclear force field (meson field), it would be expected to interact with those particles that are sources of the meson field, i.e., with nucleons. According to present thinking, π mesons should interact with nucleons in this way, and heavy mesons might do the same, but μ mesons might not show the same kind of interaction. This chapter will present experimental data concerning these interactions.

In addition to nuclear interactions, mesons have the same sort of electromagnetic interactions as other charged particles. As a matter of fact, electromagnetic interactions are very much more common than nuclear, because electromagnetic forces can be exerted at longer range than nuclear forces and interactions involving small energy transfers (i.e., small forces) are possible. Thus a meson passing through matter ionizes atoms all along its path, but only rarely, if at all, does it undergo a nuclear interaction. For that reason it is necessary to outline the effects of electromagnetic interactions first before proceeding to a discussion of the relatively rare nuclear ones. In the latter case two types of interactions are to be considered: those that lead to an actual disappearance of the meson, and those which merely change its momentum, amounting to nuclear scattering.

1. ELECTROMAGNETIC INTERACTIONS

Electromagnetic interactions have already been discussed to some extent in Chap. 1 as sources of energy loss in passing through matter. As was pointed out there, three types of interaction may result: the meson may be deflected by the electromagnetic forces resulting in a simple scattering, it may be perturbed sufficiently vigorously to emit electromagnetic radiation (bremsstrahlung),* or it may transfer energy to an electron, causing excitation or ionization of the atom to which the electron belonged. The latter process is the source of the steady energy loss in passing through matter.†

In most cases the energy given to the electron is small, little more than is necessary to ionize the atom, but in the relatively rare close collisions the electron may receive a considerable amount of energy, in which case it is called a "knock-on" electron. Actually the frequency of occurrence decreases smoothly with increasing electron energy.

There is no exactly defined energy for which the term "knock-on" becomes applicable; a value of 0.01 to 0.1 Mev would correspond to common usage. When the knock-on electron is produced in the gas of a cloud chamber, it produces a visible track called a δ ray, whose energy is usually near this minimum value. When the knock-on electron is produced in a solid absorber, it may emerge to be recognized by counter or cloud chamber. The more energetic electrons have the better probability of emerging to be detected, so that the typical energy observed for such knock-ons may be several Mev. Very energetic knock-ons produced in solid material may cause electron showers to develop.

Results on the scattering of mesons are taken up in the next section. In addition to scattering, there are three more or less distinct kinds of experimental measurement which may be compared with the theory of electromagnetic interactions. The first of these is an over-all measurement of energy loss or ionization. The second is a measurement of the number and energy of knock-on electrons produced by the mesons. The third is a measurement of the numbers and sizes of showers or bursts initiated by the mesons through high-energy knock-on and bremsstrahlung processes.

The average energy transferred from a meson to the electrons in the material through which it travels is given by the Bethe-Bloch formula, Eq. (6), Chap. 1. Figure 1 below (which is identical with Fig. 5, Chap. 1) shows the energy loss as a function of meson velocity. At the low-velocity end of the curves, the energy loss rises rapidly. The reason for this is that a slow meson loses more energy to each electron that it passes because its field has a longer time in which to act on it. The slow rise for large velocities is a relativistic effect due to the apparent lateral expansion of the field of the moving particle. There is, however, some

---

* Radiation is emitted, for example, when the meson is accelerated in an energetic collision. Interactions involving the meson spin and relativistic effects are also important in producing electromagnetic radiation, so that the complete theory is very complicated and still somewhat uncertain.

† For references to more complete discussions of this process, see Chap. 1.

reason to doubt that this relativistic rise is as marked in solid materials as indicated by the solid curves, because of the so-called "density effect," recently discussed in detail by Halpern and Hall [1]. This effect amounts to a reduction in the meson's field at distances large enough that there are intervening atoms between the meson and the point in question, and it arises because the polarization of the intervening atoms acts to shield the more distant points.

It is not very easy to measure the actual energy loss of a meson to compare with the curves given in Fig. 1. The energy lost can be esti-

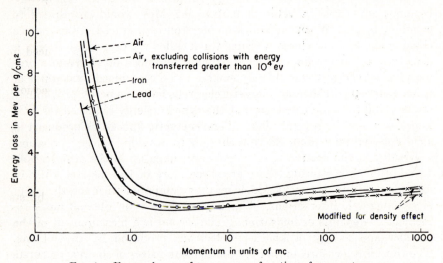

FIG. 1.   Energy losses of mesons as a function of momentum.

mated fairly closely from the number of ions produced, and this quantity is often more convenient to measure. In air, for example, each ion pair represents an energy dissipation of about 32 ev, on the average.

The density of ionization produced by mesons* has been measured by counting droplets in a cloud chamber. In such a measurement one includes only the ionization due to those electrons that are given small amounts of energy, since any energy given to a knock-on electron does not contribute to the ionization observed in the track of the meson. While such knock-ons are rare, they still account for an appreciable fraction of the total energy loss, because each knock-on gets a considerable amount of energy. The cloud-chamber measurement of density of ionization thus corresponds to an energy loss somewhat less than

---

* The measurements have been made on cosmic rays occurring at sea level with lead interposed to cut out the soft component, so that the majority of the particles are surely μ mesons.

given by the curves of Fig. 1 because it does not include the energy given to knock-on electrons.*

The results of various measurements are summarized in Table 1.

TABLE 1. DENSITY OF IONIZATION PRODUCED BY MESONS

Reference	Meson energy	Material	Density of ionization in ion pairs per cm
R. L. Sen Gupta, *Nature, 146*, 65 (1940)	10^8–5×10^9	Air	40
W. E. Hazen, *Phys. Rev., 65*, 259 (1944)	Spectrum	Air	50
W. E. Hazen, *Phys. Rev., 67*, 269 (1945)	2–6×10^8	Dry air	41
	All $> 2 \times 10^8$	Dry air	45
R. H. Frost, Thesis, Univ. of Calif., 1947	Min. ion	Hydrogen	6.78
	Min. ion	Helium	8.2
	Min. ion	Argon	55

A value of 45 ion pairs per cm in air corresponds to a value of about 1.2 Mev per g/cm². This is somewhat less than the theoretical value for air in Fig. 1 at the minimum of the curve, which is about 1.8 Mev per g/cm². The difference is about what one would expect to find due to energy transferred to knock-on electrons. The general correctness of these results has been checked by Dunlap, who measured pulses in an ionization chamber that were caused by single particles [2]. He obtained a value of 60 ion pairs per cm of air at NTP. The value is higher than that from cloud chambers because it represents all the energy going into ionization in the gas of his ionization chamber, not merely along the meson track. Thus energy transferred to knock-ons would still lead to ionization that would be measured in this experiment except in the cases where the knock-on was sufficiently energetic to pass out of the gas of the ionization chamber. The number of such knock-ons is quite small, so that this experiment gives a higher value for the density of ioniza-

* One can, for example, distinguish between "primary" and "probable" density of ionization. The number of ion pairs produced directly by the meson is its primary density of ionization. Some of the electrons involved are sufficiently energetic to produce more ion pairs, which must be added in to give the probable density of ionization, which is observed along the track. But this probable ionization does not include ionization due to secondary electrons of sufficiently great energy that their effects occur at an appreciable distance from the meson track, so that it does not include all of ionization ultimately caused by the passage of the meson.

tion, which agrees more closely with the total energy loss calculated theoretically.

It has been difficult to check the actual shape of the theoretical curve in Fig. 1 by experimental measurements on mesons, though it has been confirmed roughly by measurements on electrons. Slow mesons which would lie on the low-energy side of the minimum are very rare. When found, the data have been used in connection with the theoretical curve to estimate the meson's mass rather than to check the theoretical curve. Again, mesons of a sufficiently high energy to have a large relativistic rise in ionization are not common. Definite evidence of this rise has just been obtained, although a number of experiments of this sort have been made. As an example we can quote the results of Whittemore and Street [3], who measured the ionization in a silver chloride crystal counter for mesons of energies of about 200 Mev and greater than about 1200 Mev. The average pulse heights were 2.09×10^{-2} and 2.13×10^{-2} volt, respectively. From the curves of Fig. 1 an expected difference of about 15 per cent would be found if there were no density effect, which can be ruled out by the experimental result. It therefore provides some confirmation of the existence of a density effect. In the most recent measurements the ionization has been measured by counting droplets in a cloud chamber [82], by pulse height in proportional counters [83, 84], and pulse height from scintillation counters [85]. These have given quite definite indications of relativistic rise and density effect in agreement with theory.

In considering the production of knock-on electrons of moderate energy one has two quite different cases to consider. The first is that of knock-ons produced in a gas, where they may be detected at once, such as the gas of a cloud chamber. The second is that of knock-ons produced in a solid material which must escape to the sensitive volume of cloud chamber or counter to be observed. In the first case the typical knock-on energy is low, and the classical Rutherford formula gives the probability of a knock-on of energy E'.

$$\chi(E,E')dE' = \text{const} \left(\frac{1}{\beta}\right)^2 \left(\frac{1}{E'}\right)^2 dE' \tag{1}$$

Here $\chi(E,E')$ = probability meson of kinetic energy E, gives a knock-on electron of kinetic energy E'

   $\beta = v/c$ for the incident meson

The energies of knock-on electrons produced in argon gas in a cloud chamber were estimated from the range by Seren [4]. The results obtained for 601 mesons having a total track length of 24.2 g/cm^2 of argon are plotted in Fig. 2. The agreement with the Rutherford formula is quite good.   A total of 143 knock-on electrons were observed.   Such knock-ons are quite frequent.   Approximately 5 knock-on electrons of energy greater than 13 Kev are produced per gram per square centimeter of material traversed by fast mesons.   This frequency is checked by the

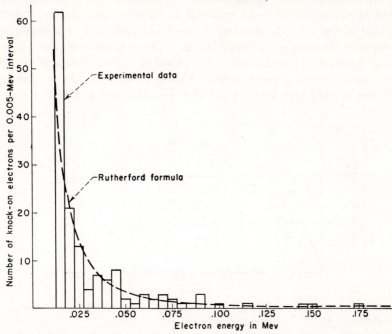

FIG. 2.   Energy spectrum of knock-on electrons produced by mesons (mainly μ mesons) in argon, according to Seren [4].

measurements of Brown, McKay, and Palmatier [5] who found 119 knock-ons produced in 21 g/cm² of argon.

The contrast with knock-ons from a solid material is evident from Table 2, taken from Brown, McKay, and Palmatier.   The number of

TABLE 2. KNOCK-ON ELECTRONS PRODUCED BY MESONS

	Number of knock-ons per meson	
Origin of knock-on	Energy <1 Mev	Energy >1 Mev
Occurs in cloud-chamber gas	0.0305	0.0035
Emerges from bottom of ½-in. lead plate	0.004	0.065

low-energy knock-ons *escaping* from the lead is very small, about 0.0003 per g/cm², while the number of higher energy electrons is about 0.005 per g/cm².

Such an interpretation is very incomplete, of course, since absorption, and even multiplication, of the electrons in the lead are important factors. If the thickness of the solid material is changed, one obtains a curve like that of Fig. 3 for the number of knock-ons produced by mesons. At the greater thicknesses, an equilibrium between production and absorption of the electrons is reached. The shape of the curve depends on the exact conditions of measurement. Values quoted for the equilibrium thickness [6 to 8] have been 10 g/cm² of Pb, 25 g/cm² of Pb, 25 g/cm² of

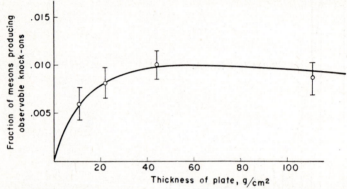

Fɪɢ. 3. Typical curve for production of knock-ons in a solid plate as a function of plate thickness (Bassi and Loria [8]).

Pb. Tamm and Belenky have estimated that at equilibrium the number of knock-on electrons of energy greater than 1 Mev emerging from lead should be ≈ 10 per cent the number of mesons [9]. The results of various experimenters are in approximate agreement with this value, as can be seen from the summary presented in Table 3.

In the above discussion of ionization and knock-on processes no effort has been made to distinguish between π mesons and μ mesons. The distinction is not important because the effects do not depend directly upon either mass or spin of the meson in question. The experiments have been performed mainly on penetrating cosmic rays at sea level, which are almost entirely μ mesons. In the case of very high-energy electromagnetic interactions, meson spin becomes important. To produce a very large energy transfer, a very close collision is required, and the dipole or other moments of the meson (and electron) must be taken into account.

High-energy mesons can produce knock-on electrons of high energy when they collide closely with an electron or bremsstrahlung photons of high energy when they collide closely with a nucleus. The theoretical expressions applicable to these two processes have been summarized by Christy and Kusaka [10] and by Rossi and Greisen [11] for mesons of spin 0, $\frac{1}{2}$, and 1. The detailed formulas are complicated and will not be reproduced here. The qualitative results are that the probability of producing knock-on electrons or bremsstrahlung photons increases with increasing meson spin. In lead, the bremsstrahlung process is the more important source of very high-energy secondaries, but this would not be the case in light materials.

TABLE 3. NUMBER OF KNOCK-ON ELECTRONS EMERGING FROM SOLID MATTER

Reference	Material	Minimum electron energy, Mev	Knock-on electrons per meson, per cent
Seren, *Phys. Rev.*, *62*, 204 (1942)	Tungsten	1	10.5
	Lead	4.3	9.7
Nassar and Hazen, *Phys. Rev.*, *69*, 298 (1946)	Lead	1	5.5
	Lead	5	2.7
	Lead	10	2
Bassi and Loria, *Nature*, *163*, 400 (1949)	Lead	10	1
Brown, McKay and Palmatier, *Phys. Rev.*, *76*, 506 (1949)	Lead	1	7
Clay, *Physica*, *13*, 433 (1947)	Iron	2	10

Christy and Kusaka [10] and also Lapp [12] showed that such processes can account for the large bursts observed under thick shields at sea level, and obtained fair quantitative agreement with the hypothesis that they are produced by μ mesons. These results have already been discussed in Chap. 2 and are in agreement with a spin of $\frac{1}{2}$ for the μ meson. There seems to be no doubt that μ mesons and presumably π mesons can produce energetic secondary electrons and photons by such processes, but such events are very rare, and have been studied mainly with ionization chambers. For any given burst in an ionization chamber, one is uncertain what particle produced it and what particles were produced in it. As a result, a detailed analysis of events of this kind is not possible on the basis of available data.

2. SCATTERING OF MESONS

One would expect theoretically that when a nuclear force meson passes near a nucleon (that is, when their respective wave functions overlap) a force is exerted between them which causes the meson to be deflected from its original course. Such nuclear scattering would be expected for π mesons and possibly for heavy mesons. For μ mesons, however, results already presented in Chaps. 3 to 5 suggest that there may not be the same nuclear scattering, since they seem to be less directly related to nuclear forces. On the other hand, scattering due to electromagnetic forces should occur for all charged mesons. In this section, data on meson scattering will be compared with these expectations.

The electromagnetic or Coulomb scattering leads to a large number of small-angle scattering processes which add together statistically when the meson passes through a scatterer of any appreciable thickness. This is known as "multiple scattering." The theory has been developed primarily by Williams, and is summarized by Rossi and Greisen [11]. The final result is a Gaussian distribution for the scattering angle with rms angle of scattering given by Eq. (2).

$$\overline{\theta^2} = \frac{E_s{}^2}{P^2 v^2} l \tag{2}$$

where θ is the net angle by which the particle is scattered in passing through a thickness l

E_s is a constant with dimensions of energy = 21 Mev

P is the momentum of the particle

v is the velocity of the particle

l is the thickness of the scatterer measured in "radiation lengths"

Coulomb scattering thus produces a rather small deflection for relativistic mesons passing through plates of moderate thickness. When present, nuclear scattering might be expected to add an occasional large-angle scattering, and has sometimes been called "anomalous scattering" for that reason.

Unfortunately, meson theory does not provide a completely definite value for the expected frequency of nuclear scattering, but one might expect that the cross section for scattering would be approximately equal to the geometrical cross section. Thus a 1-cm lead plate would scatter about 1 in 30 mesons passing through it, whereas every meson would experience a small Coulomb scattering.

The first experiments to be made on meson scattering all involved μ mesons, since the particles studied were penetrating cosmic rays at sea level. At the time they were performed, it was thought that the μ meson was to be identified with the nuclear force meson, and the results were expected to show evidence of anomalous scattering. At the present time, however, quite the opposite result would be expected. In most cases the experiment consisted of a measurement of the deflection observed for particles passing through plates in a cloud chamber. Blackett and Wilson found scattering that was in agreement with the expected Coulomb scattering without any anomalous scattering [13]. In a more detailed study, Wilson found that the scattering of all but one of 185 particles agreed with the expectations for Coulomb scattering [14]. The one particle had momentum 1.5×10^9 ev/c and was scattered through an angle of 4°, which was about six times the expected angle. The total path length observed was about 4500 g/cm^2 and indicated a cross section per nucleon of about 4×10^{-28} instead of 10^{-26}.

A similar result was obtained by Code [15], who measured the scattering of 359 particles penetrating 1.5 in. of tungsten. The average scattering angle agreed with the predictions of Coulomb scattering, and there were only a few particles which were scattered through larger angles than would be expected from the Gaussian distribution. At most six scatterings could be put in this class, and since penetration of about 26,000 g/cm^2 of material was observed, the maximum cross section per nucleon would again be about 4×10^{-28}. The data of Wilson and Code on large-angle scattering are given in Table 4.

TABLE 4. LARGE-ANGLE SCATTERINGS OBSERVED BY WILSON AND CODE [14,15]

Observed scattering angle in units of average angle	Data of Wilson (185 cases)		Data of Code (359 cases)	
	Expected	Observed	Expected	Observed
4.0–5.0	0.24	2	0.48	4
5.0–6.0	0.012	0	0.024	1
6.0–7.0	0.0004	1	0.0008	1
> 7.0	0.000005	0	0.00001	0

The numbers in Table 4 were not really large enough to permit a definite conclusion that anomalous scattering existed since the argument was a statistical one. They did, however, show that anomalous scattering was not at all common and that the cross section for such scattering must be much less than 10^{-26} cm^2/nucleon. The actual identity of the scattered particles was also uncertain. The penetrating cosmic-ray particles at sea level are largely μ mesons, but a few protons and very rarely even a π meson may also be present. Since the large-angle scatterings are very rare, they might be accounted for by protons or π mesons. From these experiments, therefore, we can only conclude that the probability for nuclear scattering of μ mesons is very small, as would be expected if π mesons are the nuclear force mesons, and μ mesons are not directly related to nuclear forces.

Additional experiments on meson scattering have been performed by Shutt [16], who employed an indirect method of analysis to produce evidence for the existence of anomalous scattering. In the case of Coulomb scattering, the average angle of scattering varies as the square root of the thickness of the absorber, and, in fact, if angles are measured in units of $l^{\frac{1}{2}}$, the observed distributions should be independent of thickness. The probability of nuclear scattering, on the other hand, is proportional to l. Shutt observed scattering in about 20,000 traversals of a 5-cm lead plate and compared the distribution with that from scattering in 40,000 traversals of a 1-cm plate. Departures from the $l^{\frac{1}{2}}$ rule were interpreted in terms of a nuclear scattering with a cross section of 5×10^{-28} cm^2. As in the previous experiments, the majority of the particles observed were surely μ mesons, but it is uncertain what fraction of the observed scatterings may have been due to other particles.

Further evidence of the rarity of large-angle μ-meson scattering has been obtained by Amaldi and Fidecaro [17]. They employed a counter telescope to select penetrating particles and a hodoscope to observe those scattered through large angles by a 6-cm thickness of iron. Only about 1 in 10^5 incident particles gave a scattered count, and the number could be explained as due to protons rather than μ mesons. They concluded that the cross section of μ mesons for nuclear scattering was not greater than about 10^{-30} cm^2.

Taken as a whole the results on the anomalous scattering of μ mesons indicate that they certainly do not have a strong nuclear interaction. These results are quite consistent with assumption that π mesons rather than μ mesons are directly related to nuclear forces, and could be explained by assuming that the μ mesons have no nuclear scattering, with the observed events due to other particles.

In the case of π mesons the early observations of Powell showed that nuclear interactions occurred when a negative π meson slowed down and was captured by a nucleus. A small star was usually produced as a result of a nuclear disruption. Detailed data on this type of event occurring at the end of the range of the meson will be presented in the final section of this chapter. On the other hand the π meson may collide with a nucleus in flight and interact with it. In such a case the π meson may be completely absorbed or scattered, but even when scattered it is likely to transfer enough energy to the scattering nucleon or nucleons to cause a nuclear disruption. It is not clear whether this type of event should be considered as an inelastic π meson scattering or as a nuclear disruption caused by a π meson in flight, but we will defer discussion of such events until the final section of the chapter. By π-meson scattering, then, we mean only elastic scattering events in which the scattering nucleus is not observed to break up.

The first attempts to obtain information on the scattering or other interactions of π mesons were made with cloud chambers. Lightly ionizing tracks from nuclear explosions and groups of penetrating tracks known as penetrating showers are thought to contain a large proportion of π mesons.* Consequently observations on the scattering of these particles in cloud chamber plates conveys some information concerning the scattering of π mesons, although a fair number of the particles involved may actually have been protons rather than π mesons.

A considerable number of such observations have been made. For example, Lovati, Mura, Salvini, and Tagliaferri have measured the scattering of 100 particles in hard showers which penetrate a 12-mm lead plate [18]; 90 per cent were scattered through angles of less than 2°; the largest scattering angle observed was 9°. It was concluded that the observations were consistent with purely Coulomb scattering. Similar data have been obtained by Brown and McKay for penetrating lightly ionizing tracks from nuclear explosions [19]. They observed a total of 750 penetrations of 1.27-cm thick lead plates. The distribution of scattering angles was in good agreement with a Gaussian curve with average scattering about 2°. In addition there were seven particles scattered through angles greater than 10° and four times the rms value for the particle in other plates. If these are considered to represent nuclear scatterings, the corresponding mean free path is about 1500 g/cm², which would imply a cross section $\sim 10^{-27}$ cm².

More recent results by Barker and Butler [20], Gregory and Tinlot [21], and by Hartzler [22] are in general agreement with these figures. The path length for scattering appears to be about 1000 g/cm² for heavy nuclei like lead, but the number of cases observed is still small, and the bias introduced by the counter selection system may introduce an effect which is hard to evaluate.

Much more clear-cut results have been obtained from observations on the tracks of artificially produced π mesons. Bradner and Rankin [23] scanned 568 cm of π^--meson tracks in nuclear emulsions and found 12 cases of scattering through more than 30°. Bernardini, Booth, Lederman, and Tinlot [24] found 11 scatterings in 1150 cm of π^--meson track. Combining these, we obtain a mean free path for scattering (not counting cases where a star was formed) of about 300 g/cm², which is only a few times that corresponding to the geometrical cross section. Thus π mesons do undergo large-angle scattering with reasonable fre-

* Evidence in this regard is presented in Chap. 7.

quency at the energies involved in these measurements, namely, about 30 to 50 Mev. A typical π-meson scattering event is shown in Fig. 4. Further results obtained with artificially produced mesons are described in Sec. 4.

As an over-all conclusion concerning the scattering of mesons we may state that:

1. Both π mesons and μ mesons probably have the expected multiple Coulomb scattering.

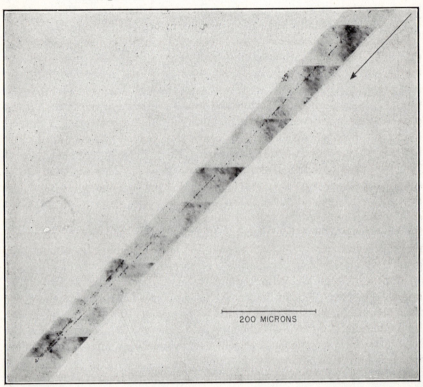

FIG. 4. Typical nuclear scattering of a π meson in a nuclear emulsion observed by Bernardini, Booth, Lederman, and Tinlot. The meson is scattered through nearly 180°.

2. μ mesons have little if any nuclear scattering.

3. π mesons probably are scattered by nuclei due to nuclear forces with a cross section of the same order of magnitude as the geometrical cross section.

4. None of the measurements concerning nuclear scattering are of great accuracy. There is need for much further work.

In general, it appears that the results bear out the hypothesis that the π meson is directly related to nuclear forces, while the μ meson is not.

3. NUCLEAR INTERACTIONS OF μ MESONS

It is already clear that except for the normal Coulomb interaction there is no strong interaction between μ mesons and nuclei. That is, there is no strong specifically nuclear interaction. Three main reasons for this conclusion have been given. In the first place, when negative μ mesons are observed to stop in a cloud chamber or a nuclear emulsion, they do not produce nuclear explosions, as they would quite certainly do if they were absorbed by nuclei in such a way as to give their rest energy to the nucleus. In the second place, large-angle scattering of μ mesons such as would be caused by a strong non-Coulomb interaction is slight or absent. Finally, experiments on the decay of μ mesons in various materials show that in light materials both positive and negative μ mesons decay after stopping, while a strong nuclear interaction would be expected to lead to very rapid absorption of the negative μ mesons before they had appreciable time in which to decay.

In materials of higher atomic number, however, negative μ mesons are not observed to decay.* Therefore they do in fact have some slight nuclear interaction. To attempt to determine how great the interaction is, the process must be analyzed in some detail. We are concerned with negative μ mesons which slow down and "stop" in the material. The meson "stops" in the sense that it is attracted to a nucleus by the Coulomb force and is trapped in a Bohr orbit around the nucleus. A general discussion and review of this subject is given by Wheeler [25]. It drops rapidly into the lowest possible orbit, the K orbit. A time of the order of 10^{-9} to 10^{-10} sec is required for the meson to lose energy from about 100 Mev to about 2000 ev, and then only about 10^{-13} sec to reach the K orbit [26,27]. These times are negligible compared with the lifetime for decay. Having arrived in the K orbit, the μ meson may either decay or interact with a nucleon, and disappear in a manner which will be discussed later.

It is clear that the probability of absorption will increase rapidly with atomic number. There are two effects tending in this direction: there are more nucleons with which to interact, and the μ meson is more tightly bound so that it spends more time near the nucleus. Wheeler assumes that the probability of absorption† by a single proton is proportional to the probability $|\Psi|^2$ for the μ meson to be at the position of the proton.

* See Chap. 5 for a discussion of these experiments.
† The process assumed is $p + \mu^- \to n + \mu^0$.

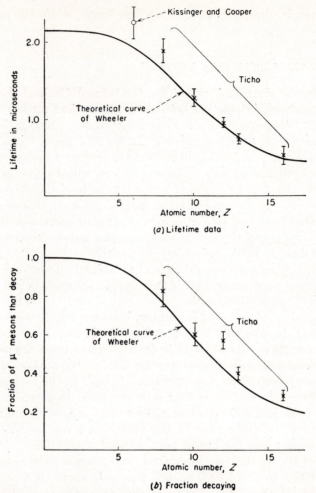

FIG. 5. Decay of negative μ mesons. Data of Ticho [26] compared with theory of Wheeler [25].

Here Ψ is the wave function of the meson bound in its K orbit. Then for a nucleus the total probability is given by Eq. (3).

$$A_{abs} = \text{const} \sum_{\text{protons}} \left| \Psi \text{ (at proton)} \right|^2 \tag{3}$$

Here A_{abs} is actually the probability of absorption per unit time, a probability rate. For a small nucleus, the Ψ function can be assumed to be like that for the electron in a hydrogen atom and to be constant over the nucleus. When the appropriate substitutions are made in Eq. (3), one obtains Eq. (4).

$$A_{abs} = \text{const} \frac{Z}{\pi} \left(\frac{Ze^2 m}{h^2} \right)^3 = \text{const}' \, Z^4 \tag{4}$$

Since the corresponding probability of decay is simply $1/\tau_\mu$, it is convenient for comparison to write the expression for the probability of absorption as in Eq. (5).

$$A_{abs} = \frac{1}{\tau_\mu} \left(\frac{Z}{Z_0} \right)^4 \qquad A_{decay} = \frac{1}{\tau_\mu} \tag{5}$$

Here $1/\tau_\mu Z_0^4$ is the value of (const') in Eq. (4). Z_0 is then the atomic number for which decay and absorption are equally probable. Actually the hydrogenic wave function is not a very good approximation for nuclei with Z greater than about 10, since the dimensions of the nucleus are comparable with those of the μ-meson orbit. A more accurate calculation leads to a Z_{eff} which is somewhat less than Z. Values are given in Table 5, assuming a value of 10 for Z_0, which gives fairly good agreement with the experimental results of Ticho [26], as can be seen from Fig. 5. Recent experiments of Harrison, Keuffel, and Reynolds [81] have checked the theory for lifetimes as short as 0.050 microsec, which was obtained for Sb.

TABLE 5. MEAN LIFE AND PROBABILITY OF DECAY FOR NEGATIVE μ MESONS IN K ORBITS ACCORDING TO WHEELER [25]

Element	Z	Z_{eff}	Assuming $Z_0 = 10$ Lifetime, microsec	Prob. of decay
Be	4	3.925	2.10	0.977
C	6	5.78	1.93	0.899
N	7	6.68	1.80	0.835
O	8	7.56	1.62	0.755
F	9	8.40	1.43	0.668
Na	11	10.02	1.07	0.498
Mg	12	10.83	0.91	0.422
Al	13	11.58	0.77	0.358
S	16	13.7	0.48	0.221
Fe	26	19.4	0.14	0.066
Br	35	23.0	0.074	0.0345
Ag	47	26.4	0.043	0.0202
I	53	27.7	0.036	0.0168
Pb	82	31.5	0.022	0.0101

From the probability of absorption it is possible to determine the strength of interaction between μ mesons and nucleons. If this interaction is considered as a nuclear potential well of radius

$$e^2/mc^2 = 2.8 \times 10^{-13} \text{ cm}$$

then its depth is ~ 1 ev, which is 10^{-6} to 10^{-7} less than usual nuclear potentials [25,27]. This is obviously a very weak interaction.

No attempt will be made here to explain this interaction in terms of any basic meson theory. The interaction may well involve the π meson as an intermediate state as suggested by Marshak and Bethe [28,29]. In that case the μ meson and nucleon would both interact with the π meson and hence weakly with each other. At any rate, a weak interaction does exist, and it is of interest to determine what the products of the reaction are, since the μ meson must disappear as the result of the reaction.

If a stopped μ^- meson gave all its rest energy to the nucleus when absorbed, a small star would result which would be similar to those found with stopped π^- mesons. As has been mentioned previously, such stars are not found, so that the absorption process must be different in some way. Since this is an important point, it is worth reviewing the evidence that stopped μ^- mesons do not produce stars similar to those produced by stopped π^- mesons.

A few negative μ mesons have been observed to stop in the gas of a cloud chamber without causing a star [30,31]. An example is shown in Fig. 6. On the other hand Valley, Leavitt, and Vitale have obtained several instances which appeared to be one-pronged stars caused by mesons [32], but the event was associated with penetrating showers, so that π mesons rather than μ mesons were probably involved. Results obtained with emulsions show very clearly that μ mesons do not usually eject charged nuclear fragments when they are absorbed. A number of μ mesons resulting from π-μ decay in the emulsion have been observed to stop without producing stars, while the mesons that do produce stars usually have the greater mass associated with π mesons [33 to 36]. Chang has observed μ mesons stopping in thin foils in a cloud chamber [37]. In 37 events that were clearly observed there were no protons produced of energy ~ 4 Mev or higher. Voorhies and Street have observed μ mesons stopping in a silver chloride crystal counter [38]. If stars occurred, large pulses should be observed. From their absence it was concluded that if any star prongs were present their total energy could be at most a few Mev. On the other hand, George and Evans [39] showed that stars were observed in emulsions underground that had to be ascribed to μ^- mesons. The number of such stars was small, and most of them had only one prong. They concluded that about 9 per cent of the μ^- mesons stopping in the emulsion produced stars with one or more prongs. The prong distribution corresponded to an excitation of the nucleus of about 15 Mev, much less than would be the case if the full rest energy of the μ^- meson was transformed into nuclear excitation.

Since most of the energy of the absorbed μ meson does not go to create a star, it is necessary to consider other possible products of μ meson absorption. One might, for example, imagine that a high-energy photon

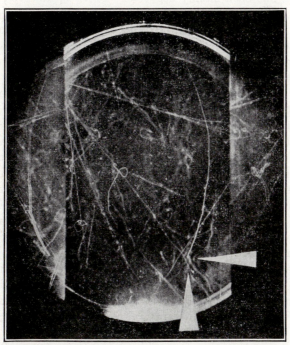

FIG. 6. μ meson, presumably negative, stopping in a cloud chamber without either decay or star production, observed by Shutt.   Mirror image visible at left.

is created which carries off the energy of the μ meson. Such a possibility is ruled out by the experiments of Piccioni and Chang [40,37]. Piccioni used a counter hodoscope (Fig. 6, Chap. 5) to look for electrons produced in a lead screen from photons arising from stopped μ mesons. None were found, proving that energetic photons (of 20 Mev or so) were not produced. Chang used a cloud chamber containing thin lead plates triggered to select μ mesons stopping in the chamber. If energetic photons were formed at μ meson absorption, electron pairs should have been observed in the lead plates. None were seen. Eight low-energy electron tracks were, however, observed which were lined up with the point at which the μ meson stopped. These electrons were probably caused by photons of a few Mev arising in the process of μ-meson absorption, either from transitions of the mesons from one Bohr orbit to another in reaching the K orbit, or from nuclear excited states arising from the capture process. These low-energy photons do not, however, account for any substantial fraction of the μ meson's rest energy.

The experimental evidence on the products of μ-meson absorption discussed above has been mainly negative. There is, however, some positive evidence for the production of *neutrons* in the process of μ-meson absorption. Sard, Ittner, Conforto, and Crouch obtained counts in a neutron detector which were associated with stopped μ mesons [41,42]. Their apparatus is shown in Fig. 7a. They observed anticoincidences AB-C which were followed by a count in N during a time interval of 80 microsec (which corresponded to the time required for the neutrons to slow to thermal energies in the paraffin and diffuse into one of the boron counters to be counted). A total of 61 counts were reported, amounting to 0.34 per hr whereas the accidental rate was about 0.001 per hr. Since the rate dropped to 0.02 per hr when the 7-cm lead absorber was removed and did not rise very greatly when the anticoincidence C tray was disconnected, it appears fairly certain that the neutron counts were due to particles, most likely μ mesons, stopping in the lead. The efficiency of the neutron detector was not known, so that no accurate absolute figure could be given for the number of neutrons produced. It was estimated that there might be 2 to 3 neutrons per stopped meson.

More recent experiments have been carried out underground in order to eliminate events caused by neutrons or protons in the cosmic radiation (which are rapidly absorbed) [66]. The general result was confirmed and the average neutron multiplicity was estimated to be 2.16 ± 0.15 from the efficiency of the neutron counters.

A similar experiment was performed by Groetzinger, Berger, and McClure [43,44] with the apparatus sketched in Fig. 7b. They were able to separate positive and negative particles, but obtained only a small number of events. For positive μ mesons, one neutron count was obtained with 1500 stopped μ mesons (2 chance counts expected), but 67 neutron counts were obtained with 5500 stopped negative μ mesons. This suggests that the neutrons do in fact come from the absorption of the negative μ mesons. From the efficiency of their neutron detector they estimated that about two neutrons were actually produced per stopped μ meson.

These results have been interpreted in terms of a "charge-exchange" reaction by Wheeler and others [45 to 47]. The elementary reaction

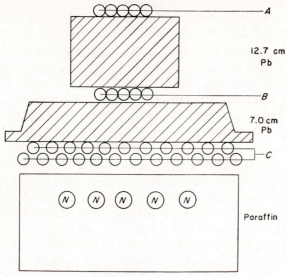

(a) Sard, Ittner, Conforto, and Crouch

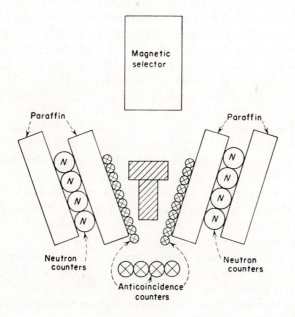

(b) Groetzinger, Berger, and McClure

FIG. 7. Apparatus for detection of neutrons associated with stopped μ mesons.

assumed is

$$\mu^- \text{ meson} + \text{proton} \rightarrow \text{neutron} + \text{neutral meson or neutrino}$$

The neutrino (or neutral meson) receives the majority of the energy available. Tiomno and Wheeler calculated that the neutron energies would be about 10 Mev. Since the neutron is part of a larger nucleus, this energy should sometimes serve to excite the nucleus. In a large nucleus, however, the Coulomb potential barrier is sufficient to make it much more likely that a neutron will be emitted than a proton, even if the energy goes into general nuclear excitation. Thus neutrons should frequently be emitted, but charged particles very rarely, following this reaction. The charge-exchange reaction is in agreement with the observations on the absorption of stopped μ mesons, in that it provides for an absorption of the meson without giving the nucleus an excitation high enough to emit many charged particles. A few very small charged particle stars would be expected, as are, in fact, observed by George and Evans.

Since the nuclear interaction between μ mesons and nucleons is very small, one would expect no observable nuclear interaction for μ mesons in flight. The great penetrating ability of μ mesons shows that they do not have a large cross section for nuclear interaction. One might be tempted to conclude that μ mesons in flight do not ever cause nuclear events such as stars or penetrating showers, were it not for an observation by George and Evans which indicates the contrary [48,49]. By exposing nuclear emulsions underground at a depth of 60 m water equivalent, they observed stars which must have been produced by μ mesons. Virtually no stars could be produced at this depth by the star-producing radiation which is effective in the atmosphere, since it is absorbed with a mean free path of about 100 to 150 g/cm^2 and would be absorbed long before penetrating to that depth. μ mesons appeared to be the only particles that could be responsible. The number of stars was small, of course, and would correspond to a cross section per nucleon for star production of about 10^{-29} cm^2 if they were due to μ mesons. A similar conclusion has been reached by Cocconi and Tongiorgi who detected nuclear events at depths up to 60 m of water by the neutrons produced [67].

To explain the presence of these stars, it is not necessary to assume the existence of any nuclear force interaction. They could be caused by electromagnetic forces alone, that is, by the electromagnetic field of the μ meson. In this way they would have a closer resemblance to photo-disintegration phenomena than anything else. Thus it appears that these nuclear disruptions do not really represent nuclear interactions and are not in contradiction with the previous conclusions about the very small nuclear interaction of μ mesons.

4. NUCLEAR INTERACTIONS OF π MESONS

In Chap. 3 the early observations of Powell and coworkers were described. They showed that pi mesons, which had the property of producing secondary decay mesons, and sigma mesons, which had the property of producing stars, both had a mass of about $280m_e$. It was thought likely that these mesons were nuclear force mesons with positive and negative charge, respectively.* In addition, some mesons were observed which simply stopped in the emulsion without causing any event. These were called rho mesons.

In the following discussion we continue to use the term π meson for *any* nuclear force meson whose mass is about $280m_e$. The results previously presented showed that a π meson which stops in an emulsion may produce a star. They did not, however, indicate how often a star is produced and how often not. They did not indicate whether π mesons in flight may interact with nuclei producing stars. These and other questions will be discussed in the following section.

The interactions of stopped π mesons will be considered first. When the first observations were made of cosmic-ray mesons stopping in a nuclear emulsion, a large number of mesons were found which ended in the emulsion without producing any visible event. These were known as rho mesons. Typical data on events due to stopped mesons from the work of Lattes, Occhialini, and Powell [50] are given in Table 6. Some

TABLE 6. CLASSIFICATION OF MESONS STOPPING IN EMULSION OF LATTES, OCCHIALINI, AND POWELL (ADJUSTED FOR EVENTS ESCAPING OBSERVATION) [50]

	Frequency in mesons per cc per day	
	Altitude 2800 m	Altitude 5500 m
pi mesons	0.8 ± 0.2	0.9 ± 0.5
sigma mesons	0.9 ± 0.2	1.0 ± 0.2
mu mesons (from pi-mu decays)	0.8 ± 0.2	0.9 ± 0.5
rho mesons unaccounted for	4.0 ± 0.7	3.3 ± 0.9

of the rho mesons were certainly μ mesons   Positive μ mesons would decay, producing an electron, which would not have been observed in the emulsions used in this experiment (since they were not sensitive to minimum ionization tracks). Negative μ mesons would usually stop without the production of any charged particle if they stopped in a grain

* See Chap. 3 for more detailed discussion and references.

of silver bromide but would decay if they stopped in the gelatin. Because of fading it was not possible to determine accurate masses for rho mesons by grain counting, so that an undetermined fraction of the rho mesons could have been π mesons failing to produce stars or pi-mu decays. It seemed more likely, however, that they were mainly μ mesons.

Scattering measurements gave some confirmation for this belief, since the mass of rho mesons was determined to be $200 \pm 10m_e$ by Goldschmidt-Clermont et al. [51]. The actual distribution of masses obtained, as is shown in Fig. 8, was not sharp enough, however, to show clearly whether some of the rho mesons might have been π mesons.

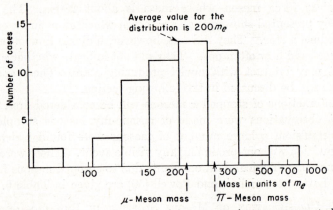

Fig. 8. Masses of rho mesons determined from scattering measurements by Goldschmidt-Clermont et al. [51].

The best evidence on this question comes from experiments on artificially produced mesons. In this case π mesons can be identified as such quite reliably, and their behavior checked. According to Smith, all but 0.3 ± 0.4 per cent of the positive π mesons produce recognizable pi-mu decays [52], so that it seems safe to assume that all positive π mesons decay when stopped. Negative π mesons, on the other hand, produce stars of one or more prongs in the majority of the cases.

Adelman and Jones have studied the events occurring at the end of tracks of π^- mesons produced in the Berkeley cyclotron [53]. They found that 26.8 per cent of the tracks ending in a nuclear emulsion showed no observable event, while the remainder produced stars of from one to five prongs. The actual prong distribution is given in Table 7. In a similar experiment Cheston and Goldfarb found that 35.2 per cent of the π^- mesons ended without an observable star [54]. In all probability these represent cases in which neutrons are emitted from the nucleus absorbing the π^- mesons, without the emission of any charged particles.

The details of the process by which the energy of the meson is transferred to the nucleus are not yet clear. If one imagines that the π^- meson is absorbed by a single proton which is transformed to a neutron, momentum cannot be conserved unless a second particle, such as a photon or neutral meson, is always produced. In such a case the photon or neutral meson must receive the majority of the energy, as in the absorption of μ^- mesons. If the original proton was a member of a large nucleus, the energy of the neutron might serve to give the nucleus a general excitation, but only a small fraction of the total 140-Mev rest energy of the π^- meson would be available to do so, since most of it would be carried off by the photon or neutral meson. If, on the other hand, the π^- meson is absorbed by two or more nucleons acting together, its whole rest energy may be transferred to them, resulting in much higher excitation of the nucleus. The fact that several charged prongs may be emitted in a star due to π^--meson absorption indicates a fairly high excitation, so that the process is fairly certainly of the latter type.

TABLE 7. PRONG DISTRIBUTIONS OF STARS PRODUCED BY THE ABSORPTION OF STOPPED π^- MESONS

No. of prongs	Adelman and Jones, per cent	Cheston and Goldfarb, per cent	Menon, Muirhead, and Rochat	
			Heavy nuclei, per cent	Light nuclei, per cent
0	26.8	35.2	36	0
1	21.5	13.3	33	34
2	27.0	21.9	22	25
3	15.2	18.9	5	38
4	7.8	8.8	5	2
5	1.8	1.9		

One might hope to compare the observed prong distribution with that calculated theoretically for a given nuclear excitation energy. In doing so, however, one must take account of the fact that stars occurring in an emulsion can arise from any of the various nuclei contained in it. There are a considerable number of light nuclei—hydrogen, carbon, nitrogen, and oxygen—in the emulsion in addition to the heavier silver and bromine. For any comparison of prong distribution with theory, one must separate stars due to absorption in light and heavy nuclei. This has been done by Menon, Muirhead, and Rochat, who have made much the most detailed investigation of the absorption of stopped π^- mesons

[55].   They used plates on which alternating layers of emulsion and pure gelatin (light elements only) were present as a "sandwich." Stars occurring in the gelatin were due to light elements only.   From their prong distribution a correction could be determined to the stars occurring in the emulsion to eliminate the light-element stars.   Other methods were also devised to determine whether a star occurred in a light or heavy element.   They concluded that about 46 per cent of the visible stars in the emulsion are due to light nuclei (C, N, O) and 54 per cent due to heavy nuclei (Ag, Br).   Their prong distributions are given in Table 7.

From the prong distribution for heavy nuclei, Menon, Muirhead, and Rochat concluded that the excitation given to the nucleus would have to be about 100 Mev to fit the experimental data.   The energies of the emitted protons were consistent with "evaporation" from a nucleus with this excitation, except that some protons were observed with higher energy than could be obtained in such a process.   It was thought that these protons might have been given the higher energy in the initial meson-absorption step.   The energy carried off by them would perhaps account for the discrepancy between 100 Mev excitation of the nucleus and the full 140 Mev rest energy of the π meson.   It seemed likely that the basic process of π^--meson absorption transferred *all* the meson's rest energy to a group of several nucleons.

Concerning the absorption by light nuclei somewhat less could be said. In many cases the nucleus was completely split up into components no larger than an a particle.   These particles were often of rather low energy, indicating that much of the energy had gone to one or more energetic neutrons.   It was not possible to identify any particles as being products of the initial meson absorption process.   It was only possible to conclude that the observations were consistent with absorption by a group of several nucleons.

It appears that in both light and heavy nuclei the π^- meson is absorbed by several nucleons acting together.   In the smallest possible nuclei, hydrogen and deuterium, such a process is not possible and one would expect somewhat different products to result.   In hydrogen, for example, the most likely reactions would involve the emission of a photon, as in Eq. (6a), or a neutral meson, as in Eq. (6b).   The latter would of course only be possible if the π^0-meson mass is less than that of the π^- meson. If produced, the π^0 meson would decay at once to two photons.   In case (6a) the photon would have virtually the whole rest energy of the π^- meson, about 140 mev, while in case (6b) each photon would have about half that energy (assuming that the π^0-meson mass is approximately equal to that of the π^- meson).   One might also imagine that two photons would be produced directly without any intervening π^0

meson, as in Eq. (6c), in which case there would be a continuous distribution of photon energies.

$$\pi^- + p \to n + \gamma \tag{6a}$$
$$\pi^- + p \to n + \pi^0 \to n + 2\gamma \tag{6b}$$
$$\pi^- + p \to n + 2\gamma \tag{6c}$$

Thus it should be possible to determine which reaction or reactions occur from an investigation of the γ rays produced.

Such an investigation has been carried out by Panofsky, Aamodt, York, and Hadley by means of a very remarkable experiment [56,57]. π mesons were produced by the Berkeley cyclotron and allowed to impinge on a stainless-steel pressure vessel containing hydrogen gas at 2700 lb pressure at liquid nitrogen temperature. Under these conditions the hydrogen density is sufficient that the majority of π^- mesons are slowed down and absorbed before decaying. Collimators were arranged so that any photons produced as a result of the π^--meson absorption could pass into a pair spectrometer by means of which the energy spectrum of the photons was measured. The apparatus is shown schematically in Fig. 9.

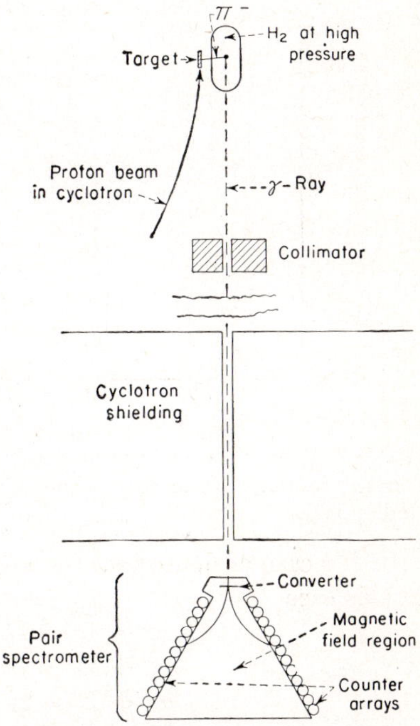

The energy spectrum obtained is shown in Fig. 10. Photons of energy equal to about 70 Mev and about 130 Mev were found, indicating that both processes (6a) and (6b) occur. The lack of photons of other energies showed that process (6c) was

FIG. 9. Schematic diagram of apparatus used to measure energy spectrum of photons resulting from the capture of π^- mesons in hydrogen and deuterium by Panofsky, Aamodt, and Hadley [57].

not important. The ratio of π^0-meson yield to single photon (radiative capture) yield was estimated to be 0.94 ± 0.20. Results of Sachs and Steinberger confirm that π^0 mesons are produced [68].

The fact that π^0 mesons are produced at all shows that they must be lighter than π^- mesons. The energy spread of the photons is due to Doppler effect from the motion of the π^0 meson, and the velocity, or energy, of the π^0 meson arises from the mass difference between π^- meson and π^0 meson.   Thus the energy spread of the 70 Mev peak can be used to obtain a value for the mass difference which is quite precise.   Panofsky, Aamodt, and Hadley obtained $m_{\pi^-} - m_{\pi^0} = 10.6 \pm 2.0 m_e$.

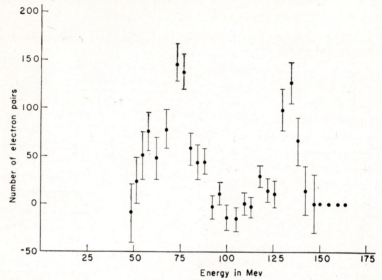

FIG. 10.   Energy spectrum of photons resulting from π^--meson capture in hydrogen. Pair spectrometer set to cover region centered at 100 Mev (Panofsky, Aamodt, and Hadley [57].

In the case of deuterium the analogous processes are listed in Eq. (7). In this case

$$\pi^- + D \rightarrow 2n \tag{7a}$$
$$\pi^- + D \rightarrow 2n + \gamma \tag{7b}$$
$$\pi^- + D \rightarrow 2n + \pi^0 \rightarrow 2n + 2\gamma \tag{7c}$$

There was no evidence for π^0-meson emission, case (7c), and full energy photons, case (7b), were observed with smaller frequency than in the case of absorption by hydrogen.   If it was assumed that the actual number of mesons absorbed was the same in hydrogen and deuterium, then case (7a), which would lead to no observable photons, must have taken place in about 70 per cent of the cases [58].   This is the simplest case of a nuclear disintegration caused by π^--meson absorption.

So much for the absorption of π^- mesons that have "stopped," that is, lost energy until they are captured in a bound orbit around a nucleus. It remains to discuss the nuclear interactions of π mesons in flight.   Since π mesons are produced in energetic collisions between nucleons, the inverse process in which a π meson striking a nucleus is absorbed giving its energy to the nucleons should also occur with a corresponding probability. In addition, a meson may be scattered by a nucleon without being absorbed, since the nucleon will experience a force due to the meson field acting on it. This may cause an elastic scattering as mentioned in Sec. 2, but if the energy transferred to the recoil nucleon is large enough, it may cause a disintegration of the nucleus of which it is a part, an inelastic scattering. "Charge-exchange" reactions in which the π^+ or π^- meson gives its charge to a nucleon, emerging as a π^0 meson, might also be possible. Thus elastic scattering, inelastic scattering, charge-exchange scattering, and absorption may all be possible.

The evidence concerning processes of this sort is rather fragmentary. The first problem involved in studying the nuclear interactions of π mesons in flight is that of obtaining, or identifying, a π meson to study. Positive identification of cosmic-ray mesons is difficult, and only recently have beams of artificially produced π mesons been available for study.

Some evidence concerning the interaction of π mesons has been obtained from observations on penetrating particles produced in energetic nuclear events in cosmic radiation. As previously mentioned, there is evidence that many of these particles are π mesons. The evidence is discussed in detail in Chap. 7. One can therefore assume that results concerning penetrating shower particles can be considered to be results on π mesons, although some of the particles may well be protons, instead.

Penetrating shower particles have been observed in cloud chambers by many investigators, among them Fretter [65], Lovati, Mura, Salvini and Tagliaferri [18], Brown and McKay [19], Butler, Rosser, and Barker [59], Barker and Butler [20], Gregory and Tinlot [21], and Hartzler [22]. Each cloud chamber contained a number of lead plates. The results are summarized in Table 8. Three types of nuclear interaction are included: (1) stars in which one or more heavily ionizing particles, presumably protons (or a particles) are produced, (2) penetrating events in which the original penetrating particle produces penetrating secondaries, and (3) large-angle scattering (discussed in Sec. 2). In each case the apparent mean free path is an upper limit to the true mean free path because events occurring entirely inside the plates would not be counted. Possible events of this sort are shown schematically in Fig. 11. An event such as that shown in Fig. 11a would appear like an uneventful penetration, whereas that shown in Fig. 11b would appear like a stopped particle. When an adjustment is made for events of this sort, it appears that the true mean free path for nuclear interaction of the penetrating particles (including elastic scattering) is most likely about 200 g/cm², although the value is by no means a reliable one, especially since it is not certain how many of the particles involved were protons.

Piccioni has interpreted experiments on penetrating showers as showing very slight absorption of π mesons, corresponding to a mean free path of 1200 g/cm² or more [60]. Such a low value of the absorption might mean that π-meson interactions frequently involve scattering or the production of additional secondary π mesons, suggestions advanced by Greisen [61]. The interpretation of this experiment seems to be uncertain.

Somewhat more clear-cut results concerning the interactions of π mesons in flight have been obtained with nuclear emulsions by scanning many long tracks that could be identified as π mesons. Camerini, Fowler, Lock, and Muirhead observed π mesons emitted from stars [62], using scattering and grain density to identify the π mesons.* They scanned 128 cm of track which could be identified as due to π mesons. Six stars were observed, leading to a path length for nuclear interactions in the emulsion of 21 ± 9 cm, or 82 g/cm². While the statistical precision of this determination is not very satisfying, there is no uncertainty as to the nature of the particle, and no doubt as to the number of events occurring, so that this figure is probably more reliable than the previous ones.

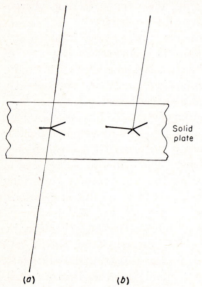

Fig. 11. Possible nuclear interactions of penetrating particles which would be overlooked in a cloud chamber.

A considerable number of experiments have recently been performed using artificially produced beams of π mesons. Observations of Bernardini and coworkers, and others, with nuclear emulsions have shown that π mesons with energies of 50 to 100 Mev interact with approximately geometrical cross section [23,24,69,70]. Total cross sections measured with a countertelescope by Chedester, Isaacs, Sachs, and Steinberger gave approximately geometrical cross sections for elements from lithium to lead [71]. Cloud-chamber measurements by Shapiro et al. gave a slightly smaller cross section for carbon and aluminum [72,73].

Cloud-chamber and emulsion results permit the different types of events to be distinguished. Data from Bernardini, Booth, and Lederman [69] and Bernardini and Levy [70] are given in Table 9. Cases in which the meson disappears without producing any event might be considered

* See Sec. 4, Chap. 7, for a discussion of this method.

TABLE 8. INTERACTION OF PENETRATING SHOWER PARTICLES IN LEAD

Investigator	Fretter	Lovati et al.	Brown and McKay	Barker and Butler	Gregory and Tinlot	Hartzler (gold plates)
Amount of lead traversed, g/cm²	67,000	23,300	28,500	9,000	6,000	19,400
No. of stars and penetrating showers	78	29	65	23	25	57
Amount of lead traversed, g/cm²	67,000	23,300	10,800	9,000	6,000	19,400
No. of large-angle scatterings	12 ($>15°$)	7 ($\geq 10°$)	7 ($>8°$)	8	10	12
Apparent meson free path for stars and penetrating events, g/cm²	860	810	440	400	240	340
Apparent meson free path for scattering, g/cm²	5,600	3,300	1,550	1,100	600	1,600
Combined meson free path for interaction, g/cm²	750	650	345	290	170	280

TABLE 9. INTERACTIONS OBSERVED WITH ARTIFICIALLY PRODUCED π MESONS

	Cross section for process stated in millibarns $(10^{-27}$ cm²) per average emulsion nucleus			
	Elastic scattering*	Inelastic scattering	Stars and disappearances	Total
π^- mesons				
30–50 Mev	190	60	620	870
60–90 Mev	100	190	760	1050
100–110 Mev	160	250	750	1160
π^+ mesons				
35–50 Mev	170	10	370	550
70–80 Mev	150	80	580	810

* Minimum angle of 30° for π^- mesons and 40° for π^+ mesons.

to represent charge-exchange events, but more likely are zero-prong stars in which only neutrons are emitted, since Wilson and Perry have shown that the cross section for charge exchange of π^+ mesons is negligible [74]. Accordingly they are grouped with stars. While the number of cases

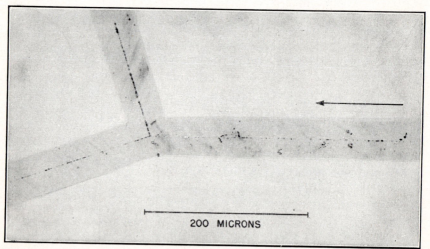

200 MICRONS

FIG. 12.   An absorption of a π^- meson by which two fast protons are ejected, observed by Bernardini, Booth, Lederman, and Tinlot.

represented by Table 9 is small, it is possible to conclude that stars are the most common type of event. A typical interaction in which two fast protons are produced is shown in Fig. 12. There is no great difference between positive and negative mesons. The cross sections appear to increase somewhat with increasing energy. Geometrical cross section corresponds to about 1100 millibarns, so that the values given are slightly less than geometrical. Shapiro observed interactions in thin carbon plates in a cloud chamber and found elastic scatterings relatively rare also [73]. It is possible to interpret some of the elastic scatterings as diffraction scattering due to the other nuclear interactions.

Mesons cannot be absorbed by free protons because two product particles are necessary to conserve energy and momentum. Absorption in deuterium is consequently of special interest as the simplest absorption reaction. Durbin, Loar, and Steinberger [75] and Clark, Roberts, and Wilson [76] have measured the cross section for the reaction $\pi^+ + D \rightarrow p + p$ and obtained values of 3 to 7 millibarns for meson energies of 20 to 50 Mev. Comparison of this value with that for the inverse process was used to show that the spin of the π^+ meson is zero and not any higher integer.

Scattering of π mesons by hydrogen should give direct evidence concerning the interaction between π mesons and nucleons. At energies of about 50 Mev the cross section is small [71,77] but rises rapidly in the range from 50 to 150 Mev, as shown by the work of Anderson, Fermi, and coworkers [78 to 80]. They have also found that the cross section is about three times as large for positive mesons as for negative [80], and that charge-exchange scattering does occur frequently for π^- mesons scattered by hydrogen [79], although this does not appear to be the case for scattering by larger nuclei.

Many experiments on the interactions of π mesons with nuclei are now in progress, and further results should soon be available.

5. NUCLEAR INTERACTIONS OF HEAVY MESONS

Nothing is really known about the nuclear interactions of heavy mesons. There are, however, two reasons for believing that heavy mesons resemble π mesons in this respect. In the first place, there is evidence that heavy mesons are associated with penetrating showers and are therefore probably produced in energetic nuclear collisions in the same way that π mesons are. Therefore they should also be expected to be absorbed by nuclei in the same way as π mesons. In the second place, Leprince-Ringuet [63] and Forster [64] have reported stars which appeared to be caused by stopped heavy mesons. It seems probable that if heavy mesons really exist they have strong nuclear interaction comparable with that of π mesons.

6. SUMMARY

1. Electromagnetic interactions of mesons lead to energy loss by ionization, to the production of knock-on secondary electrons, and to the

production of bremsstrahlung photons. The latter process becomes important only at very high energies.

2. μ mesons in flight probably have a negligible specifically nuclear interaction. They can, however, cause nuclear disruptions by electromagnetic interactions with a very small cross section.

3. π mesons in flight undergo nuclear scattering and cause nuclear interactions with a total cross section roughly equal to the geometrical cross section in nuclear emulsions.

4. Stopped positive mesons undergo decay without nuclear interaction for both π and μ mesons.

5. Negative μ mesons which are stopped in solid or liquid absorbers interact by charge exchange with nuclei of charge greater than about 10. The nucleus is usually excited sufficiently to emit a few neutrons and occasionally a proton.   In absorbers of smaller atomic number, μ mesons usually decay, indicating a very weak nuclear interaction.

6. Negative π mesons which are stopped in solids or liquids (or even compressed gases) are usually absorbed, producing a small star.   Absorption by hydrogen is exceptional in that a γ ray or neutral meson is emitted in order to satisfy conservation laws.

REFERENCES

1. Halpern, O., and H. Hall, *Phys. Rev.*, *73*, 477 (1948).
2. Dunlap, W. C., *Phys. Rev.*, *67*, 67 (1945).
3. Whittemore, W. L., and J. C. Street, *Phys. Rev.*, *76*, 1786 (1949).
4. Seren, L., *Phys. Rev.*, *62*, 204 (1942).
5. Brown, W. W., A. S. McKay, and E. D. Palmatier, *Phys. Rev.*, *76*, 506 (1949).
6. Tongiorgi, V., *Nuovo cimento*, *3*, 342 (1946).
7. Clay, J., and A. Venema, *Physica*, *10*, 735 (1943).
8. Bassi, P., and A. Loria, *Nature*, *163*, 400 (1949).
9. Tamm, I., and S. Belenky, *J. Phys.* (*U.S.S.R.*), *1*, 177 (1939).
10. Christy, R. F., and S. Kusaka, *Phys. Rev.*, *59*, 405, 414 (1941).
11. Rossi, B., and K. Greisen, *Revs. Modern Phys.*, *13*, 240 (1941).
12. Lapp, R. E., *Phys. Rev.*, *69*, 321 (1946).
13. Blackett, P. M. S., and J. G. Wilson, *Proc. Roy. Soc.* (*London*), (A)*165*, 209 (1938).
14. Wilson, J. G., *Proc. Roy. Soc.* (*London*), (A)*174*, 73 (1940).
15. Code, F. L., *Phys. Rev.*, *59*, 229 (1941).
16. Shutt, R. P., *Phys. Rev.*, *61*, 6 (1942); *69*, 261 (1946).
17. Amaldi, E., and G. Fidecaro, *Phys. Rev.*, *81*, 339 (1951).
18. Lovati, A., A. Mura, G. Salvini, and G. Tagliaferri, *Nuovo cimento*, *6*, 207 (1949).
19. Brown, W. W., and A. S. McKay, *Phys. Rev.*, *77*, 342 (1950).
20. Barker, K. H., and C. C. Butler, *Proc. Phys. Soc.* (*London*), (A)*64*, 4 (1951).

21. Gregory, B. P., and J. H. Tinlot, *Phys. Rev.*, *81*, 667, 675 (1951).
22. Hartzler, A. J., *Phys. Rev.*, *82*, 359 (1951).
23. Bradner, H., and B. Rankin, *Phys. Rev.*, *80*, 916 (1950).
24. Bernardini, G., E. T. Booth, L. Lederman, and J. Tinlot, *Phys. Rev.*, *80*, 924 (1950); *82*, 105 (1951).
25. Wheeler, J. A., *Revs. Modern Phys.*, *21*, 133 (1949).
26. Ticho, H. K., *Phys. Rev.*, *74*, 1337 (1948).
27. Tiomno, J., and J. A. Wheeler, *Revs. Modern Phys.*, *21*, 153 (1949).
28. Marshak, R. E., and H. A. Bethe, *Phys. Rev.*, *72*, 506 (1947).
29. Lodge, A. S., *Nature*, *161*, 809 (1948).
30. Johnson, T. H., and R. P. Shutt, *Phys. Rev.*, *61*, 380 (1942).
31. Piccioni, O., *Phys. Rev.*, *73*, 411 (1948).
32. Valley, G. E., C. P. Leavitt, and J. A. Vitale, *Phys. Rev.*, *75*, 201 (1949).
33. Brown, R., U. Camerini, P. H. Fowler, H. Muirhead, C. F. Powell, and D. M. Ritson, *Nature*, *163*, 47 (1949).
34. Barbour, I., *Phys. Rev.*, *76*, 320 (1949); *78*, 518 (1950).
35. Cosyns, M. G. E., C. C. Dilworth, G. P. S. Occhialini, M. Schoenberg, and N. Page, *Proc. Phys. Soc. (London)*, (A)*62*, 801 (1949).
36. Franzinetti, C., *Phil. Mag.*, *41*, 86 (1950).
37. Chang, W. Y., *Revs. Modern Phys.*, *21*, 166 (1949).
38. Voorhies, H. G., and J. C. Street, *Phys. Rev.*, *76*, 1100 (1949).
39. George, E. P., and J. Evans, *Proc. Phys. Soc. (London)*, (A)*64*, 193 (1951).
40. Piccioni, O., *Phys. Rev.*, *74*, 1754 (1948).
41. Sard, R. D., W. B. Ittner, III, A. M. Conforto, and M. F. Crouch, *Phys. Rev.*, *74*, 97 (1948).
42. Sard, R. D., A. M. Conforto, and M. F. Crouch, *Phys. Rev.*, *76*, 1134 (1949).
43. Groetzinger, G., and G. W. McClure, *Phys. Rev.*, *74*, 341 (1948).
44. Groetzinger, G., M. J. Berger, and G. W. McClure, *Phys. Rev.*, *81*, 969 (1951).
45. Tiomno, J., and J. A. Wheeler, *Revs. Modern Phys.*, *21*, 153 (1949).
46. Rosenbluth, M., *Phys. Rev.*, *75*, 532 (1949).
47. Perkins, D. H., *Nature*, 682 (1949).
48. Evans, J., and E. P. George, *Nature*, *164*, 20 (1949).
49. George, E. P., and J. Evans, *Proc. Phys. Soc. (London)*, (A)*63*, 1248 (1950).
50. Lattes, C. M. G., G. P. S. Occhialini and C. F. Powell, *Nature*, *160*, 486 (1947).
51. Goldschmidt-Clermont, Y., D. T. King, H. Muirhead, and D. M. Ritson, *Proc. Phys. Soc. (London)*, (A)*61*, 183 (1948).
52. Smith, F. M., *Phys. Rev.*, *81*, 897 (1951).
53. Adelman, F. L., and S. B. Jones, *Science*, *111*, 226 (1950).
54. Cheston, W. B., and L. J. B. Goldfarb, *Phys. Rev.*, *78*, 683 (1950).
55. Menon, M. G. K., H. Muirhead, and O. Rochat, *Phil. Mag.*, *41*, 583 (1950).
56. Panofsky, W. K. H., R. L. Aamodt, and H. F. York, *Phys. Rev.*, *78*, 825 (1950).
57. Panofsky, W. K. H., R. L. Aamodt, and J. Hadley, *Phys. Rev.*, *81*, 565 (1951).
58. Aamodt, L., J. Hadley, and W. Panofsky, *Phys. Rev.*, *80*, 282 (1950).

59. Butler, C. C., W. G. V. Rosser, and K. H. Barker, *Proc. Phys. Soc. (London)*, (A)*63*, 145 (1950).

60. Piccioni, O., *Phys. Rev.*, *77*, 6 (1950); *78*, 78 (1950).

61. Greisen, K., *Phys. Rev.*, *77*, 713 (1950).

62. Camerini, U., P. H. Fowler, W. O. Lock, and H. Muirhead, *Phil. Mag.*, *41*, 413 (1950).

63. Leprince-Ringuet, L., Hoang Tchang-Fong, L. Janeau, and D. Morellet, *Comptes rend.*, *226*, 1897 (1948); L. Leprince-Ringuet, *Revs. Modern Phys.*, *21*, 42 (1949).

64. Forster, H. H., *Phys. Rev.*, *77*, 733 (1950).

65. Fretter, W. B., *Phys. Rev.*, *76*, 511 (1949).

66. Crouch, M. F., and R. D. Sard, *Phys. Rev.*, *85*, 120 (1952).

67. Cocconi, G., and V. Cocconi Tongiorgi, *Phys. Rev.*, *84*, 29 (1951).

68. Sachs, A., and J. Steinberger, *Phys. Rev.*, *82*, 973 (1951).

69. Bernardini, G., E. T. Booth, and L. Lederman, *Phys. Rev.*, *83*, 1075, 1277 (1951).

70. Bernardini, G., and F. Levy, *Phys. Rev.*, *84*, 610 (1951).

71. Chedester, C., P. Isaacs, A. Sachs, and J. Steinberger, *Phys. Rev.*, *82*, 958 (1951).

72. Camac, M., D. R. Corson, R. M. Littauer, A. M. Shapiro, A. Silverman, R. R. Wilson, and W. M. Woodward, *Phys. Rev.*, *82*, 745 (1951).

73. Shapiro, A. M., *Phys. Rev.*, *84*, 1063 (1951).

74. Wilson, R., and J. P. Perry, *Phys. Rev.*, *84*, 163 (1951).

75. Durbin, R., H. Loar, and J. Steinberger, *Phys. Rev. 83*, 646 (1951) and *84*, 581 (1951).

76. Clark, D. L., A. Roberts, and R. Wilson, *Phys. Rev.*, *83*, 649 (1951).

77. Shutt, R. P., E. C. Fowler, D. H. Miller, A. M. Thorndike, and W. B. Fowler, *Phys. Rev.*, *84*, 1247 (1951).

78. Anderson, H. L., E. Fermi, E. A. Long, R. Martin, and D. E. Nagle, *Phys. Rev.*, *85*, 934 (1952).

79. Fermi, E., H. L. Anderson, A. Lundby, D. E. Nagle, and G. Yodh, *Phys. Rev.*, *85*, 935 (1952).

80. Anderson, H. L., E. Fermi, E. A. Long, and D. E. Nagle, *Phys. Rev.*, *85*, 936 (1952).

81. Harrison, F. B., J. W. Keuffel, and G. T. Reynolds, *Phys. Rev.*, *83*, 680 (1951).

82. Ghosh, S. K., G. M. D. B. Jones, and J. G. Wilson, *Proc. Phys. Soc. (London)*, (A)*65*, 68 (1952).

83. Kuperian, J. E., Jr., and E. D. Palmatier, *Phys. Rev.*, *85*, 1043 (1952).

84. Becker, J., P. Chanson, E. Nageotte, T. Price, P. Rothwell, and P. Treille, *Comptes rend.*, *234*, 1155 (1952).

85. Bowen, T., and F. X. Roser, *Phys. Rev.*, *85*, 992 (1952).

CHAPTER 7

PRODUCTION OF MESONS IN COSMIC RADIATION

In this chapter we will discuss the production of the mesons observed in cosmic radiation. The laboratory production of "artificial" mesons has already been described in some detail, and we know that mesons, actually π mesons, can be produced by collisions between nucleons and by the action of photons on nuclei. We might expect to observe similar phenomena in cosmic radiation. The energies involved in cosmic-ray events are, however, usually considerably higher than has so far been achieved by accelerating machines. The protons produced by the Berkeley cyclotron have an energy of about 340 Mev, whereas most of the primary protons striking the earth's atmosphere have an energy of a few Bev (at latitudes of 40° to 50° where most experiments have been done). The experiments on artificial production of mesons so far carried out have to do with their production at energies near threshold, while their production in cosmic rays often occurs at much higher energies. Consequently the phenomena are likely to appear rather different in the two cases. As a matter of fact, many of the results concerning the production of mesons in cosmic radiation were actually obtained before mesons were produced in the laboratory, so that there is some historical justification for proceeding with a discussion which is largely independent of that given in Chap. 4.

The short lifetime of the cosmic-ray mesons is sufficient proof that they must be produced somewhere in the earth's atmosphere. Neither π nor μ mesons could travel to the earth from any external source without decaying en route. The apparent lifetime of a moving meson, τ', is given by Eq. (1).

$$\tau' = \tau \frac{W}{mc^2} \tag{1}$$

where τ = rest lifetime, W = total energy, and m = rest mass of the meson involved. With the known rest lifetimes and velocity $\approx c$, the path length before decay will be of the order of 10 m for π mesons and 1000 m for μ mesons, if their energy is in each case a few times the rest energy. (Evidence presented later shows that mesons are most frequently produced with such an energy.) All mesons must have been produced at some point not very far from that at which they are observed.

The basic theoretical notion of meson formation is that π mesons bear the same relation to the nuclear force field that photons bear to the electromagnetic field. When a nucleon, which is the source of the meson field, is sufficiently vigorously accelerated, a meson field quantum, or π meson, is actually liberated, and travels off. That is to say, a π meson is formed. Such an event would be expected to take place in energetic collisions between nucleons. μ mesons, on the other hand, would be expected to arise from the decay of π mesons, and not to be produced directly. The primary aim of experiments on meson formation is to demonstrate whether or not this picture is correct. The question can thus be stated very simply. It is not, however, simple experimentally to identify the particles taking part in such high energy reactions, so that a great many experiments have been carried out which do not have a simple clear-cut interpretation.*

A great deal of theoretical work has been done in an effort to establish detailed predictions concerning the production of π mesons. We cannot attempt to describe these developments. It is not possible, at present, to carry out rigorous calculations based on meson theory to such a point that unambiguous results are obtained. Most theoretical calculations are based on one or the other of two pictures of the meson-production process. In the first, a nucleon-nucleon collision is considered to produce a single π meson in most cases, but a nucleon passing through a nucleus of any size is likely to experience several collisions, so that several π mesons are produced during traversal of one nucleus. The term "plural" production of mesons has been applied to this version, which has been developed by Heitler and various collaborators [1,2]. In the alternative version, a single nucleon-nucleon collision is considered to produce several π mesons simultaneously. Such a process is termed "multiple" production, and has been supported by Heisenberg [3]. A similar approach was followed by Lewis, Oppenheimer, and Wouthuysen [4]. A simplified statistical theory of multiple π-meson formation in nucleon-nucleon collisions has been proposed by Fermi [5].

The predictions of the two versions of the theory are not radically different, so that they cannot easily be distinguished experimentally by results on collisions involving large nuclei. A study of meson production in hydrogen by nucleons of a few Bev would, of course, distinguish

* Prior to 1947 the existence of the π meson was unknown, and it was tacitly assumed that μ mesons were involved in meson-production events. This fact tends to make the literature somewhat more confusing than it would otherwise be.

between the two possibilities.   Unfortunately the difficulties of carrying out such an experiment with cosmic rays are so great that it has not so far been done.   When accelerators in the Bev range are available, such experiments will become more practical.

Since π mesons are electrically charged, they may be released from their home nucleon by an electromagnetic field in a sort of photo-disintegration process.   In this way photons may also be expected to form π mesons in passing through matter, as has been done artificially.   Thus π mesons may be produced by protons, neutrons, or photons.   On the other hand, π mesons in collision with nuclei may cause disruptions producing protons and neutrons.   Thus meson-nucleon cascades are possible, in principle, at least.   In addition the photons produced by the decay of neutral π mesons, bremsstrahlung radiation, and knock-on electrons of charged mesons represent the soft component produced by mesons, whereas photoproduction of π mesons implies the possibility of π mesons produced by the soft component!   Thus meson-nucleon cascades and photon-electron cascades may be somewhat interdependent. The complexity of the processes by which π mesons are produced in cosmic radiation is very great.

With these theoretical possibilities for π-meson production, what experimental methods are applicable in order to recognize and identify them?   In Fig. 1 some of the possible phenomena resulting in π mesons are diagramed.   In Fig. 1a a fast proton produces a single fast meson. Since both proton and meson are penetrating, energetic, lightly ionizing particles, it would be very hard to devise an experiment to detect the event.   As a rule, however, a nucleon-nucleon collision producing a π meson should also knock out various nuclear fragments, as shown in Fig. 1g.   Thus fast particles from stars might well be instances of π-meson formation.   Of course the star may not be due to a proton. Hypothetical stars resulting from an energetic neutron and photon are shown in Figs. 1h and 1i accompanied by the emission of a π meson. Events like Figs. 1b and 1c should not be difficult to recognize since the π meson is created by an uncharged particle.   Events like Figs. 1d, 1e, and 1f should be recognizable since several penetrating particles are present, a penetrating shower.   In addition to events like those diagramed in Fig. 1, groups of mesons are found in large air showers which are predominantly electronic, and must, therefore, either be produced by the soft shower particles or by the primary event in which the shower originated.

There are thus four main types of experimentally observable phenomena which may sometimes (or, conceivably, always) be examples of meson production.

1. The production of penetrating ionizing particles by non-ionizing radiation

2. The occurrence of groups of penetrating particles—"penetrating showers"

3. The occurrence of relativistic particles from nuclear disruptions

4. The occurrence of penetrating particles in large air showers

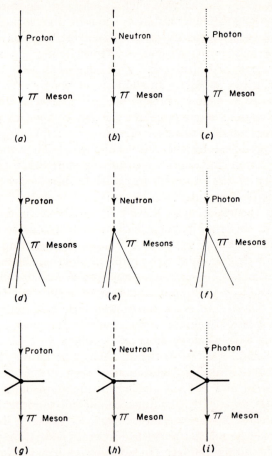

FIG. 1.   Schematic diagram of hypothetical methods of π-meson formation, illustrating the types of events which may be recognized experimentally.

Experiments on these four types of phenomena in cosmic radiation have been made in great number, but it is not often easy to derive definite information on π-meson formation from the results.   The main difficulty is that an event producing π mesons is generally very likely to produce fairly energetic protons as well.   Both energetic protons and

π mesons are penetrating particles with fairly low density of ionization. It is difficult to distinguish between them. To accomplish an unambiguous distinction, it is practically necessary either to measure the mass or to identify the meson by a characteristic decay time through delayed coincidences. Needless to say, very few experiments have done either.

In the remainder of this chapter each of these four types of observation will be discussed separately. The events will appear somewhat different in each case because of observational bias, but the basic process of meson production is presumably about the same in all of them.

1. PRODUCTION OF PENETRATING PARTICLES BY NON-IONIZING RADIATION

Most of the experiments which have been interpreted as demonstrating the production of mesons by non-ionizing radiation were made before the existence of two types of meson—π and μ—was realized. The data indicate directly that some penetrating ionizing radiation is produced by some non-ionizing radiation. We will first summarize the evidence for the existence of such a process and then see what can be said about the actual identity of the particles concerned.

The type of apparatus used in most of these experiments is shown schematically in Fig. 2. The counting rate of telescope (b) is compared with that of (a). The lower lead absorber selects penetrating particles. Telescope (a) counts penetrating particles incident from the air above and penetrating particles produced in the material A by *ionizing* radiation. Telescope (b) counts these counts, and in addition, penetrating particles produced in A by non-ionizing radiation. Hence a comparison of the two counting rates can show the effect in question if it is substantially larger than statistical fluctuations.

A number of early experiments failed to show any such effects at sea level or 14,000 ft altitude, but Schein and Wilson [6] obtained a positive result at higher altitudes in an airplane. In this case 2.2 cm of lead was used for the material in position A, and the following results were obtained: at 13,000 to 20,000 ft, (b) 4.8 ± 0.7, (a) 5.2 ± 0.7; at 20,000 to 25,000 ft, (b) 9.2 ± 1.0, (a) 6.0 ± 0.7; at 25,000 ft, (b) 11.0 ± 0.9, (a) 5.2 ± 0.6.

The investigation was extended to higher altitudes by Schein, Jesse, and Wollan using free balloons [7]. They found that production of penetrating particles began at about 6000 m and increased with increasing altitude to 17,600 m. The number of penetrating particles produced in a 2-cm lead block was about 25 per cent of the number of penetrating particles incident on the telescope from the air at the higher altitudes.

The detection of events due to non-ionizing particles can be made more conclusive by the use of anticoincidence counters. Using such a scheme, Rossi and Regener [8] were able to show the production of penetrating particles by non-ionizing radiation at mountain altitudes (4300 m). Their apparatus is shown in Fig. 3; 5 cm of lead was moved from position 2 to position 1, and an excess of counts found when the added requirement was made that there be no count in A. The actual $BCDE$-A counting rates were for 5 cm of Pb in position 2, 0.8 ± 0.2; for 5 cm of Pb in position 1, 2.83 ± 0.15. The total rate $BCDE$ for penetrating particles was 198, so that the observed production is about 1 per cent of the normal penetrating particle rate.

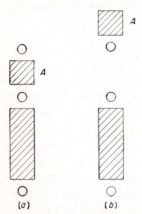

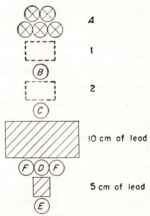

Fig. 2. Schematic diagram of counter telescopes for demonstrating the production of penetrating particles by non-ionizing radiation.

Fig. 3. Counter telescope with anticoincidence tray for demonstrating production of penetrating particles by non-ionizing radiation, used by Rossi and Regener [8].

Using a similar anticoincidence procedure, Rossi, Janossy, Rochester, and Bound obtained a negative result at sea level [9], but Janossy and Rochester subsequently showed that the effect *was* present at sea level, although the number of penetrating particles produced by non-ionizing radiation was only about 0.1 per cent of the total flux of penetrating particles through their counter telescope [10].

Thus the existence of this process is well established, but there is still no definite identification of the particles concerned. It has generally been presumed that the penetrating particles are mesons, and we would accordingly presume them to be π mesons. There is, however, no direct experimental demonstration that they are π mesons rather than μ mesons, and there is no real proof that they are mesons of any kind. It is fairly clear, of course, that they are not electrons, since they penetrate 10 to

15 cm of lead.   Rossi and Regener showed that showers are not often produced, as would certainly be the case if the particles were electrons. Hence they must be either mesons or protons.   Protons have been considered unlikely because protons are not a common constituent of cosmic rays at low altitudes.   In fact, the experiments were undertaken mainly in an effort to learn about the mechanism for the formation of mesons, which were known to be abundant.   While it seems reasonable to consider these particles to be mesons, it is not logically necessary to do so. Data presented in the following sections show that in penetrating showers and stars both energetic π mesons and protons are produced.   Accordingly it is very likely that both π mesons and protons are involved in these instances of penetrating particle production by non-ionizing radiation.

The identification of the non-ionizing particle is also uncertain. Schein and collaborators have supported the photon hypothesis, while other investigators have favored the neutron alternative.   The evidence has been based largely on the effect of absorbers placed above the telescope in which the events are detected.   Schein, Wollan, and Groetzinger found that a 6-cm block of lead above the telescope removed the meson-production effect [11].   Tabin found that the number of meson-production events showed a maximum at about 4 cm of lead for various thicknesses placed above the telescope, and no maximum for paraffin [12]. In addition, the variation of meson-production events with altitude resembles that of the soft component.   All these data suggest formation by photons.

Rossi and Regener showed, however, that covering their telescope with 2.5 cm of lead gave a decrease in counting rate only from 2.83 to 2.37, while initiating photons should surely produce showers in the lead which would discharge the anticoincidence counters just below it [8].   Addition of further layers of lead gave a slow reduction in counting rate such as might have been expected of a neutron as initiating particle.   Similar results were obtained by Janossy and Rochester [10] and by Sirkar and Bhattacharjee [13].   The altitude dependence of the event would also be consistent with a neutron component absorbed exponentially in the atmosphere with absorption length ≈ 100 g/cm^2.   It does not at present appear possible to decide definitely between the two possibilities, though the neutron hypothesis appears to be the more promising.   A combination of the two may very likely be involved.

2. PENETRATING SHOWERS

Very soon after the discovery of mesons the search for the mechanism of their production was begun.   Since electrons were produced in cascade showers, it seemed likely that analogous showers of penetrating particles might be examples of meson production. As a result, many investigators tried to find events in which two or more penetrating particles came from a common point. Such events we call penetrating showers.* In some early work such a term is used to describe a shower initiated by a penetrating particle, for example, by Schmeiser and Bothe [14], but we will require two or more penetrating particles.

The first evidence for such events was obtained in cloud-chamber photographs in which two or more penetrating tracks occurred. Discussion of these instances and bibliography thereto are given by Montgomery [15], Janossy [16], and Fretter [17]. The orientation of the tracks was such

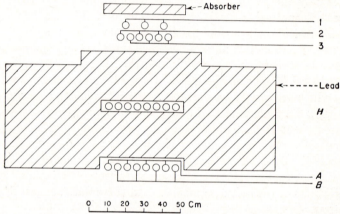

FIG. 4. Penetrating shower detector used by Janossy and Ingleby [18].

that they could have arisen from a single originating event, and it therefore seemed reasonably certain that they did in fact do so. Counter methods for detecting such events have been used extensively by Janossy and coworkers [18,19]. The type of detector used by Janossy and Ingleby is shown in Fig. 4. The controlling counters were connected in five groups: 1, 2, 3, A, and B. For each fivefold coincidence $123AB$, the number of counters discharged in the tray H is recorded. The lead absorber is much too thick to permit electronic cascade showers to discharge counters both above and below it. Some $123AB$ coincidences are to be expected from penetrating particles which produce knock-ons just above counters 123 and again above A and B. In such events 0

---

* These events are sometimes called "local" penetrating showers. Other events are also found in which there are time-associated penetrating particles which cannot be shown to have a common point of origin. These are usually associated with cascade air showers and are sometimes called "extensive" penetrating showers. They will be discussed in more detail in the next section on Penetrating Particles in Air Showers.

or 1 counter in H should be discharged.   The probability of also producing a knock-on there is about 1 per cent.   The number of fivefold coincidences with 0 or 1 counts in H is consistent with such a picture, but, as shown in Table 1, there are a considerable number of instances in which 2 or more counts occur in H, but none would be expected from knock-ons.   Such events must, therefore, be showers of penetrating particles.   A counter arrangement like that of Fig. 4, but requiring two or more counts in H can therefore be used as a penetrating shower

TABLE 1. NUMBER OF COUNTS IN HODOSCOPE TRAY H WITH FIVEFOLD COINCIDENCE 123AB OBTAINED BY JANOSSY AND INGLEBY [18]

Counts in H	0	1	2	3	4	5	6	7	8
No. of cases	77	65	14	9	13	9	7	7	5

detector.   Such a device has been used by Janossy and coworkers for an extensive series of experiments.

A somewhat different counter arrangement was used by Wataghin, de Souza Santos, and Pompeia, in which fourfold coincidences were detected between two shielded counter telescopes, thereby requiring two or more penetrating particles [20].

In order to check the occurrence of penetrating particles, the penetrating shower selector of Janossy has been made to control a cloud chamber in which a thick lead plate was placed [21 to 25].   Penetrating particles were observed in the cloud chamber as expected, though their number was not very great, indicating a fairly small number of penetrating particles in a typical penetrating shower.

A number of other detailed cloud-chamber investigations have been made in which groups of penetrating particles have been observed [26 to 38].   For example, Fretter observed 177 penetrating showers most of which had 2, 3, or 4 penetrating particles.   He used a large cloud chamber containing 16 half-inch lead plates at an altitude of 3000 m, with counter control to select showers passing through the chamber. Electron showers or low-energy electrons are usually associated with the penetrating showers and heavy tracks of slow mesons or protons are often seen as well.   Typical photographs of penetrating showers are given in Fig. 5.

The existence of penetrating showers is thus established beyond any doubt.   It seems highly probable that many of the penetrating particles are mesons, but there is not very much data which can be used to prove that such is actually the case.   The only two alternatives, of course, are mesons or protons, but it is difficult to identify a fast penetrating particle as being definitely one or the other.

MESONS

(a)   (b)

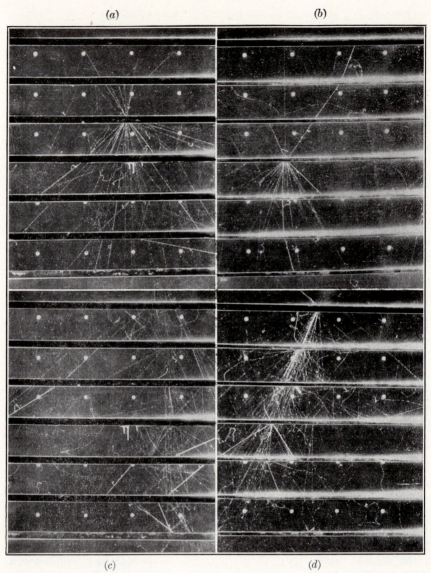

(c)   (d)

FIG. 5. Typical cloud-chamber photographs showing penetrating showers observed by Fretter. "V particles" produce tracks in (a) between third and fourth plates, in (b) between fifth and sixth, and in (c) above the top plate.

Some mesons certainly are present and so are some protons.   Fretter was able to identify 35 mesons and 21 protons which stopped in his cloud chamber after traversing one or more lead plates, on the basis of scattering and density of ionization.   Measurements with a magnetic field show a preponderance of positive particles.   Butler, Rosser, and Barker [25], for example, found 52 positive particles to 15 negative.   If one assumes that the negative ones are all mesons and that there are an equal number of positive mesons, then this leads to 30 mesons and 37 protons.   They were able to identify 20 mesons and 4 protons by density of ionization and magnetic curvature.

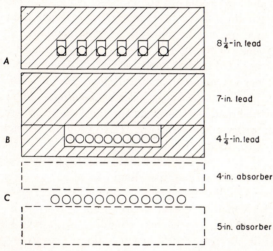

FIG. 6.   Piccioni's apparatus for detecting delayed coincidences due to mesons in penetrating showers [39].

An extremely ingenious identification of mesons in penetrating showers has been accomplished by Piccioni using delayed coincidences [39]. Penetrating showers were detected by requiring two or more counts in layer A of the apparatus shown in Fig. 6 in coincidence with a count in layer B.* He then counted delayed coincidences in which a counter in layer C was discharged 1.3 to 8.4 microsec later.   Such delayed coincidences indicate mesons stopping in the absorber.   Thus an A_1BC_{del} coincidence indicates decay of a μ meson incident on the equipment

* Such a simple arrangement does, in fact, select penetrating showers at mountain altitudes where this experiment was performed.   The lead shielding between A counters makes it unlikely that a knock-on electron from a penetrating particle would discharge a second counter.   Experimentally, the events recorded were about eighteen times as numerous at mountain altitudes as at sea level.   Approximately 90 per cent of the events recorded were penetrating showers.

above while an A_2BC_{del} coincidence indicates decay of a μ meson resulting from a penetrating shower. The lifetime will be that of the μ meson, although the original particle produced may have been a π meson which, after stopping, decayed to form a μ meson, since the π-meson lifetime is very short.

Piccioni found that 15 out of each 1000 penetrating shower events involved μ-meson decays, while only 3 out of each 1000 normal penetrating particles did so. Both figures were much larger than could be due to chance. Therefore mesons were certainly produced in the penetrating shower events. Only a small fraction of the mesons actually produced would stop so as to give delayed coincidences, so that the total number of mesons produced must have been many times larger than 15 per 1000, but the number could not be determined from his data.

In order to show whether the mesons were originally produced as π mesons or μ mesons, Piccioni compared the frequency of delayed coincidences with carbon and sulfur absorbers. In the case of π mesons, only positive particles decay in either absorber. Thus the delayed coincidence rate should be the same for the two absorbers, if the penetrating shower mesons are π mesons which stop and decay to μ mesons which decay to electrons. In the case of μ mesons, only positive particles decay in sulfur, whereas both positive and negative decay in carbon. Thus the delayed coincidence rate should be about twice as high for the carbon absorber as sulfur if the penetrating shower particles are μ mesons formed directly, which stop and decay. For μ mesons incident on the equipment from above, the carbon to sulfur ratio was 1.85 ± 0.05, as expected. (It is not exactly 2 because there are more positive than negative μ mesons.) In the case of penetrating shower particles the ratio was 1.11 ± 0.1, showing that they were produced as π mesons in most cases.

Thus we can say with considerable certainty that mesons are produced in penetrating showers, and that they are mainly produced as π mesons. We cannot, however, determine from these data the number of π mesons produced per penetrating shower or the fraction of all penetrating particles that are π mesons. Despite many investigations of penetrating showers there is very little information on this point. What information there is suggests that protons and π mesons are present in about equal numbers in the high-energy penetrating shower particles.

In addition to the penetrating particles discussed above slow particle tracks are very often associated with penetrating showers. They are mainly slow protons, some of which are ejected by interactions of the shower particles, some of which are ejected in the event originating the shower. Electronic showers are also usually present in penetrating showers [25,30,31,32,37,38]. They may arise from knock-ons of the penetrating particles. In addition, it seems fairly certain that some are formed by the decay of neutral mesons into photons. It is not, of course, possible to demonstrate the presence of the π^0 meson directly, since its lifetime is so short. The electronic showers associated with penetrating showers do, however, seem to have the general characteristics that would be expected on the hypothesis that they are produced by π^0 mesons. With such an origin one would expect two or more somewhat separate electron showers to arise, one from each photon produced by the π^0 mesons. Such multiple showers have been observed by Chao [31]. Green has shown that there is a photon link between the originating penetrating shower event and the electronic showers [40]. The evidence is as follows: If the penetrating showers are observed in a cloud chamber with lead plates, the electrons appear at or near the origin of the penetrating shower, but if the plates are of carbon, the electrons usually appear in plates at a considerable distance. The thickness of carbon between originating event and appearance of electrons is, in fact, about one radiation length, so that it seems fairly clear that the electrons are produced by photons, not directly.

Thus it is very likely that neutral mesons, actually π^0 mesons, are formed in penetrating showers. The experimental information on electrons in such showers is consistent with such a picture, and there seems to be no reason to doubt its accuracy.

So much for the identity of the penetrating shower particles; what can be said concerning the particles that produce them? Considerable confusion existed on this score in early experiments because penetrating showers of local origin were not kept separate from groups of penetrating particles in air showers. The two types were studied separately by Broadbent and Janossy [41]. They found that when lead or paraffin was placed above the penetrating shower detector (shown in Fig. 4) the frequency of events was increased, and a given number of grams per square centimeter had the same effect on (local) penetrating showers whether it was lead or paraffin. Extensive showers, however (in which a distant unshielded counter tray was also discharged) were unaffected by paraffin and showed the characteristic transition effect of electronic showers in lead.* The data are shown in Fig. 7. They concluded that the local penetrating showers certainly were not formed by the soft component and were therefore presumably formed by a nucleonic component, protons and neutrons. Similar results have been obtained by

---

* This transition effect in lead is, in a sense, spurious, since it arises from events in which the 123 counters are discharged by electronic showers generated in the lead by the air-shower particles, rather than by penetrating particles.

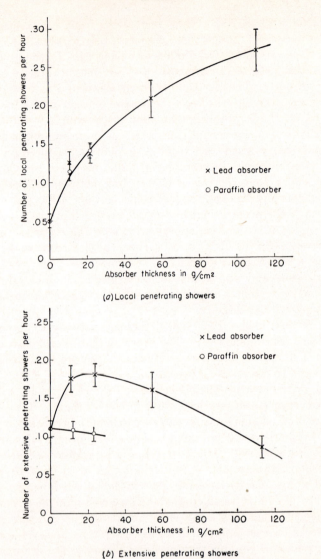

(a) Local penetrating showers

(b) Extensive penetrating showers

FIG. 7. Effect on "local" penetrating showers and "extensive" penetrating showers (penetrating particles in air showers) of absorbing material placed above the penetrating shower detector (Broadbent and Janossy [41]).

George and Jason [42]. A somewhat contradictory result has been obtained by Mezzetti and Querzoli who find carbon to be equivalent to 4.4 times its weight of lead in producing penetrating showers, suggesting that they may be produced in proportion to the geometrical cross section of the nucleus [43]. This would still indicate production by a nucleonic component.

Other data on the absorption of the particles causing penetrating showers support the conclusion that they are due to a nucleonic component, in particular data on absorption in the atmosphere. The frequency of penetrating showers decreases markedly for increasing barometric pressure, about -11 per cent per cm Hg pressure [44]. This corresponds to an absorption of 0.0081 per g/cm^2 for the particles producing the penetrating showers, or an absorption thickness in air of about 120 g/cm^2. Even more striking is the increase in the frequency of penetrating showers with increase in altitude as observed by Sala and Wataghin [45], Tinlot [46], and others. The results of Tinlot, shown in Fig. 8, have an exponential dependence on atmospheric depth with an absorption thickness of 118 ± 2 g/cm^2. In a further experiment Tinlot and Gregory measured the absorption in lead and iron of charged particles producing penetrating showers [47]. Again the absorption followed an exponential law in each case, with absorption thicknesses of 200 g/cm^2 for iron and 310 g/cm^2 for lead.* Electrons or μ mesons would certainly not show absorption of such a type, so that it seems certain that the nucleonic component must be involved. Sitte [48], Walker, Walker, and Greisen [49], and Gottlieb [38] have obtained similar results, but with smaller values for the absorption thickness of the initiating particle.

Neutrons must be included as well as protons. Janossy and Rochester showed that some penetrating showers were observed even when a layer of anticoincidence counters was placed above the penetrating shower detector, so that some initiating particles were neutral [50]. The neutral particles were penetrating, since a 35-cm lead absorber placed above the apparatus reduced the frequency of events only by a factor of 2.6. (Which corresponds approximately to a 310 g/cm^2 absorption thickness.) Hence photons were ruled out, and one must conclude that the particles were fast neutrons.

We would expect that the nucleons responsible for such energetic events as penetrating showers would have to be ones of very high energy. This expectation is confirmed by the absence of any large latitude effect

---

* In this case the penetrating shower detector was such that events occurring in the absorber would not be counted, so that the increase in rate due to the absorber which was observed by Broadbent and Janossy and by George and Jason did not take place.

for penetrating showers. At sea level, Appapillai and Mailvaganam
found no latitude effect with a penetrating shower detector of the type
used by Janossy [51]. Walsh and Piccioni found a latitude effect of
about 12 per cent at airplane altitudes (atmospheric depth 300 g/cm²)
between 55°N and 21°N (geomagnetic latitudes) [52]. This small effect
indicates that the primary particles responsible for the penetrating
showers observed have average energies of 20 to 30 Bev.

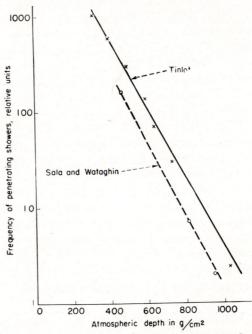

FIG. 8. Variation of penetrating shower frequency with altitude according to Sala
and Wataghin [45] and Tinlot [46].

It seems fairly clear therefore, that penetrating showers are produced
by high-energy nucleons and that π mesons are produced in them. Such
production supports the idea that π mesons are nuclear force mesons.

These results on penetrating showers are thus consistent with the
assumption that mesons are produced in nucleon-nucleon collisions.
They do not, however, determine any details of the process, even to the
extent of distinguishing between the plural and multiple theories of
meson production. To do so, it would be necessary to know how many
π mesons are produced in penetrating showers under various conditions,
but this information is not available. There is some information as to
the number of penetrating particles, some of which are π mesons and

some protons (about 50-50 according to Butler *et al.*).   Typical data are given in Table 2.   The data are somewhat biased by the methods used to select penetrating shower events, so that interpretation of the data in terms of π-meson formation is not easy.   According to Green the smaller multiplicity observed for carbon is due to a difference in geometry, penetrating particles being harder to identify in that case [40].   When corrected for this effect, the multiplicities in carbon and lead are the same.   Such a result would be consistent with multiple, but not plural, meson production.   Freier and Ney have observed a difference in multiplicity between lead and carbon, the average multiplicity being 10.1 for lead, 6.8 for carbon, and 5.5 for lucite [33].   These figures, however, would not be inconsistent with the hypothesis of multiple production.   Fretter has observed penetrating showers with

TABLE 2. MULTIPLICITIES OF PENETRATING SHOWERS*

Material in which produced	Number of penetrating tracks					
	2	3	4	5	6	7
Lead (Fretter)	45	63	31	15	10	13
Carbon (Green)	30	20	7	5	2	4

* The figures displayed give the number of penetrating showers observed with a given number of tracks.

up to 10 penetrating particles produced in a block of lithium [53].   Such events could hardly occur if only one meson is formed per nucleon-nucleon collision, as in the plural theory, because the lithium nucleus is too small for so many collisions to occur.   These observations provide added evidence that multiple production of mesons takes place.

The angular distribution of the shower particles is also of interest. The particles are contained in a fairly narrow cone.   Fretter found that the average projected angle from the direction of the initiating track was 18.6° for events from lead.   In the case of carbon, Green found 20.0°, which was effectively the same as for lead.   Freier and Ney found 24°, 15°, and 16° for the projected angle, including 50 per cent of the tracks for showers from carbon, lucite, and lead, respectively.   This close agreement between lead and carbon seems to favor the multiple rather than plural picture of meson formation.

The energy of the π mesons found in the penetrating showers is, of course, determined to a large extent by the apparatus used to select the event.   In a cloud chamber, particles may be required to penetrate only a fairly thin lead plate to be classed as penetrating, so that the lower limit is 50 to 100 Mev. With counter selectors which require penetration of 10 to 20 cm of lead or more, energies of several hundred Mev are the minimum. Butler, Rosser, and Barker found that the average momentum of mesons measured with their arrangement was about 800 Mev/c. It seems probable, therefore, that the events called penetrating showers involve particles of quite high energy.

3. PENETRATING PARTICLES IN AIR SHOWERS

As was noted in the previous section, an unshielded counter tray in the vicinity of a penetrating shower detector is often discharged in coincidence with the penetrating shower. The fraction of discharges of the penetrating shower selector that is accompanied by counts in the nearby tray varies from a few per cent to about 50 per cent depending on the condition of the experiment. It is thought that in such cases the penetrating particles are associated with extensive air showers. These extensive air showers were discovered by the observation of coincident discharges in two or more counters placed in a horizontal plane with large separations. The coincidence rate decreases for increasing separation, but is still appreciable for distances as large as a hundred meters or more. The air showers are characterized by a core in which the number of particles per unit area is very large, with decreasing density toward the periphery. The particles are mainly electrons (and photons), and there are many in each shower, millions in the largest that have been observed. Consequently, the total energy involved in the shower may be extremely large. It is not appropriate to give a detailed discussion of air showers here. Summaries have been given by Montgomery [15], Janossy [16], and Cocconi [54]. We will simply try to show some evidence for the existence of showers of mesons in the extensive air showers and to indicate how the mesons are thought to have been produced.

Early experiments on air showers showed that the particles involved were more penetrating than the normal soft component of cosmic rays [55 to 57]. It was clear, however, that the majority of the shower particles were electrons, because of their multiplication in lead, and it was not certain to what extent the ability of the air showers to discharge counters under 5, 10, or even 20 cm of lead was due to electrons and photons of very high energy and to what extent it was due to mesons or other penetrating particles [58].

Janossy, however, found penetrating showers associated with air showers [19]. Since these showers penetrated 50 cm of lead, which would require energies $\sim 10^{19}$ ev if the particles were electrons, it was safe to conclude that *some* penetrating particles were involved.   Mura, Salvini, and Tagliaferri showed the presence of particles that penetrated 15 to 20 cm of lead without discharging adjacent counters, *i.e.*, without generating any cascade shower [59].   Such particles had to be considered penetrating; they could not be high-energy electrons.   Treat and Greisen concluded that penetrating particles were present in all air showers although much less numerous than the electrons [60].

The penetration of air-shower particles has been investigated over a wide range by Cocconi, Tongiorgi, and Greisen [61].   Three unshielded

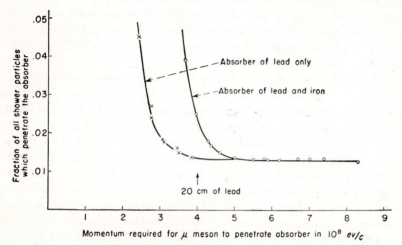

Fig. 9.   Fraction of extensive air-shower particles capable of penetrating thick absorbers, according to Cocconi, Tongiorgi, and Greisen [61].

trays selected air showers, and a series of shielded trays in coincidence registered particles capable of penetrating up to about 500 g/cm² of lead and iron.   The results are shown in Fig. 9.   The first point to be noticed is that lead is a more effective absorber than iron for the less penetrating particles, suggesting that they are electrons and photons. If the absorber thicknesses are plotted in radiation units, the two curves coincide, proving quite definitely that many of the particles penetrating up to 200 g/cm² of lead are photons and electrons.   The particles which are capable of further penetration are clearly different.   They have an absorption length of about 3600 g/cm² of iron.   This is about ten or twenty times that normally found for protons or π mesons so that the penetrating particles appear to be μ mesons.

Figure 9 shows that about 1.4 per cent of the air-shower particles were in the penetrating class under the conditions of that experiment. Cocconi, Tongiorgi, and Greisen [61] have shown that this fraction varies somewhat with the size of shower, position relative to the shower core, and altitude of observation, the extreme values which they observed being about 1.0 and 2.6 per cent. They found that the fraction of penetrating particles was somewhat greater in air showers with few electrons than those with many, was somewhat greater at the periphery of the shower than near its core, and was about twice as great at sea level as at 3000 m elevation. In a similar experiment Ise and Fretter obtained 2.25 per cent as many penetrating particles as electrons, in general agreement with the other results [62]. (They detected coincidences between three shielded trays, rather than one shielded and several unshielded.) These figures are somewhat lower than those obtained in earlier investigations, many of which used lead shields that were not thick enough to eliminate electrons and photons completely.

Since the discovery of penetrating particles associated with air showers, the origin of the penetrating particles has been uncertain. There are two main possibilities: the penetrating particles may either be locally produced in the detecting apparatus by other particles present in the shower or they may be produced in the air and strike the detector from outside. This question is related to the identification of the penetrating particles. Those that are locally produced in the apparatus are presumably protons and π mesons produced in nuclear events. Those that strike the detector from outside are presumably μ mesons from the decay of π mesons produced in nuclear events in the air above, with some protons from the same source. Both possibilities are inherently plausible, and almost certainly both take place to some extent. In cloud-chamber photographs of sections of extensive air showers, Ise and Fretter observed many instances both of parallel penetrating particles incident from outside and of penetrating showers formed inside the chamber. Similar observations have been made by Brown and McKay [63]. The real uncertainty is whether local or remote production predominates, and on this score different experiments have led to different results.

Evidence for the predominance of local production has been presented by Broadbent and Janossy [64]. They concluded that the density of the air showers was too low, on the average, for there to be appreciable probability for two penetrating particles to be incident on their penetrating shower selector. Salvini and Tagliaferri found that when several counters are placed under lead shielding two were sometimes discharged in coincidence [65]. When this happened, the counters that discharged were adjacent in three out of four cases, indicating local production as an important effect.

The experiments of Cocconi, Tongiorgi, and Greisen, on the other hand, indicated that most of the penetrating particles were produced in the air [61].   The strongest argument was an indirect one based on the variation of penetrating and other air shower particles with altitude. Since the ratio of penetrating air-shower particles at 3260 m to those at 260 m was 2.3 to 1, whereas that for the soft shower particles was 5.0 to 1, and that for a nucleonic component was at least 10 to 1, the penetrating particles could not be mainly local secondaries of either of the other two.   They also found that the frequency of multiple discharges in shielded counter trays was consistent with random statistics for particles incident from outside with just a few locally produced multiple events.

A summary of considerations concerning the origin of the penetrating particles can be quoted from Cocconi, Tongiorgi, and Greisen.

"In the first place, production of penetrating particles in the lead plates of a cloud chamber has been seen in association with air showers; hence, *some* of the penetrating particles observed under lead are locally produced.   This implies that production can also occur in the air. Several experiments have shown that the number of penetrating particles observed is independent of the atomic number of the absorber.   Hence, either the particles are *not* locally produced or the amount of production is independent of atomic number.   Finally, we observe that the penetrating particles have very small average absorption coefficients in lead and iron, and increase in number slowly with elevation.   Therefore the particles can be produced in air, even at great height above the apparatus, and still be observed.   The number produced in the air is in general much greater than the number produced locally, because the weight of air above the apparatus is greater than the weight of absorber, and the average intensity of the producing agents is greater in the air.

"The penetrating particles produced in the air, however, are separated from each other because of their initial angular divergence and their scattering, so they are only rarely found close together.   If one designs a counter arrangement that exerts a strong bias in favor of close-packed groups of penetrating particles, one may record most frequently those groups of penetrating particles that are locally produced, even though these are a small fraction of all the penetrating particles in the showers. If, however, one uses a single shielded counter, or a group of widely separated counters, one will detect most frequently the penetrating particles that were produced in the air above the apparatus.   This explanation accounts fairly well for the differences among the experimental results. . . . "

In more recent experiments the behavior of the penetrating particles
in air showers has been observed with counter hodoscopes. The apparatus used by Sitte [48] is shown in Fig. 10. He was able to show that
some of the penetrating particles produced secondaries in two of the
hodoscope trays. These were considered to be due to nuclear interactions of the penetrating particles. These interacting particles could
not be μ mesons and were considered to be protons. In addition events

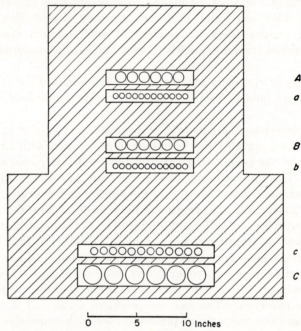

FIG. 10. Schematic diagram of hodoscope arrangement used by Sitte for studying
penetrating particles in air showers [48]. Showers are selected by trays A, B, and C,
while a, b, and c are hodoscope trays.

due to neutral particles, presumably neutrons, were found. Sitte
estimated the ratio of noninteracting to charged interacting to neutral
interacting particles to be 1 to 0.10 to 0.16, at an altitude of 3260 m. In
a similar experiment Greisen, Walker, and Walker [66] obtained ratios
of 1 to 0.36 to 0.24. The presence of interacting particles has also been
pointed out by McCusker [67]. Thus it seems clear that an appreciable
fraction of the penetrating particles are nucleons rather than μ mesons,
even though the absorption measured by Cocconi, Tongiorgi, and Greisen
was very low. This may mean that the interactions are of such a kind
that either the penetrating particle is not really absorbed or further
charged particles are generated.

It appears probable that the air showers are initiated by very energetic nuclear events near the top of the atmosphere. In the initial event energetic nucleons and π mesons are created. The π^0 mesons decay to form photons which initiate the soft component which multiplies rapidly. The charged π mesons mainly decay to form μ mesons, though some may interact in secondary nuclear events. The energetic nucleons give secondary nuclear events in which the process is repeated, developing a nucleonic cascade in addition to the electronic cascade. Through the production of π^0 mesons and photons the nucleonic cascade continually generates further electronic cascades. To a lesser extent energetic photons may cause nuclear events. The over-all phenomenon is surely one of very great complexity.

4. MESONS FROM STARS

In both nuclear emulsions and cloud chambers, events are observed in which two or more densely ionizing particles diverge from a common point. Such events are usually called "stars."* The tracks of the emergent particles are called "prongs." Stars are considered to represent the explosive disintegration of nuclei, with the emission of protons, deuterons, tritons, α particles and heavier nuclear fragments. Neutrons are also emitted but are unobserved since they are non-ionizing. We will not discuss the properties of stars as such, but will only present some results which show that mesons are emitted from stars in addition to the heavier nuclear fragments. For general discussions, see Heisenberg [68] and Montgomery [15]. An excellent summary has been given by Camerini, Lock, and Perkins [96].

In some of the earliest observations of cosmic-ray showers, a few stars were observed, and in some of these, lightly ionizing tracks were seen which did not appear to be electrons [69]. Since energetic nucleon-nucleon collisions must be involved in stars, it has seemed probable for some time that mesons would be emitted fairly frequently from them, at least from those of high energy. Only recently, however, has definite proof been presented. As an example of suggestive results we may take cloud-chamber photographs of Hazen's [26], which showed 58 stars during random operation at 10,000 ft. He found 71 star prongs which penetrated 0.7 cm of lead with only a few cases of multiplication or substantial scattering. Such particles could not be electrons, but could be either mesons or protons. On the other hand, of 166 prongs which

---

* Investigators differ in their criteria for the selection of stars for study, some requiring at least three particles emerging, some at least four, or some other special characteristic. Such differences must be allowed for in comparing results.

failed to penetrate a plate 70 were lightly ionizing and therefore of high speed. These particles could not be protons, since the most energetic proton that would be stopped in such a plate would have density of ionization about four times minimum, but could be electrons or mesons. The simplest assumption would seem to be that at least some of the particles were mesons. In a similar cloud-chamber investigation Powell was able to show that a number of particles produced in stars were fairly certainly mesons because their density of ionization, range, and scattering in passing through lead plates were not consistent with any other assumption [29]. Rochester, Butler, and Runcorn identified a star prong whose curvature in a magnetic field was $2.2 \times 10^7 \pm 25$ per cent ev/c as a meson, since its density of ionization was estimated at 7 times minimum, whereas a proton would have had 150 times minimum, and an electron would have had minimum ionization [70].

At about this time nuclear emulsions became available in which mesons gave recognizable tracks whenever they stopped in the emulsion.* A few such mesons were found to be produced in stars. Lattes, Muirhead, Occhialini, and Powell identified two mesons emitted in a total of 1600 stars with three or more prongs [71]. The meson-producing stars were rare, but mainly because only slow mesons could be observed in the emulsions then available. Mesons of energies greater than a few Mev gave too low an ionization to be recorded in the emulsion, and these might be expected to be emitted much more frequently than those which could be seen. In addition, the meson had to end in the emulsion to be identified positively, so that many were missed because they left the emulsion. By the time that 10,000 stars had been inspected, 20 mesons had been found—17 sigma mesons ending in secondary stars and 3 rho mesons stopping uneventfully [72]. The majority of these mesons were therefore negative π mesons. The explanation for the lack of positive π mesons is simply that any that were actually emitted would be accelerated by the Coulomb repulsion of the nucleus so that their energy would be too high to be observed in the emulsion. Similar results were obtained by other investigators [73 to 75]. Examples of stars in which slow mesons are produced are shown in Fig. 11.

When emulsions that were capable of detecting particles of minimum ionization became available, numerous investigators reported the presence of minimum ionization tracks from stars, often occurring in

---

* The procedure for recognizing mesons depends on measuring the density of ionization through grain density as a function of range. The multiple scattering also serves to identify mesons. At a given distance from the end of the track a meson will, for example, have a lower grain density and higher scattering than a proton. Nuclear emulsion techniques are discussed briefly in Chap. 3.

well-defined groups [76 to 79].   The groups were usually oriented in a
downward direction.   While there was no proof at first, it seemed likely
that the particles might be mesons.   Some very large stars were observed
in which there were more star prongs than there were protons in any
nuclei in the emulsion [80,81].   Such stars certainly indicate the production of charged particles, presumably mesons.   Reproductions of typical
stars with groups of minimum ionization prongs are shown in Fig. 12.

The most definite evidence that many of the lightly ionizing particles
from stars are mesons was obtained by Fowler from a study of the grain

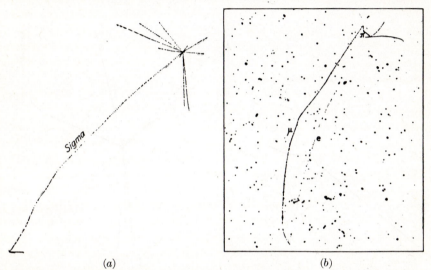

(a)   (b)

FIG. 11.   (a) Star from which a slow sigma meson is ejected.   (b) Star from which a
slow pi meson is ejected.   The resulting μ meson and electron can be seen (the latter
very faintly), showing a complete $\pi - \mu - e$ sequence (Hornbostel and Salant).

density and multiple Coulomb scattering of tracks that were long enough
to give a statistically meaningful estimate of scattering [82].   Measurement of these two quantities determines the mass of the particle, provided it is singly charged.   This method had, of course, been used
previously to determine meson masses.   Fowler's remarkable accomplish-
ment was the development of methods of measuring the extremely small
angles of scattering of the high-energy particles, in some cases less than
$0.01°/100$ microns.   Fowler's results are summarized in Fig. 13.   He concluded that mesons were in fact produced in stars, about 90 per cent of
the prongs with grain density less than 1.5 times minimum being caused
by mesons.   Practically all the mesons were π mesons, with mass estimated by him as $283 \pm 14m_e$.   There were very few, if any, electrons,
μ mesons, or heavy mesons, at least in the energy ranges where they could

readily be identified. These results show quite conclusively that π mesons are produced fairly frequently in energetic stars. More recent data show that about 60 per cent of the lightly ionizing prongs which are long enough to permit determinations of their multiple scattering to be made can be identified as π mesons [94]. Another 20 per cent can be identified as protons, and the final 20 per cent are of such high energy that it is not possible to tell which they are.

These results have been extended to include information on the energy spectrum of the π mesons by Camerini, Fowler, Lock, and Muirhead [83].

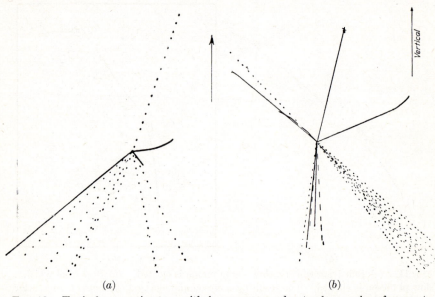

(a)   (b)

FIG. 12. Typical energetic stars with heavy prongs due to slow nuclear fragments and groups of minimum ionization prongs presumably due to mesons (Hornbostel and Salant).

Their results for protons and mesons are shown in Fig. 14. For energies up to about 100 Mev, protons are much the more abundant, but at higher energies π mesons and protons are approximately equally numerous. There is some indication that the energy spectrum of the protons varies somewhat more rapidly with energy than is the case for π mesons. Thus about half the prongs with energy above 100 Mev are π mesons, but since these π mesons are lightly ionizing whereas most of the protons are more heavily ionizing, most of the lightly ionizing prongs are π mesons.

It would be desirable to have data on the multiplicity and angular spread of the mesons—or, more precisely, π mesons—produced in stars. The best data available give multiplicity and spread for lightly ionized prongs [84,85,94]. These prongs are not all caused by π mesons, but Fowler's results indicate that most of them are, and a rough identification of π mesons with light tracks is therefore justified. Data are plotted in Table 3 giving the frequencies of stars with various numbers of light tracks at altitudes of 11,000 ft and 68,000 ft. If there is a light prong in the upper hemisphere, it is considered to be an incoming initiating particle, and the star is then thought to have been caused by a

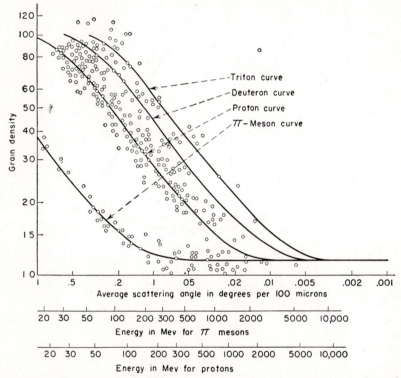

FIG. 13. Grain count vs. scattering observed by Fowler compared with theoretical curves for known particles [82].

proton with energy in excess of 1 Bev. (A few are actually due to π mesons.) If there is no such initiating particle, the star is thought to have been caused by a neutron. A few small stars may have been produced by slower protons, and an appreciable number caused by α particles, whose ionization is never less than four times that of a minimum ionization particle (of single charge). About 20 per cent of the incoming primary cosmic rays are α particles, so that stars due to them are fairly frequent at balloon altitudes.

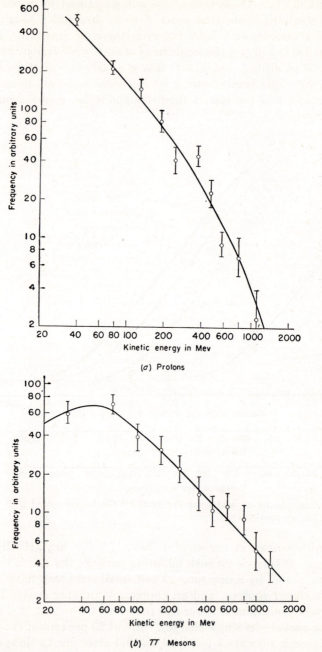

(a) Protons

(b) π Mesons

FIG. 14.   Energy spectra of protons and π mesons emitted in cosmic-ray stars occurring in nuclear emulsions at balloon altitudes (Camerini, Fowler, Lock, and Muirhead [83]).

The data in Table 3 show that there are more stars with several light prongs produced by protons than by neutrons (or other causes), but most of the low-energy stars without light prongs are caused by neutrons. This probably means that stars with several light prongs are to a large extent due to primary protons.   The low-energy stars are caused by lower energy initiating particles, and low energy neutrons are more abundant than the corresponding protons, because the latter are eliminated by ionization losses.

TABLE 3. NUMBER OF STARS OBSERVED WITH VARIOUS NUMBERS OF PRONGS HAVING GRAIN DENSITY UP TO 1.5 TIMES MINIMUM BY BRISTOL GROUP [84,94]

No. of light prongs	With initiating particle		No initiating particle	
	No. of cases	Per cent	No. of cases	Per cent
At 11,000 feet				
0	525	10.7	3729	75.5
1	208	4.2	238	4.9
2	69	1.4	54	1.1
3	21	0.43	16	0.79
4–6	26	0.53	16	0.79
7–10	8	0.16	5	0.10
>10	4	0.08	5	0.10
Total	861	17.6	4063	82.4
At 68,000 feet				
0	2117	13.8	8977	58.6
1	1063	7.0	1378	9.0
2	424	2.8	437	2.9
3	229	1.5	83	0.54
4–6	313	2.0	126	0.82
7–10	100	0.65	20	0.13
>10	29	0.19	4	0.03
Total	4275	27.9	11025	72.1

A total of 200 stars had charged initiating particles whose energies could be measured [94].   In these cases the number of lightly ionizing prongs increased rapidly with increasing energy, showing that the probability for meson production continues to increase at energies above the range discussed in Chap. 4.   The results are shown in detail in Table 4.

Data on the angular spread of the light tracks are given in Fig. 15.

The tracks were quite well collimated along the direction of the incident particle. The average angle of deviation was 13.6°.

It is not very practical to attempt to decide between plural and multiple theories of meson production by comparing the theoretical predictions with these data. In either case the theoretical calculations require assumptions concerning the energy spectrum of the protons causing the stars, concerning their cross section for interaction with the nucleons in the nuclei, and concerning the energy to be radiated in the form of mesons. Since these parameters are not accurately known from other considerations, there is considerable freedom to adjust them. For

TABLE 4. NUMBER OF STARS OBSERVED WITH VARIOUS NUMBERS OF LIGHTLY IONIZING PRONGS AS A FUNCTION OF ENERGY OF INITIATING CHARGED PARTICLE, BRISTOL GROUP [94]

Number of light prongs	Initiating proton			Initiating π meson			Initiating particle not identifiable		
	Kinetic energy, Bev			Kinetic energy, Bev			Kinetic energy, Bev		
	0.24 to 0.54	0.54 to 0.81	0.81 to 1.24	0.09 to 0.33	0.33 to 0.74	0.74 to 1.10	1.24 to 1.91	1.91 to 4.3	4.3 to 9.4
0	17	10	23	11	11	10	9	6	2
1		1	9		3	8	12	13	4
2			1			1	2	4	3
3							1	3	1
4								4	3
5									1
6									1

either theory they can be chosen so as to give reasonable agreement with the observations; thus it is not possible to rule out either theory, nor, of course, the possibility that the true state of affairs is a mixture of both. One can, however, conclude that the mere existence of groups of mesons does not indicate true multiple production in a single nucleon-nucleon collision. The plural picture of singly produced mesons originating in a sort of cascade process in the nucleus can indeed lead to the emission of as many as 10 or more mesons from a single star.

A fairly clear distinction between the two theories could, in principle, be made by comparing stars occurring in large nuclei with those in small ones. If meson production is wholly multiple, there would be no difference between them. If, however, meson production is plural, the larger nuclei should give a larger number of mesons.   Some rather fragmentary data have been obtained which can be interpreted in this way.

When stars which involve sufficient energy transfer to produce mesons occur in an emulsion, the number of heavy prongs can be used to tell whether the star was due to one of the small nuclei (C, N, and O) in the emulsion or one of the large ones (Ag and Br).   If there are more than

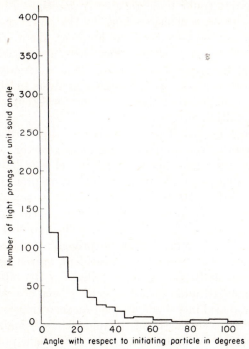

Fig. 15.   Angular distribution of mesons from stars; *i.e.*, number of star prongs with grain count up to 1.5 times minimum at various angles to the direction of initiating particle (Bristol Group [84]).

nine heavy prongs, the nucleus must have been a large one, because there are not that many protons in the smaller nuclei.   It is possible to show that most of the stars with two to five heavy prongs came from small nuclei.

With a criterion of this sort Feld, Lebow, and Osborne showed that the angular spread of the mesons (actually minimum ionization prongs) from large nucleus stars was greater than from small nucleus stars in which the same number of mesons were formed [86].   This difference was interpreted as indicating a cascade multiplication in the larger nuclei.   In a similar way Salant, Hornbostel, Fisk, and Smith showed that a change in incident particle energy (achieved by changing the latitude of observation from 57°N to 31°N) had a different effect on stars from large and small nuclei [87].   For the small nuclei primaries of less than 8 Bev gave the same number of mesons (minimum ionization prongs) as primaries of over 8 Bev.   For the large nuclei, however, the more energetic primaries gave about 5.2 mesons per star instead of 2.7.   It was concluded that a cascade process was effective in the larger nuclei so that the more energetic primaries could undergo greater multiplication and produce more mesons.   These conclusions both fit the plural meson-production picture.   As pointed out by Osborne, however, there are some stars in which more mesons are produced than there are nucleon-nucleon collisions [88].   Such examples would rule out a strictly one-at-a-time meson-production process.   In a detailed analysis of their results the Bristol group concluded that they were not consistent with either pure plural or pure multiple production [95].

A very interesting star has been observed by Lord, Fainberg, and Schein which may be considered to be evidence for the multiple production of mesons in a single nucleon-nucleon collision [89].   It is shown in Fig. 16.   In this event 15 minimum ionization prongs are emitted in the forward direction, 10 of which are virtually superimposed, while only 2 heavier prongs are present.   The prongs appear to be of very high energy from scattering measurements.   The number and angular distribution of the minimum ionization prongs are consistent with the predictions of Fermi's theory for an incident proton energy of about 10,000 Bev which undergoes a single collision.   Recently in emulsions exposed at balloon altitudes several stars have been observed that appear to have been produced in a single nucleon-nucleon collision.   Pickup and Voyvodic observed events with 6, 7, 12, and 13 lightly ionizing prongs and no heavy ones [92].   A similar event with seven light prongs was found by Hopper, Biswas, and Darby [93].   These all appear to be examples of multiple meson production.

These results indicate that successive meson-production events can occur in a large nucleus in a sort of cascade, but that more than one meson can be produced in a single event.   In all probability the multiplicity of the individual events is low for incident proton (or neutron) energies of a few Bev, with singly produced mesons predominating.   At higher energies the multiplicity of the individual collision may become larger, but the possibility of a cascade development in a large nucleus presumably remains.

In the preceding discussion of mesons formed in stars only charged mesons have been discussed.   It is fairly certain that neutral π^0 mesons are also formed in comparable numbers, although the evidence is indirect.   The π^0 meson cannot be observed directly, nor can the two photons into which it is believed to decay.   Only when one of the photons produces an electron pair does an observable effect occur.   Such electron pairs have been observed in connection with stars, but they are rather rare since the

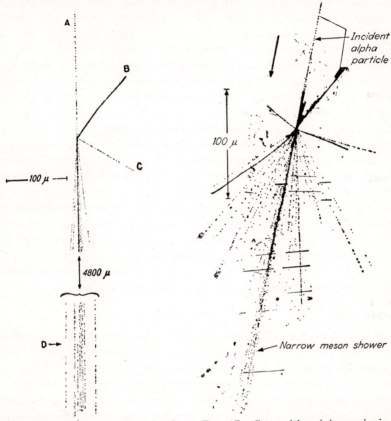

FIG. 16. Star observed by Lord, Fainberg, and Schein in which a very well-collimated group of minimum ionization tracks is emitted with only two heavier prongs. Probably represents a single energetic nucleon-nucleon collision [89].

FIG. 17. Star with minimum ionization group of mesons, including electron pairs produced by photons from the decay of π^0 mesons, observed by Kaplon, Bradt, and Peters [81].

photons do not have a very high probability of producing pairs in the emulsion.

Pairs of this type were observed by Kaplon, Peters, and Bradt [81,90] in a very large star in emulsions flown to 100,000 ft.   This star, shown in Fig. 17, had a group of 23 minimum ionization prongs emerging with an angular spread of 2.5°.   An additional 33 minimum ionization prongs were spread over a wide angle.   Two pairs were observed in the emulsion. The angles between the two tracks were very small in each pair, and their energies were estimated at ~ 10 Bev and ~ 50 Bev.   In addition it was possible to observe the narrow group of tracks in a second emulsion after passing through 2 cm of glass.   Eleven additional tracks were observed. If these were considered to be due to electron pairs formed by photons in the glass, there must have been about 35 photons involved.   This would imply at least 18 π^0 mesons, assuming that their lifetime is short enough that most of them decay to produce photons before going an appreciable fraction of a centimeter.   (Data presented in Chap. 5 show that their half-life is indeed that short.)

Carlson, Hooper, and King have made a careful survey of emulsions exposed at balloon altitudes for electron pairs [91].   They found about 15 electron pairs which were lined up with the origin of a star sufficiently closely that they were probably caused by photons from the decay of π^0 mesons.   They concluded that the ratio of the number of neutral mesons to that of charged mesons was 0.45 ± 0.10.   In addition, they measured the energy spectrum of all the pairs observed at that altitude and showed that this spectrum was indeed that to be expected if the pairs were produced by photons from the decay of π^0 mesons and the π^0 mesons had approximately the same mass as charged π mesons and were produced in stars with the same energy spectrum.

5. SUMMARY

It is clear from the foregoing discussion that a great many experiments have been performed in an effort to obtain information concerning the production of mesons in the cosmic radiation.   A great variety of results have been obtained, and these are not always completely consistent, nor is their interpretation always clear.   One can, however, give a general qualitative picture of the meson-formation process, which seems to be in agreement with the vast majority of the observations.

One imagines that π^+, π^-, and π^0 mesons may be produced in nuclear events whenever there is sufficient energy available to create their rest mass.   Each type may be produced with approximately equal probability.   There is no evidence that μ mesons are formed directly.   Heavy mesons may very likely be formed in such events, but they are considerably less numerous than π mesons, and virtually nothing is known concerning their production.   Heavy mesons will not be discussed further.

The π^0 mesons decay within a very short distance to form two photons, which may then generate a soft component made up of further photons and electrons.   The π^- and π^+ mesons may go distances of many meters before decaying in flight to form μ^- and μ^+ mesons. In the atmosphere the π mesons usually decay, but if they are produced in a solid (or liquid) nuclear collisions may be observed before decay.

When the mesons are formed by nucleon-nucleon collisions occurring in a large nucleus, fast nucleons are produced in addition to the mesons, and in comparable numbers. The over-all production process may be a complicated one involving successive events inside the same nucleus, a sort of intranuclear cascade. Similarly the π mesons and fast nucleons may generate successive events in other nuclei in a nucleonic cascade process. In these cases slow nucleons are also usually produced in each nuclear event.

In the general discussion there were four sections, each devoted to a different way of identifying the meson-production event: (1) production by non-ionizing particles, (2) penetrating showers, (3) penetrating particles in air showers, and (4) mesons from stars. In the case of mesons from stars, the event is selected by the presence of the heavy star prongs. Only a small fraction of all stars have mesons emitted, but virtually all meson-formation events have associated heavy prongs, so that these cases give a reasonably unbiased sample of meson-formation events. In the case of penetrating showers, the event is selected by the presence of fast mesons and/or fast nucleons. In general, these events involve a higher energy initiating particle and a greater energy transfer than stars which emit mesons. Heavy prongs and a soft component are often observed in addition to the penetrating particles. In the case of penetrating particles in air showers, the event is selected by the presence of the extensive electronic cascade. Mesons formed in the air are usually recorded as μ mesons. Energetic protons and neutrons are also present which may generate π mesons and additional generations of fast nucleons in the apparatus used to detect penetrating particles. The air shower as a whole may be thought of as resulting from an initial nuclear event of very high energy. The subsequent nuclear events in the air shower need not all be especially energetic, however. In the case of production by non-ionizing particles, the event in which the meson is formed is probably similar to those classed as penetrating showers.

Thus the different ways of selecting meson-formation events tend to favor events involving different energy ranges, but the basic type of event is the same in all cases.

REFERENCES

1. Heitler, W., *Revs. Modern Phys.*, *21*, 113 (1949).
2. Heitler, W., and L. Janossy, *Proc. Phys. Soc. (London)*, (A)*62*, 669 (1949).
3. Heisenberg, W., *Z. Physik*, *126*, 569 (1949); *Nature*, *164*, 65 (1949).

4. Lewis, H. W., J. R. Oppenheimer, and S. A. Wouthuysen, *Phys. Rev.*, *73*, 127 (1948).

5. Fermi, E., *Progress Theor. Phys.*, *5*, 570 (1950); *Phys. Rev.*, *81*, 683 (1951).

6. Schein, M., and V. C. Wilson, *Revs. Modern Phys.*, *11*, 292 (1939).

7. Schein, M., W. P. Jesse, and E. O. Wollan, *Phys. Rev.*, *57*, 847 (1940).

8. Rossi, B., and V. H. Regener, *Phys. Rev.*, *58*, 837 (1940).

9. Rossi, B., L. Janossy, G. D. Rochester, and M. Bound, *Phys. Rev.*, *58*, 761 (1940).

10. Janossy, L., and G. D. Rochester, *Nature*, *148*, 531 (1941).

11. Schein, M., E. O. Wollan, and G. Groetzinger, *Phys. Rev.*, *58*, 1027 (1940).

12. Tabin, J., *Phys. Rev.*, *66*, 86 (1944).

13. Sirkar and Bhattacharjee, *Science and Culture*, *8*, 89 (1942).

14. Schmeiser, K., and W. Bothe, *Ann. Physik*, *32*, 161 (1938).

15. Montgomery, D. J. X., "Cosmic Ray Physics," Princeton University Press, Princeton, N.J., 1949.

16. Janossy, L., "Cosmic Rays," Oxford University Press, New York, 1948.

17. Fretter, W. B., *Phys. Rev.*, *73*, 41 (1948).

18. Janossy, L., and P. Ingleby, *Nature*, *145*, 511 (1940).

19. Janossy, L., *Proc. Roy. Soc. (London)*, (A)*179*, 361 (1942).

20. Wataghin, G., M. D. de Souza Santos, and P. A. Pompeia, *Phys. Rev.*, *57*, 61 (1940).

21. Janossy, L., C. B. A. McCusker, and G. D. Rochester, *Nature*, *148*, 660 (1941).

22. Rochester, G. D., *Nature*, *154*, 399 (1944).

23. Rochester, G. D., *Proc. Roy. Soc. (London)*, (A)*187*, 464 (1946).

24. Rochester, G. D., and C. C. Butler, *Proc. Phys. Soc. (London)*, (A)*61*, 307, 535 (1948).

25. Butler, C. C., W. G. V. Rosser, and K. H. Barker, *Proc. Phys. Soc. (London)*, (A)*63*, 145 (1950).

26. Hazen, W. E., *Phys. Rev.*, *64*, 257 (1943); *65*, 67 (1944).

27. Fretter, W. B., and W. E. Hazen, *Phys. Rev.* *70*, 230 (1946).

28. Shutt, R. P., *Phys. Rev.*, *69*, 261 (1946).

29. Powell, W. M., *Phys. Rev.*, *69*, 385 (1946).

30. Fretter, W. B., *Phys. Rev.*, *73*, 41 (1948); *76*, 511 (1949).

31. Chao, C. Y., *Phys. Rev.*, *74*, 492 (1948); *75*, 581 (1949).

32. Bridge, H., and W. E. Hazen, *Phys. Rev.*, *74*, 579 (1948).

33. Freier, P., and E. P. Ney, *Phys. Rev.*, *77*, 337 (1950).

34. Lovati, A., A. Mura, G. Salvini, and G. Tagliaferri, *Phys. Rev.*, *77*, 284 (1950).

35. Brown, W. W., and A. S. McKay, *Phys. Rev.*, *77*, 342 (1950).

36. Nooh, M. G., and S. R. Haddara, *Proc. Phys. Soc. (London)*, (A)*63*, 606 (1950).

37. Gottlieb, M. B., A. J. Hartzler, and M. Schein, *Phys. Rev.*, *79*, 741 (1950).

38. Gottlieb, M. B., *Phys. Rev.*, *82*, 349 (1951).

39. Piccioni, O., *Phys. Rev.*, *77*, 1 (1950).

40. Green, J. R., *Phys. Rev.*, *80*, 832 (1950).

41. Broadbent, D., and L. Janossy, *Proc. Roy. Soc. (London)*, (A)*190*, 497 (1947).

42. George, E. P., and A. C. Jason, *Nature*, *161*, 248 (1948).
43. Mezzetti, L., and R. Querzoli, *Phys. Rev.*, *79*, 168 (1950); *Nuovo cimento*, *7*, 470 (1950).
44. Janossy, L., and G. D. Rochester, *Nature*, *152*, 445 (1943); *Proc. Roy. Soc. (London)*, (A)*183*, 186 (1944).
45. Sala, O., and G. Wataghin, *Phys. Rev.*, *67*, 55 (1945); *70*, 430 (1946).
46. Tinlot, J., *Phys. Rev.*, *73*, 1476 (1948); *74*, 1197 (1948).
47. Tinlot, J., and B. Gregory, *Phys. Rev.*, *75*, 519 (1949).
48. Sitte, K., *Phys. Rev.*, *78*, 714, 721 (1950).
49. Walker, W. D., S. P. Walker, and K. Greisen, *Phys. Rev.*, *80*, 546 (1950).
50. Janossy, L., and G. D. Rochester, *Nature*, *150*, 633 (1942).
51. Appapillai, V., and A. W. Mailvaganam, *Nature*, *162*, 887 (1948); *Proc. Phys. Soc. (London)*, (A)*63*, 856 (1950).
52. Walsh, T. G., and O. Piccioni, *Phys. Rev.*, *80*, 619 (1950).
53. Fretter, W. B., *Phys. Rev.*, *80*, 921 (1950).
54. Cocconi, G., *Revs. Modern Phys.*, *21*, 26 (1949).
55. Auger, P., R. Maze, and J. Grivet-Meyer, *Compt. rend.*, *206*, 1721 (1938).
56. Auger, P., R. Maze, and Robley, *Compt. rend.*, *208*, 1641 (1935).
57. Cocconi, G., A. Loverdo, and V. Tongiorgi, *Nuovo cimento*, *1*, 49 (1943); *2*, 28 (1944).
58. Auger, P., and J. Daudin, *Compt. rend.*, *209*, 481 (1939).
59. Mura, A., G. Salvini, and G. Tagliaferri, *Nature*, *159*, 367 (1947).
60. Treat, J. E., and K. I. Greisen, *Phys. Rev.*, *74*, 414 (1948).
61. Cocconi, G., V. Cocconi-Tongiorgi, and K. Greisen, *Phys. Rev.*, *75*, 1063 (1949); *76*, 1020 (1949).
62. Ise, J., Jr., and W. B. Fretter, *Phys. Rev.*, *76*, 933 (1949).
63. Brown, W. W., and A. S. McKay, *Phys. Rev.*, *76*, 1034 (1949).
64. Broadbent, D., and L. Janossy, *Proc. Roy. Soc. (London)*, (A)*191*, 517 (1947); (A)*192*, 364 (1948).
65. Salvini, G., and G. Tagliaferri, *Phys. Rev.*, *73*, 260 (1948); *75*, 1112 (1949); *Nuovo cimento*, *6*, 108 (1949).
66. Greisen, K., W. D. Walker, and S. P. Walker, *Phys. Rev.*, *80*, 535 (1950).
67. McCusker, C. B. A., *Proc. Phys. Soc. (London)*, (A)*63*, 1340 (1950).
68. Heisenberg, W., "Cosmic Radiation," Dover Publications, New York, 1946.
69. Street, J. C., *J. Franklin Inst.*, *227*, 765 (1939).
70. Rochester, G. D., C. C. Butler, and S. K. Runcorn, *Nature*, *159*, 227 (1947).
71. Lattes, C. M. G., H. Muirhead, G. P. S. Occhialini, and C. F. Powell, *Nature*, *159*, 694 (1947).
72. Occhialini, G. P. S., and C. F. Powell, *Nature*, *162*, 168 (1948).
73. Schein, M., and J. J. Lord, *Phys. Rev.*, *73*, 189 (1948).
74. Lord, J. J., and M. Schein, *Science*, *109*, 114 (1949).
75. Pickup, E., and A. Morrison, *Phys. Rev.*, *75*, 686 (1949).
76. Brown, R., U. Camerini, P. H. Fowler, H. Muirhead, C. F. Powell, and D. M. Ritson, *Nature*, *163*, 47 (1949).
77. Pickup, E., and L. Voyvodic, *Phys. Rev.*, *76*, 447 (1949).
78. Hornbostel, J., and E. O. Salant, *Phys. Rev.*, *76*, 859 (1949).

79. Lord, J. J., and M. Schein, *Phys. Rev.*, *77*, 19 (1950).
80. Leprince-Ringuet, L., F. Bousser, Hoang-Tchang Fong, L. Jauneau, and D. Morellet, *Compt. rend.*, *229*, 163 (1949); *Phys. Rev.*, *76*, 1273 (1949).
81. Kaplon, M. F., B. Peters, and H. L. Bradt, *Phys. Rev.*, *76*, 1735 (1949).
82. Fowler, P. H., *Phil. Mag.*, *41*, 169 (1950).
83. Camerini, U., P. H. Fowler, W. O. Lock, and H. Muirhead, *Phil. Mag.*, *41*, 413 (1950).
84. Brown, R. H., U. Camerini, P. H. Fowler, H. Heitler, D. T. King, and C. F. Powell, *Phil. Mag.*, *40*, 862 (1949).
85. Camerini, U., T. Coor, J. H. Davies, P. H. Fowler, W. O. Lock, H. Muirhead, and N. Tobin, *Phil. Mag.*, *40*, 1073 (1949).
86. Feld, B. T., I. L. Lebow, and L. S. Osborne, *Phys. Rev.*, *77*, 731 (1950).
87. Salant, E. O., J. Hornbostel, C. B. Fisk, and J. E. Smith, *Phys. Rev.*, *79*, 184 (1950).
88. Osborne, L. S., *Phys. Rev.*, *81*, 239 (1951).
89. Lord, J. J., J. Fainberg, and M. Schein, *Phys. Rev.*, *80*, 970 (1950); *Nuovo cimento*, *7*, 774 (1950).
90. Bradt, H. L., M. F. Kaplon, and B. Peters, *Helv. Phys. Acta*, *23*, 24 (1950).
91. Carlson, A. G., J. E. Hooper, and D. T. King, *Phil. Mag.*, *41*, 701 (1950).
92. Pickup, E., and L. Voyvodic, *Phys. Rev.*, *82*, 265 (1951) and *84*, 1190 (1951).
93. Hopper, V. D., S. Biswas, and J. F. Darby, *Phys. Rev.*, *84*, 457 (1951).
94. Camerini, U., J. H. Davies, P. H. Fowler, C. Franzinetti, H. Muirhead, W. O. Lock, D. H. Perkins, and G. Yekutieli, *Phil. Mag.*, *42*, 1241 (1951).
95. Camerini, U., J. H. Davies, C. Franzinetti, W. O. Lock, D. H. Perkins, and G. Yekutieli, *Phil. Mag.*, *42*, 1261 (1951).
96. Camerini, U., W. O. Lock, and D. H. Perkins, "Progress in Cosmic Ray Physics," Chap. I, Interscience Publishers, Inc., New York, 1952.

CHAPTER 8

OCCURRENCE OF MESONS IN COSMIC RADIATION

While mesons have recently been produced "artificially" in the laboratory, by far the majority of the mesons which have existed have been produced naturally in cosmic radiation. By far the majority of the experiments on mesons have dealt with mesons occurring naturally in cosmic radiation. For this reason it is appropriate to include an outline of our present knowledge concerning the occurrence of mesons in cosmic radiation, although this outline concerns experiments of a rather different type from those dealt with in previous chapters. The role played by mesons in cosmic-ray phenomena is a very important one, and a complete discussion of it would require a more detailed description of cosmic-ray experiments than is possible here.

In this chapter no attempt will be made to present the historical development of our present ideas or to include all pertinent references, especially to early work. For such information the reader should consult discussions of cosmic rays as such.* Instead a brief outline will be given of our current knowledge concerning the occurrence of mesons at sea level, below ground, and in the atmosphere. In so far as possible their occurrence will be described as a function of sign, energy, time variations, direction, and position relative to the earth's magnetic field.

The mesons observed in cosmic radiation are, of course, terrestrial rather than cosmic. They are secondaries produced in the earth's atmosphere by the primary cosmic rays which enter from outside space.

* For general discussions of cosmic rays, see:

H. J. J. Braddick, "Cosmic Rays and Mesotrons," Cambridge University Press, New York, 1939.

R. A. Millikan, "Electrons (+ and −), Protons, Photons, Neutrons, Mesotrons, and Cosmic Rays," rev. ed., University of Chicago Press, Chicago, 1947.

W. Heisenberg, "Cosmic Radiation," Dover Publications, New York, 1946.

L. Janossy, "Cosmic Rays," 2d ed., Oxford University Press, New York, 1950.

D. J. X. Montgomery, "Cosmic Ray Physics," Princeton University Press, Princeton, N.J., 1949.

L. Leprince-Ringuet, "Cosmic Rays," Prentice-Hall, Inc., New York, 1950.

An excellent summary of recent work is given in "Progress in Cosmic Ray Physics," J. G. Wilson, editor, Interscience Publishers, Inc., New York, 1952.

The primary rays are mainly protons, with about a quarter as many α particles, and 1 per cent as many stripped nuclei having charges from 6 (carbon) to 26 (iron) [1]. Their energies are usually several Bev. Much higher energies occur occasionally, but much lower energies are bent away from the earth by the earth's magnetic field. When these energetic particles hit air nuclei, complicated interactions take place in which there are emitted: (1) nuclear fragments (protons, neutrons, deuterons, tritons, α particles, and larger) of lower energy; (2) π^+, π^-, and π^0 mesons; and (3) probably some γ rays. Electrons and positrons may possibly be created directly, though there is no clear proof of this, and heavy mesons are probably formed. The charged nuclear fragments are mainly stopped by ionization if they are slow, but in many cases cause another lower energy nuclear disintegration if their energy is a few hundred Mev or more. The neutrons are moderated by nuclear collisions if their energy is not too high and finally captured uneventfully by the air nuclei. If, however, their energy is a few hundred Mev or more they too will cause secondary nuclear disruptions when they collide with nuclei. Thus a nuclear cascade may develop until the energy of the nucleons is degraded to a point at which further disruptions are impossible. In most cases only a few successive events are involved, but the highest energy primaries, which create large air showers, may produce complicated nuclear cascades as well.

The π^+ and π^- mesons mainly decay to form μ mesons since their lifetime is short and the density of the air where they are created is small. They may also occasionally be absorbed by nuclei which they hit. The neutral mesons decay at once to photons, which are thought to be the main source of the electronic component of cosmic rays. γ rays produced directly in the nuclear disruption may also contribute to the electronic component. These electrons and photons multiply considerably in the top part of the atmosphere, are then absorbed, and constitute a rather small fraction of the cosmic radiation at sea level. The μ mesons generate additional electrons by collision processes along their path and finally produce electrons when they decay. At sea level the nucleonic component is rare, μ mesons make up about 80 per cent of the charged particles (in the vertical direction) and electrons 20 per cent. Underground the fraction that are μ mesons is even higher.

At sea level, μ mesons are very much more numerous than π mesons for two reasons. In the first place the μ-meson lifetime is about 2×10^{-6} sec, whereas that of the π meson is only about 2×10^{-8} sec, so that there is a factor of 100 in favor of the μ meson. In addition, the π mesons are actually produced in the upper atmosphere and mainly decay or are absorbed by nuclei before reaching sea level. It is fairly safe, therefore, to assume any meson at sea level to be a μ meson unless there is some special reason to think otherwise. Furthermore, since high-energy protons are rare at sea level and slow mesons not very numerous, it is approximately correct, at sea level, to identify μ mesons with penetrating particles. At high altitudes, however, where protons and π mesons are more common, such an assumption would not be strictly justified. In most cases, however, experiments have detected penetrating particles without permitting an analysis into protons, π mesons, and μ mesons (which is, of course, a very difficult thing to do).

1. MESONS AT SEA LEVEL

As has already been noted, the majority of cosmic-ray particles observed at sea level are mesons, and practically all these mesons are μ mesons. Rossi [2] gives values for the vertical intensity, flux, and integrated intensity of the hard component at sea level (at geomagnetic latitudes of 45° or greater):

$$\text{Vertical intensity} \equiv I_v = 0.83 \times 10^{-2} \text{ cm}^{-2} \text{ sec}^{-1} \text{ sterad}^{-1}$$
$$\text{Flux} \equiv J_1 = 1.27 \times 10^{-2} \text{ cm}^{-2} \text{ sec}^{-1}$$
$$\text{Integrated intensity} \equiv J_2 = 1.68 \times 10^{-2} \text{ cm}^{-2} \text{ sec}^{-1}$$

The values are accurate to a few per cent and to this accuracy (at sea level) μ mesons and the hard component may be considered identical.

The terms used above are defined as follows:

1. Vertical intensity I_v. $I_v \, d\omega \, d\sigma \, dt$ represents the number of particles of a given kind incident in time dt on a horizontal area $d\sigma$ in an element of solid angle $d\omega$ centered on the vertical direction.

2. Flux J_1. $J_1 \, d\sigma \, dt$ represents the number of particles in time dt traversing a horizontal area $d\sigma$ in a downward sense.

3. Integrated intensity J_2. $J_2 \, d\sigma \, dt$ represents the number of particles in time dt passing through a sphere of cross section $d\sigma$.

If I_θ is the directional intensity at any angle analogous to I_v, then these quantities are related by Eq. (1).

$$J_1 = \int_{\substack{\text{upper} \\ \text{hemisphere}}} I_\theta \cos \theta \, d\omega \qquad J_2 = \int_{\substack{\text{all} \\ \text{directions}}} I_\theta \, d\omega \qquad (1)$$

In a recent series of measurements Kraushaar [3] has obtained values which are consistent with the previous ones but are considered to have an accuracy of better than 1 per cent. His results (for particles of range ≥ 80 g/cm^2 of air) are

$$I_v = 0.845 \times 10^{-2} \text{ cm}^{-2} \text{ sec}^{-1} \text{ sterad}^{-1}$$
$$J_2 = 1.71 \times 10^{-2} \text{ cm}^{-2} \text{ sec}^{-1}$$

1.1. Positive excess. That a "positive excess" exists for μ mesons at sea level has been known for some time. That is, the number of positive μ mesons is greater than the number of negative ones. The usual definition of positive excess in terms of N_+ and N_-, the observed numbers of positive and negative particles, is given by Eq. (2).

$$\text{Positive excess} \equiv \epsilon = \frac{N_+ - N_-}{(\frac{1}{2})(N_+ + N_-)} \tag{2}$$

Early measurements indicated a positive excess of about 15 per cent. The most accurate measurements appear to be those of Owen and Wilson who used a "magnetic spectrograph" in which hodograph trays of counters were used to determine deflections in a magnetic field [4]. They were able to measure the positive excess as a function of μ-meson momentum but found no significant correlation. Their data are given in Table 1. The corresponding results of Bassi, Clementel, Filosofo, and Puppi are also included [5].

TABLE 1. POSITIVE EXCESS OF μ MESONS AT SEA LEVEL

Observers	Meson momentum, Bev/c	Positive excess, $\epsilon = \dfrac{N_+ - N_-}{(\frac{1}{2})(N_+ + N_-)}$
Bassi, Clementel, Filosofo, and	0.57	0.16 ± 0.10
Puppi	0.88	0.22 ± 0.12
	1.7	0.25 ± 0.07
Owen and Wilson	1.16*	0.16 ± 0.02
	1.91*	0.21 ± 0.02
	2.75*	0.22 ± 0.02
	4.90*	0.23 ± 0.02
	6.76*	0.21 ± 0.02
	11.6*	0.21 ± 0.03

* Mean momentum.

The positive excess of μ mesons is of interest since it presumably arises from the positive charge of the protons which produced the π mesons which decayed to form the μ mesons. In this process the proton may either transform into a neutron, in which case the mesons produced will have a net positive charge (*i.e.*, a positive excess), or not transform, in which case they will not; but there is no plausible compensating process to give a negative excess.   On the average the mesons will have a positive excess related to the number of mesons generated by each primary proton. If the proton contributes its charge to the mesons in half the cases, the average value of $(N_+ - N_-)$ would be $\frac{1}{2}$, since $(N_+ - N_-)$ is simply the net charge given to the mesons.   Substituting this value in Eq. (2) one obtains Eq. (3) in which $\bar{N}_+$ and $\bar{N}_-$ are to be interpreted as the average number of $+$ and $-$ mesons produced by each proton.   (The effect of the primary α particles and heavier nuclei is neglected.)

$$ \epsilon = \frac{1}{\bar{N}_+ + \bar{N}_-} \tag{3} $$

Since the measured value of ϵ is about 0.25, we would infer from Eq. (3) that in first approximation each proton produces about four mesons.

It is reasonable to expect, theoretically, that the more mesons a proton produced, the higher their energy would be, in which case the positive excess should decrease for increasing μ-meson energies.   The data of Table 1 suggest that such is not the case.   On the other hand, Ballario, Benini, and Calamai [6] found a decrease in positive excess at increasing zenith angle (angle from vertical).   Since increased energy is required to penetrate the atmosphere at increasing zenith angles, this result is in contrast with that of Owen and Wilson and might be interpreted as supporting such an energy dependence of meson production.   On the other hand, Caro, Parry, and Rathgeber found evidence for an increase of positive excess with increasing energy in an experiment closely resembling that of Owen and Wilson [7].   Since the changes of positive excess with change in meson energy are small, it is not certain whether these results are actually contrary to theoretical predictions, but there appears to be a discrepancy needing further investigation.

1.2. Energy spectrum.   The energies of cosmic-ray mesons must clearly be high in order for them to penetrate thick layers of absorbing material.   The most direct way to measure the energy of such particles is based on curvature in a magnetic field, the radius of curvature being proportional to the momentum of the particle.   Thus a series of curvature measurements on tracks photographed in a cloud chamber with a magnetic field leads to a momentum spectrum for the particles, which can also be expressed as an energy spectrum if the mass of the particles is known.   The experimental data of Blackett, Wilson, *et al.* have been summarized by Rossi [2].   The differential momentum spectrum is given in Fig. 1.   The circles represent experimental points from cloud-chamber measurements; the curve is an estimated best curve based on both these and counter results.   The curve is normalized so that it gives the number of mesons occurring in a 1 Mev/c momentum interval.

More recent investigations, such as those of Owen and Wilson [4], Caro, Parry, and Rathgeber [7], and Glaser, Hamermesh, and Safonov [8], have employed detectors above and below the magnetic field region, which has given better accuracy at high energies. The results are in good agreement with the curve of Fig. 1 up to about 10 Bev/c but show a slightly steeper slope at high momenta. In the range from about 2

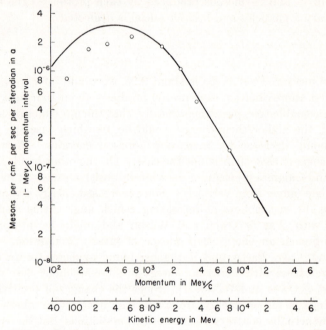

Fig. 1. Differential momentum spectrum of mesons at sea level from Rossi [2].

to 100 Bev/c the differential spectrum can be quite well represented by a power law, as in Eq. (4)

$$N(P) = \text{const } P^{-1.9} \tag{4}$$

where $N(P)$ is the number of μ mesons with momentum between P and $P + dP$.

Data on the energy spectrum can also be obtained from measurements of the number of particles penetrating various thicknesses of absorber, for which a counter telescope is normally employed. A curve in which the number of particles capable of penetrating a thickness, R, is plotted against R is an integral range spectrum since all particles of range greater than R are counted. If the particles counted penetrate R but *not* $R + dR$, then a differential range spectrum is obtained. To obtain an energy spectrum, the energy corresponding to range R must then be taken from curves or calculations. Range measurements of various experimenters have been collected by Rossi [2] and summarized in Fig. 2. The results are consistent with the cloud-chamber momentum measurements. Again circles represent experimental points while the curve is Rossi's best estimated spectrum on the basis of all available data.* Uncertainties involved in the identification of the particles and the effect of scattering make the results for thicknesses less than a few hundred g/cm² somewhat doubtful. This problem has been studied by Kraushaar [3] and by Germain [9].

It would be desirable to compare these observed spectra with those to be expected from knowledge of the energy with which mesons are produced and their energy losses. Comparison with Fig. 14, Chap. 7, shows a plausible resemblance, but since the results on mesons from stars concern production in emulsions at a certain altitude while those observed at sea level were produced in air nuclei at various altitudes, no simple quantitative comparison is possible.

1.3. Effect of meteorological variations. The intensity of cosmic rays at sea level has been found to depend on the pressure and temperature of the atmosphere in many experiments, for example, those of Regener and Rau [10], Ehmert [11], Benedetto, Altmann, and Hess [12], Nicolson and Sarabhai [13], and Duperier [14]. The main effect of pressure is an obvious one. Increased pressure simply means that there is a greater mass of air above the apparatus to absorb the mesons. Duperier gives a value of $-(0.63 \pm 0.18) \times 10^{-3}$ per g/cm² for the fractional change of intensity with changing air pressure of mesons penetrating 25 cm of lead. (The effect of other atmospheric variables has been eliminated from this figure by using partial regression coefficients.) From Fig. 2 we can see that the differential range spectrum gives 5.7×10^{-6} per g/cm² at that range (200 g/cm² of air) while the total number penetrating 25 cm of lead is about 0.76×10^{-2}. Then we would expect the pressure effect to be a decrease of $(5.7/7.6) \times 10^{-3} = 0.75 \times 10^{-3}$, which is in good agreement with Duperier's figure.

The observed temperature coefficient is negative, that is, the intensity of mesons decreases for increasing temperature. The decrease occurs because an increase of temperature causes an expansion of the atmosphere so that the top of the atmosphere, where most mesons are produced, is farther away from the point of observation, and therefore a larger fraction of the mesons decay before reaching the apparatus. It is actually the μ-meson lifetime which governs this effect. This explanation was given

* The subsequent measurements of Kraushaar are in good agreement with these curves.

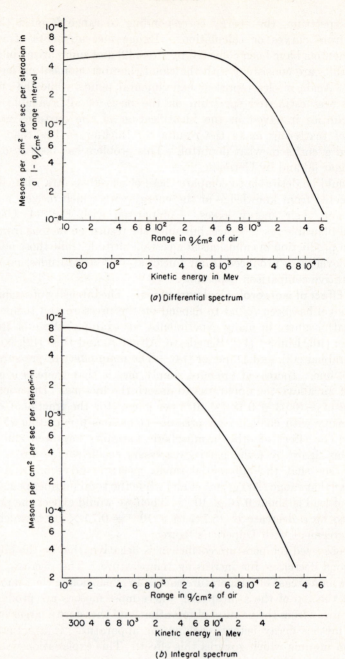

FIG. 2. Range spectra of mesons at sea level from Rossi [2]: (a) differential spectrum; (b) integral spectrum.

by Blackett [15].   As a matter of fact meson intensity is not very highly correlated with ground temperature since it is the temperature distribution throughout the atmosphere that determines the height to which the atmosphere extends.   Duperier has shown that the actual height of the 100-millibar level (100 mb = 102 g/cm^2) is a good quantity to correlate with meson intensity, the variation being $-(3.8 \pm 1.0)$ per cent per km.   This corresponds to a mean range of 26 km before decay, which would be that of a μ meson of about 4 Bev.   Actually, however, the μ mesons involved have a range of energies which must be taken into account in comparing the observed coefficient with the μ-meson lifetime.   When this is done, the coefficient is found to be consistent with the known lifetime of 2.22 microsec.

The best correlation with meteorological conditions is obtained when still another variable is considered.   This is the temperature at the level where mesons are produced, *i.e.*, the 100-mb level.   Duperier found an increase of 0.12 ± 0.02 per cent per deg C change in temperature at this level.   He explained this effect as resulting from a competition between decay and nuclear interaction of π mesons.   An increase in temperature means decreased air density and therefore fewer collisions with nuclear interaction.   The number of π mesons decaying to μ mesons would then increase.   This explanation predicts an effect of the observed order of magnitude but does not provide a quantitative interpretation of the observations.

We can conclude, therefore, that these effects are at least roughly consistent with the known properties of mesons.

1.4. Variations with zenith angle.   The directional intensity of mesons at sea level is by no means isotropic, the greatest intensity being in the vertical direction.   At other zenith angles the intensity is less, because the oblique incidence requires the mesons to traverse an increased thickness of air to reach sea level.   In addition there is an east-west asymmetry due to the bending of the trajectories of the mesons and their primaries by the magnetic field of the earth.

The zenith-angle effect for the total cosmic-ray intensity is given fairly accurate by a $\cos^2 \theta$ law, that is, at any angle, θ, from the vertical the intensity is given by Eq. (5).

$$I(\theta) = I(0) \cos^n \theta \tag{5}$$

with $n = $ about 2.   Measurements of Clay, Jonker, and Wiersma [16], Greisen [17], and Rogozinsky and Voisin [18] show that approximately the same is true for mesons.   The data plotted in Fig. 3 indicate values of $n = 1.7$, 2.1, and 2.20, respectively.   According to Freon and Tsai-Chou, the value decreases somewhat as the energy of the mesons is increased [19].   They obtained 2.05 and 1.95 for n, when the minimum momentum of meson that would penetrate their telescope was 320 and 540 Mev/c, respectively.

While this empirical law for zenith-angle distribution is a simple one, it is not easy to interpret because two effects are involved, the absorption of mesons due to ionization losses in crossing the atmosphere and decay

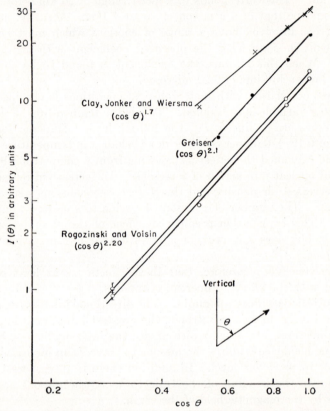

Fig. 3.   Dependence of meson intensity on zenith angle at sea level.

into electrons.   In addition, the production of mesons may not be isotropic.   We can make a very crude separation into these two factors by first imagining that the μ mesons did not decay.   Consider $\theta = 60°$ as an example ($\cos \theta = \frac{1}{2}$).   Then, if we assume the mesons to be produced at the 100-mb level (≈ 0.1 atm), they have to traverse 1800 g/cm^2 of air instead of 900, which additional absorber will reduce their number by a factor of about 2.2.   The actual height of this pressure level is about 16 km.   If we take Duperier's figure of 3.8 per cent per km for the average decay probability, decay introduces another factor of 1.8. We would expect the total effect of changing from 0 to 60° to be a factor of $1/2.2 \times 1.8 = \frac{1}{4}$, which is in fact $(\cos 60)^2$. The figures presented are, therefore, roughly consistent, but detailed calculations are beyond the scope of this discussion.

1.5. Geomagnetic effects. At a given zenith angle, however, the meson intensity is greater from the west than from the east. This is a "geomagnetic" effect due to the deflection of charged particles in the magnetic field of the earth, as is the "latitude effect" which involves a decrease in cosmic-ray intensity as the equator is approached from higher latitudes. The quantitative explanation of these and other less well-defined, geomagnetic effects is a complicated one. Only the major principles can be discussed here. Charged particles traveling so as to intersect the lines of force of the earth's field will be deflected by it. The effect is therefore large at the magnetic equator where particles of a vertical trajectory are traveling perpendicular to the field, but vanishes at the poles where they are parallel. Since the earth's field extends far beyond the atmosphere, by far the greatest effect is on the cosmic-ray primaries, but there is an appreciable effect on the secondary mesons as well. The effect of the field on the primaries is as follows: In its absence they would be incident on the atmosphere from all directions in the upper hemisphere with random distribution and with a certain energy spectrum. The lower energy ones are, however, bent away and cannot reach the earth's surface. This introduces a cutoff energy which is about 10 Bev at the geomagnetic equator and drops to zero at the poles. That is, no particle of lower energy may reach the earth's surface, or, for all practical purposes, the thin layer of atmosphere around it. For certain angles of incidence on the earth, the energy required is even higher. It is difficult for positive particles to be incident from the east, an effect which is greatest at the equator and least at high latitudes. At zenith angle 90°, a primary approaching from the east at the equator must have an energy of about 60 Bev or more.

This magnetic cutoff means that the total number of particles incident on the top of the atmosphere is considerably less at the equator than at the poles and less from the east than the west. It is not, however, obvious what effect this will have on observations made at sea level. Primaries of very low energy could not possibly produce secondaries capable of penetrating to sea level, and for this reason the latitude effect at sea level would be expected to be less than at high altitudes. The relation between primary energy and that of the secondary mesons produced is still unknown, so that it is not possible to interpret observations at sea level in terms of primary energies. It is generally believed that the secondaries will be produced in directions that approximately preserve the direction of the primary particle, in which case angular asymmetries in the primaries will still exist in the secondaries observed at low altitudes, but it is not certain how precisely this is the case.

The theoretical calculations of geomagnetic effects are thus applicable to the primary radiation, while experimental measurements have been made on the secondaries whose relation to the primaries is not precisely known.* As a result, direct quantitative interpretation is not possible.

The latitude effect (meaning the variation with latitude of the vertical intensity) of the penetrating component (which may be considered to consist of μ mesons at sea level) is quite small, indicating that the mesons sufficiently energetic to reach sea level are mainly produced by primary protons whose energies are greater than 10 Bev. Recent measurements by Morris, Swann, and Taylor [20] give a change of 5.3 ± 0.5 per cent between the equator and 30°N with no appreciable change after about 30°. Earlier measurements summarized by Johnson [21] indicated a value of 8 to 12 per cent depending on longitude, with the "knee" occurring at about 40°,† and these may well be more accurate. The latitude effect of the meson component at sea level is not actually known very precisely.

At low latitudes, the east-west asymmetry of the primary radiation manifests itself to some extent in an east-west asymmetry of the mesons produced by it, even at sea level. The effect at sea level does not seem to have been measured very extensively.‡ Early measurements quoted by Johnson [21] indicate an excess from the west of the order of 10 per cent.

At high latitudes the primary radiation sufficiently energetic to produce mesons which reach sea level is isotropic, but the mesons are bent in passing through the atmosphere so that positive particles incident from the west travel a shorter distance through the atmosphere than those incident from the east, and are therefore more numerous. The converse is true for negative particles. Since there is a positive excess, there is a small net east-west asymmetry [22]. At a zenith angle of 20°, Seidl [23] found an asymmetry of 0.7 per cent at 54°N geomagnetic latitude. If positive and negative mesons are separated, however, each

---

* Recent measurements have been made using balloons and rockets to achieve altitudes where a large fraction of the particles involved are primaries.

† The early measurements were made without lead shielding, so that soft radiation was also included. Morris, Swann, and Taylor find, however, no difference between latitude effects for penetrating and total radiation. This is reasonable because the electrons are mainly produced by the mesons.

‡ The main reason being that such measurements would have no clear physical interpretation, even if they were made, for the reasons just mentioned.

shows a considerable asymmetry.   Measurements of this type have been made by Groetzinger and McClure using a magnetic-lens type of telescope [24].   They found 7 ± 2 per cent more positives from the west and 4 ± 2 per cent more negatives from the east at zenith angle 24°, while at 58° zenith angle the figures were 13 ± 5 per cent and 19 ± 6 per cent, respectively.   The results are consistent with Johnson's theory.

2. OCCURRENCE OF MESONS BELOW GROUND

A large number of experiments have been carried out to show the existence of cosmic rays at various depths under water and earth, for example, by Kolhörster [25], Barnothy and Forro [26], Wilson [27], Clay and Van Gemert [28], and Miyazaki [29].   The greatest depths have been achieved under ground.   Wilson and Clay and Van Gemert measured the cosmic-ray intensity in mines at depths equivalent to about 1400 m of water. Miyazaki succeeded in making measurements at 3000 m of water equivalent in a tunnel.

It seems natural to presume that the cosmic rays which penetrate to such depths are indeed identical with the penetrating component observed at sea level, since neither soft component nor nucleonic component could possibly penetrate to such depths.   The particles which penetrate to great depths must therefore be either μ mesons or some previously unobserved radiation.   (It has been suggested that they are neutrinos, secondaries of which are actually detected by the apparatus.)   If the particles are μ mesons, their original energy must have been very high indeed.   In order to penetrate to 1000 m of water, an energy of about 250 Bev would be required.

At moderate depths there is considerable evidence to support the hypothesis that the particles are μ mesons.   Cloud-chamber photographs show that in most cases the controlling counters are discharged by a single ionizing particle which penetrates a lead plate without producing secondaries [30,31].   A few soft secondaries, presumably electrons, are seen.   The phenomena appear identical with those observed at sea level.   If the absorption in lead is measured with a counter telescope, it is found that the ionizing particles observed are very penetrating [31,32].

At depths in excess of 500 m of water equivalent the nature of the penetrating particle is less certain.   Barnothy and Forro have concluded that the particles penetrating to these depths are neutral decay particles from mesons [26].   Several arguments are involved: (1) the presence of uncharged particles is indicated by frequent double coincidences of a counter telescope which are not accompanied by triple coincidences,

(2) the absorption curve giving number of triple coincidences versus thickness of lead appears not to be smooth, but to have maxima suggestive of transition effects involving the production of fairly penetrating charged particles by neutral ones, and (3) the temperature coefficient of intensity at great depths is positive whereas that for μ mesons at sea level is negative. On the other hand, Miesowicz, Jurkiewicz, and Massalski feel that the frequent double coincidences may be due to γ rays from radioactive substances [33]. Tiffany and Hazen used a cloud chamber triggered by a twofold coincidence telescope at a depth of 860 m of water equivalent and concluded that practically all the coincidences were due to single ionizing particles or showers [34]. At most 3 per cent of the coincidences could have been due to products of neutral particles. Similarly, Randall, Sherman, and Hazen find that the particles are highly penetrating [35]; 84 cm of lead reduced the counting rate of a telescope by only about 6 per cent. On the other hand, larger absorption was reported by Miyazaki [29]. On the basis of these rather conflicting data it is not possible to be certain whether the particles are μ mesons or not, but it seems most probable that they actually are. There is, of course, a small admixture of soft component, which appears to consist of electrons which are produced by the mesons [36].

The data on the variation of intensity with depth below sea level have been summarized by Clay [37]. The results of various investigators are in fairly good agreement and can be represented by a curve such as that given in Fig. 4. When plotted on a logarithmic scale, there is a transition period for short distances under ground. The data at greater depths are usually represented by two straight lines, intersecting at about 300 m depth. They correspond to the two equations:

$$
\begin{aligned}
I &= I_0 h^{-1.9} \qquad \text{above 300 m water equivalent} \\
I &= I_0 h^{-2.9} \qquad \text{below 300 m water equivalent}
\end{aligned}
\tag{6}
$$

No compelling evidence exists, however, for a discontinuity in slope at that depth. Clay's results seem to show a definite break, but when those of other investigators are included, it appears that a smooth curve would be equally appropriate. There is, however, a definite increase in slope at approximately that depth.

The curve shown in Fig. 4 can be considered to represent the energy spectrum of the μ mesons incident on the earth's surface. At high energies, the energy loss is constant, so that the depth of penetration is proportional to the energy.* In this case the energy spectrum has a

---

* One might imagine that the more rapid absorption at the great depths was due to an added energy loss, possibly a loss by radiation in addition to ionization, but this does not now seem likely.

break at about 60 Bev, which is the energy required to penetrate to 300 m. The integral spectrum would be $E^{-1.9}$ at lower energies, $E^{-2.9}$ at higher.

This change in spectrum has been explained in terms of the decay of the π meson by Greisen [38] and by Hayakawa [39,40]. It is assumed that the particles occurring at great depths are μ mesons arising from the decay of π mesons in the atmosphere. The π mesons are formed with

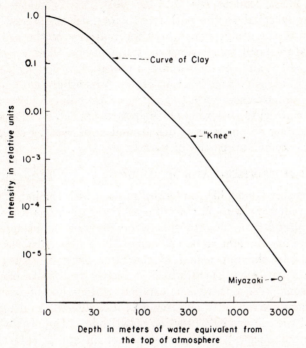

FIG. 4. Dependence of meson intensity on depth below ground, according to Clay [37].

an $E^{-1.9}$ spectrum. π mesons of low energy almost all decay rather than interact with material in their path, whereas at high energy an appreciable fraction, or even majority, may interact before decaying. The fraction decaying will be approximately as in Eq. (7).

$$\text{Fraction decaying} = \frac{\lambda}{L + \lambda} \approx \frac{\lambda}{\tau_\pi' c + \lambda} = \frac{\lambda}{\tau_\pi c (W/m_\pi c^2) + \lambda} \quad (7)$$

where L = mean range before decay of π mesons
$\quad \lambda$ = mean free path for interaction of π mesons
$\quad \tau_\pi'$ = apparent lifetime of π mesons
$\quad c$ = velocity of light

τ_π = rest lifetime of π mesons

m_π = rest mass of π mesons

W = total energy of π mesons

For sufficiently high energies, this fraction becomes approximately proportional to W^{-1} or E^{-1}, so that the number of μ mesons found at great depth becomes $E^{-2.9}$ rather than $E^{-1.9}$. The transition occurs approximately when $L = \lambda$. The values $\tau_\pi = 2.6 \times 10^{-8}$, $W = 60$ Bev, and $m_\pi = 277 m_e$ lead to $L \approx 3 \times 10^5$ cm. This is indeed a distance approximately equal to the path length for nuclear interaction in the upper part of the atmosphere where the majority of the π mesons are formed. More exact calculations show that if one takes $\lambda \approx 125$ g/cm² of air, $\tau_\pi \sim 10^{-8}$, and the known meson masses, it is possible to calculate the μ-meson intensity as a function of depth under ground and obtain a curve in good agreement with the experimental points. The steepening of the curve at depths below 300 m is, in fact, predicted. Thus the main facts concerning cosmic rays under ground appear to be explainable in terms of the known properties of mesons.

3. OCCURRENCE OF MESONS AT HIGH ALTITUDES

At sea level it is possible to identify mesons with the hard component of cosmic radiation with fair accuracy because protons are very rare. At the extreme top of the atmosphere, on the other hand, most cosmic-ray particles are thought to be protons. There mesons are negligible in proportion. In the upper half of the atmosphere a transition takes place from a hard component which is mainly protons to one which is mainly mesons. Since there is no experimental method of distinguishing between them conveniently and directly, it is difficult to determine the intensity of the mesons as a function of altitude. The problem is made even more complicated by the existence of an appreciable number of slow mesons in the soft component. μ mesons of low energy can, however, be identified quite well by counting delayed coincidences between the meson stopping in an absorber and the decay electron. For the fast particles, it is usually only possible to distinguish between particles causing nuclear interactions and those which do not. The latter are presumably μ mesons. The former may be either protons or π mesons, with protons predominating, since π mesons decay before traveling very far through the atmosphere.

Thus the frequency of occurrence of mesons as a function of altitude is not known with great accuracy or reliability in spite of the considerable amount of experimental work on the altitude variation of the hard component. In the upper half of the atmosphere especially, the details of the interpretation of the data are uncertain.

The data existing prior to 1948 have been summarized and analyzed by Rossi [2]. His final data are presented in Fig. 5. Curves are given for the hard component (particles capable of penetrating 167 g/cm² of lead) and the soft component (particles capable of penetrating 5 g/cm² of brass but not 167 g/cm² of lead), fast and slow mesons. Fast mesons

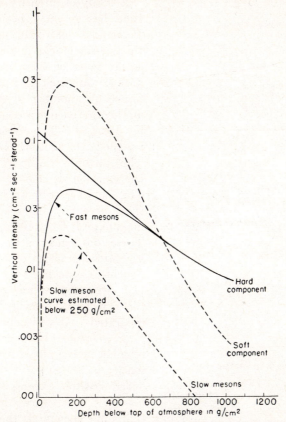

Fig. 5. Intensity of mesons as a function of altitude, according to Rossi [2].

are those in the hard component, slow mesons those in the soft component. The fast-meson curve is obtained by subtracting from the hard component a proton contribution.* The slow-meson curve was measured

* The proton contribution is taken to be equal to the primary flux at the top of the atmosphere and to decrease with depth as exp $(-x/125)$. This decrease is characteristic of rays capable of producing nuclear interactions. If some nuclear interactions are caused by π mesons produced by the protons, the absorption of the protons themselves would be more rapid. The correction made would, then, in effect class the τ mesons as protons rather than as mesons.

by Sands up to an atmospheric depth of 250 g/cm², using delayed coincidence identification of μ mesons stopping after penetrating various thicknesses of absorber. The details of these experiments have been described by Sands [41]. Similar results have been obtained by Conversi [42].

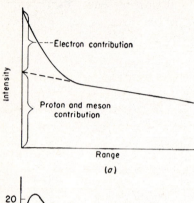

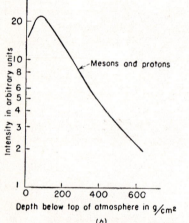

FIG. 6. (a) Typical curve of intensity vs. range (at a given altitude), showing the extrapolation procedure used by Pomerantz for assigning contributions to electrons and protons + mesons. (b) Proton + meson contributions as a function of atmospheric depth, according to Pomerantz [43].

A study of intensity at high altitude has recently been made by Pomerantz [43]. He used various thicknesses of lead in a counter telescope, most of them less than 167 g/cm². At each altitude he estimated the number of electrons by an extrapolation procedure, as shown in Fig. 6a. The remainder was assigned to protons and mesons. The altitude dependence of this contribution is shown in Fig. 6b. This curve rises more steeply than those given by Rossi and shows a maximum at 50 to 100 g/cm² depth. These differences arise because a substantial fraction of the soft component is considered by Pomerantz to consist of slow mesons and protons, which, however, cannot be separated. At altitudes above 250 g/cm², considerable uncertainty still remains in the curve for meson intensity vs. altitude.

3.1. Positive excess. In measuring the positive excess at high altitudes, one encounters the usual difficulty of separating mesons from protons. Cloud-chamber measurements by Adams, Anderson, Lloyd, Rau, and Saxena [44] at 30,000 ft gave about twice as many positive particles as negative (positive excess is equal to 67 per cent). These data are based on singly occurring tracks in the cloud chamber, and may well have included some electrons. They concluded, however, that most of the excess positive particles were protons. This conclusion is consistent with the data of Fig. 5, in which it is estimated that about 25 per cent of the hard component consists of protons at that altitude.

Measurements have been made with a magnetic lens by Quercia, Rispoli, and Sciuti [45], which indicate a positive excess of about 40 per cent at 5100 m and no further increase at 7300 m.   More accurate measurements of Groetzinger and McClure [24] gave a positive excess of 18 ± 1.5 per cent at 4300 m for mesons of energy about 800 Mev, compared with 13.5 ± 1.1 per cent at sea level.   In their apparatus, protons of the required curvature would not have been able to penetrate the magnetized iron absorbers, so that these values may better represent the positive excess of the mesons (very largely μ mesons) themselves.

Conversi [42] has used a delayed-coincidence scheme for measuring the positive excess of μ mesons at 30,000 ft. μ-meson decay events are counted for mesons stopped in carbon (in which both μ^+ and μ^- mesons decay) and sulfur (in which most μ^- mesons interact).   For energies of about 240 Mev, he obtained a positive-negative ratio of $1.54^{+0.39}_{-0.26}$, leading to a positive excess of 42 per cent.*

While the main contribution to the positive excess of cosmic rays at high altitude is thus probably due to protons, there is some evidence for an increased positive excess of the mesons.   Such an increase appears reasonable since, in general, mesons occurring at sea level must have been more energetic when produced, and therefore have been produced by higher energy primary protons, probably with a greater multiplicity (or plurality).   Neither the increase nor its interpretation are very certain at present, however.

3.2. Energy spectrum.   Measurements of the ranges of cosmic-ray particles have been made with counter telescopes by Hall [46] at 4350 m and Carr, Schein, and Barbour [47] at 5490 m.   The data are plotted in Fig. 7, with the sea-level curve given for comparison.   It is evident that the mesons tend to have lower energies at high altitude than at sea level.   To some extent, however, the contributions of protons and electrons may be responsible for the increase in low-energy particles.   The absorbers used by Carr, Schein, and Barbour (10 to 50 cm of lead) would cut out most electrons, but there was no discrimination against protons. Hall employed additional shower-detecting counters and considered particles failing to discharge these to be single mesons.   Again no discrimination against protons was employed.

Cloud-chamber measurements of momentum have been made at 30,000 ft by Anderson and coworkers [44,48].   They found that there was a marked difference between positive and negative momentum

* This value is not affected by the presence of protons, but the high value may be partly due to π mesons produced in the absorber.   Negative π mesons will always interact when stopped but positive π mesons stopping in either carbon or sulfur will decay to positive μ mesons, whose decay will then be recorded and contribute to the positive excess.

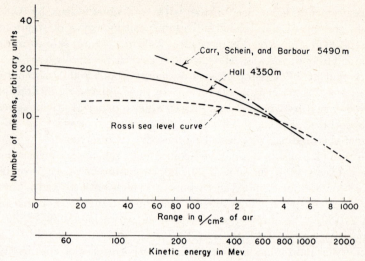

Fig. 7.   Integral range spectra of penetrating particles at various altitudes

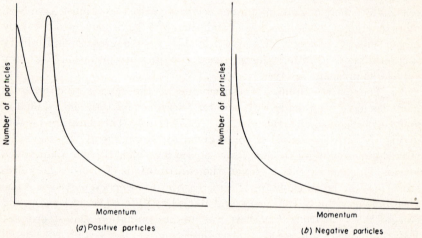

Fig. 8.   Momentum spectra of positive and negative particles at 30,000 ft, according to Anderson and coworkers [44,48].

distributions for single nonshower tracks as indicated schematically in Fig. 8.   They considered the excess in the positive spectrum to be protons, so that the negative particle spectrum should be taken as typical of mesons.   An adjustment is necessary for electrons, however, since some of the single tracks of low energy are, in fact, electrons.   The corrected (differential) momentum distribution is plotted in Fig. 9.

Similar measurements have been made by Miller and coworkers [49] at 3400 m. They also found an excess of positive particles which was believed to be due to protons. Their momentum spectrum based on negative particles is also given in Fig. 9. Only particles occurring singly under 5 cm of lead were included so that the effect of electrons should be small.

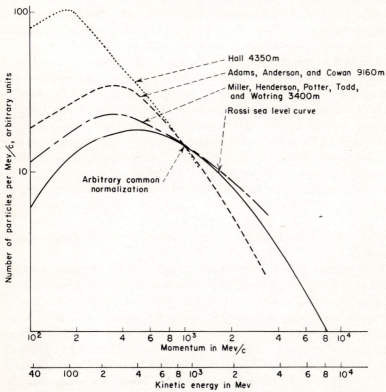

FIG. 9. Differential momentum spectra of penetrating particles (mainly mesons) at various altitudes.

For comparison, the sea-level differential momentum spectrum given by Rossi is plotted, and an analogous spectrum derived from the counter telescope measurements of Hall. The high-altitude spectra show more mesons in the momentum range below 500 Mev than the sea-level spectrum. Hall's data appear to indicate a much larger number of low-energy mesons than the cloud-chamber results, but this is probably spurious. Two effects probably contribute to the discrepancy: (1) cloud-chamber data have a slight bias against low energies because the particle must have some energy to reach the lower control counters to discharge them, and (2) the data of Hall may include some electrons as mesons, since his discrimination against electrons probably was not perfect. At high momenta the sea-level and high-altitude curves seem to have much the same slopes, but the maximum in the curve is shifted to lower momenta at high altitude.

This increased number of relatively low-energy mesons no doubt arises from the production of mesons in the nearby air. When produced, low-energy mesons predominate, but decay and ionization losses remove them in traveling any substantial distance through the atmosphere.

3.3. Effect of meteorological variations. Barometer and temperature effects have not been studied at high altitude to any appreciable extent. Presumably the effects would be about the same as at sea level.

3.4. Variations with zenith angle. The intensity of the hard component of cosmic rays has been studied as a function of zenith angle over a wide range of altitudes. At low altitudes, these data may be considered with fair accuracy to represent mesons. At high altitudes, the protons in the hard component probably have a sharper zenith-angle dependence than the mesons, while the less energetic mesons in the soft component would be expected to be even more nearly isotropic, since they are probably produced in less energetic and less well-collimated events. With these provisos data on the hard component may be considered applicable to mesons.

The most extensive data are those of Greisen [17] who measured $I(\theta)$ for zenith angles, θ, from 0 to 56° for rays penetrating 167 g/cm² of lead at 259, 1616, 3240, and 4300 m (1007, 857, 708, and 616 g/cm²). He found that the intensity was proportional to $(\cos \theta)^{2.1}$ at each altitude. That is, the zenith-angle dependence was independent of altitude. Any difference is certainly very small. Freon and Tsai-Chu [19] found an exponent of 2.05 ± 0.02 at sea level, 2.16 ± 0.02 at 2058 m. Voisin [50] found 2.18 and 2.20 at 148 and 2860 m, respectively. There is good agreement on the form of the distribution.

At higher altitudes, however, the distribution of the hard component becomes more nearly isotropic. Jenkins [51] has measured counting rates at 0° and 45° at altitudes up to 36,000 ft. He finds that the ratio of intensities rises from 0.5 at low altitudes to about 0.75 at 36,000 ft. Winckler and Stroud [52] have extended zenith-angle measurements to balloon altitudes. They find that the intensity of the hard component becomes practically isotropic near the top of the atmosphere (1 to 5 cm Hg pressure) except for a decrease in the horizontal direction where the amount of atmosphere penetrated becomes large. A large fraction of the particles involved at such altitudes are certainly protons, rather than mesons, however.

3.5. Geomagnetic Effects. At high altitudes, the latitude and east-west effects are considerably larger than at sea level. At 33,000 ft, Gill, Schein, and Yngve [53] found the vertical intensity at 40° to be 30 per cent greater than at the equator for particles penetrating 20 cm of lead. Biehl, Neher, and Roesch [54] found values of 40 per cent and 34 per cent for particles penetrating 10 and 20 cm of lead, respectively. Their altitude was 30,000 ft.

Conversi has measured the latitude effect for mesons using delayed coincidences to identify mesons stopping in a graphite block [55]. At an altitude of 30,000 ft, he found about 1.9 times the frequency at 59° as at 9°, but the statistical uncertainties were rather large.

The increased latitude effect at higher altitudes has a simple interpretation. The mesons observed at high altitudes are, in general, produced with lower energies than those reaching sea level. Correspondingly they are presumably produced by lower energy primary nucleons, i.e., by those that have the greatest deflections in the earth's field and hence the greatest latitude effect.

The east-west asymmetry becomes considerable at such altitudes for latitudes less than about 30°. For a zenith angle of 45°, 22-cm Pb absorber, altitude 34,500 ft, and latitude 27°18′, Schein, Yngve, and Kraybill found an excess of 46 ± 7 per cent from the westerly direction [56]. Biehl, Neher, and Roesch obtained 27.6 per cent and 30.4 per cent with zenith angle 45°, 10- and 20-cm Pb absorbers, respectively, altitude 30,000 ft, and latitude 0°. They concluded that these asymmetries were consistent with the assumption that all the cosmic-ray primaries were positively charged. As was the case for the latitude effect, the east-west asymmetry is greater at high altitudes because the particles observed there are due to lower energy primaries which are more field sensitive.

REFERENCES

1. Bradt, H. L., and B. Peters, *Phys. Rev.*, *77*, 54 (1950).
2. Rossi, B., *Revs. Modern Phys.*, *20*, 537 (1948).
3. Kraushaar, W. L., *Phys. Rev.*, *76*, 1045 (1949).
4. Owen, B. G., and J. G. Wilson, *Proc. Phys. Soc. (London)*, (A)*62*, 601 (1949); (A)*64*, 417 (1951).
5. Bassi, P., E. Clementel, I. Filosofo, and G. Puppi, *Phys. Rev.*, *76*, 854 (1949); *Nuovo cimento*, *6*, 484 (1949).
6. Ballario, C., M. Benini, and G. Calamai, *Phys. Rev.*, *74*, 1729 (1948).

7. Caro, D. E., J. K. Parry, and H. D. Rathgeber, *Nature, 165*, 688 (1950).
8. Glaser, D. A., B. Hamermesh, and G. Safonov, *Phys. Rev., 80*, 625 (1950).
9. Germain, L., *Phys. Rev., 80*, 616 (1950).
10. Regener, E., and W. Rau, *Naturwissenschaften, 27*, 803 (1939).
11. Ehmert, A., *Naturwissenschaften, 28*, 28 (1940).
12. Benedetto, F. A., G. O. Altmann, and V. F. Hess, *Phys. Rev., 61*, 266 (1942).
13. Nicolson, P., and V. Sarabhai, *Proc. Phys. Soc. (London)*, (A)*60*, 509 (1948).
14. Duperier, A., *Proc. Phys. Soc. (London)*, (A)*61*, 34 (1948); (A)*62*, 683 (1949); *Nature, 167*, 312 (1951).
15. Blackett, P. M. S., *Phys. Rev., 54*, 973 (1938).
16. Clay, J., K. H. J. Jonker, and J. T. Wiersma, *Physica, 6*, 174 (1939).
17. Greisen, K., *Phys. Rev., 61*, 212 (1942).
18. Rogozinski, A., and A. Voisin, *Compt. rend., 227*, 1092 (1948).
19. Freon, A., and Tsai-Chou, *Compt. rend., 229*, 753 (1949).
20. Morris, P. A., W. F. G. Swann, and H. C. Taylor, *Phys. Rev., 74*, 1102 (1948).
21. Johnson, T. H., *Revs. Modern Phys., 10*, 193 (1938).
22. Johnson, T. H., *Phys. Rev., 59*, 11 (1941).
23. Seidl, F. G. P., *Phys. Rev., 59*, 7 (1941).
24. Groetzinger, G., and G. W. McClure, *Phys. Rev., 77*, 777 (1950).
25. Kolhörster, W., *Z. Physik, 88*, 536 (1934).
26. Barnothy, J., and M. Forro, *Z. Physik, 104*, 744 (1937); *Phys. Rev., 74*, 1300 (1948).
27. Wilson, V. C., *Phys. Rev., 53*, 337 (1938).
28. Clay, J., and A. G. M. Van Gemert, *Proc. Acad. Sci. Amsterdam, 42*, 672 (1939).
29. Miyazaki, Y., *Phys. Rev., 76*, 1733 (1949).
30. Braddick, H. J. J., and G. S. Hensby, *Nature, 144*, 1012 (1939).
31. Wilson, V. C., and D. J. Hughes, *Phys. Rev., 63*, 161 (1943).
32. Nielsen, W. M., and K. Z. Morgan, *Phys. Rev., 54*, 245 (1938).
33. Miesowicz, M., L. Jurkiewicz, and J. M. Massalski, *Phys. Rev., 77*, 380 (1950).
34. Tiffany, O. L., and W. E. Hazen, *Phys. Rev., 77*, 849 (1950).
35. Randall, C. A., N. Sherman, and W. E. Hazen, *Phys. Rev., 79*, 905 (1950).
36. Randall, C. A., and W. E. Hazen, *Phys. Rev., 81*, 144 (1951).
37. Clay, J., *Revs. Modern Phys., 11*, 128 (1939).
38. Greisen, K., *Phys. Rev., 73*, 521 (1948); *76*, 1718 (1949).
39. Hayakawa, S., *Progr. Theor. Phys., 3*, 199 (1949).
40. Hayakawa, S., and S. Tomonaga, *Phys. Rev., 75*, 1958 (1949); *Progr. Theor. Phys., 4*, 287 (1949).
41. Sands, M., *Phys. Rev., 77*, 180 (1950).
42. Conversi, M., *Phys. Rev., 79*, 749 (1950).
43. Pomerantz, M. A., *Phys. Rev., 75*, 68, 1721 (1949).
44. Adams, R. V., C. D. Anderson, P. E. Lloyd, R. R. Rau, and R. C. Saxena, *Revs. Modern Phys., 20*, 334 (1948).
45. Quercia, I. F., B. Rispoli, and S. Sciuti, *Phys. Rev., 73*, 516 (1948); *74*, 1728 (1948); *78*, 824 (1950).
46. Hall, D. B., *Phys. Rev., 66*, 321 (1944).

47. Carr, T. D., M. Schein, and I. Barbour, *Phys. Rev.*, *73*, 1419 (1948).
48. Adams, R. V., C. D. Anderson, and E. W. Cowan, *Revs. Modern Phys.*, *21*, 72 (1949).
49. Miller, C. E., J. E. Henderson, D. S. Potter, J. Todd, Jr., and A. W. Wotring, *Phys. Rev.*, *79*, 459 (1950).
50. Voisin, A., *Compt. rend.*, *230*, 1396 (1950).
51. Jenkins, J. F., Jr., *Phys. Rev.*, *76*, 992 (1949).
52. Winckler, J. R., and W. G. Stroud, *Phys. Rev.*, *76*, 1012 (1949).
53. Gill, P. S., M. Schein, and V. Yngve, *Phys. Rev.*, *72*, 733 (1947).
54. Biehl, A. T., H. V. Neher, and W. C. Roesch, *Phys. Rev.*, *76*, 914 (1949).
55. Conversi, M., *Phys. Rev.*, *76*, 444 (1949).
56. Schein, M., V. H. Yngve, and H. L. Kraybill, *Phys. Rev.*, *73*, 928 (1948).

Absorption thickness (or length). If particles are absorbed exponentially so that the number penetrating a thickness l is $N(l) = N(0) \exp(-l/\lambda)$, then λ is their absorption thickness (or length).

Air showers. Simultaneous groups of particles existing in the atmosphere, which may contain large numbers of particles spread over large areas. Sometimes called Auger showers.

Anomalous scattering. Large-angle scattering which cannot be explained by electromagnetic interactions and is presumably due to specifically nuclear forces.

Anticoincidence. A particle detector or counter is in anticoincidence with respect to a certain event if it is required that it detect *no* particle at the time of the event.

Bremsstrahlung. Radiation of a photon due to a change in momentum (or spin) of a charged particle.

Burst (in ionization chamber). A current pulse in an ionization chamber due to the formation of a great many ions in it.

Cascade. A process in which one particle causes one or more secondaries, which in turn cause further particles, and so on.

Cloud chamber. An enclosure in which vapor is caused to become supersaturated so as to form droplets on ions in the tracks of charged particles.

Coincidence. A particle detector or counter is in coincidence with respect to a certain event if it is required that it detect a particle at the time of the event.

Core (of air shower). An area in an air shower where there is an exceptionally high density of particles per unit area.

Counter. A device which produces a useful signal when a particle hits it.

Counter telescope. An arrangement of several counters in coincidence so that only particles whose paths lie within certain angles are counted.

Decay. A spontaneous process in which a particle is transformed into others, capable of taking place in free space. In free space, conservation of energy and momentum requires that at least two particles be created.

Delayed coincidence. A counter is in delayed coincidence with respect to a certain event if it is required that it detect a particle within certain time limits after the event.

Density of ionization. The density of ionization produced by a charged particle under given conditions is the number of ions per unit length produced by it. Sometimes called "specific ionization" or abbreviated to simply "ionization" (see page 129 for discussion).

Electron-sensitive emulsions. A term sometimes used for emulsions capable of recording tracks of minimum ionization.

227

East-west effect (east-west asymmetry). Difference in cosmic-ray intensity between easterly and westerly directions caused by bending of trajectories by the earth's magnetic field.

Emulsion (nuclear). A silver bromide photographic emulsion capable of registering the tracks of ionizing particles as a series of developable grains.

Extensive penetrating showers. Events in which two or more penetrating particles occur in coincidence with distant particles.

Geiger counter. A device in which high voltage placed on a wire in a gas-filled enclosure causes an electrical breakdown when an ionizing particle traverses the gas. The resulting current indicates passage of the particle.

Grain (in emulsion). A small amount of silver bromide which acts as a unit and can be reduced to a silver grain by appropriate chemical development if acted on by light or, in the case of nuclear emulsions, ionization.

Grain count. The number of (silver) grains in a certain section of charged particle track, usually counted from the end of the track at which the particle stopped.

Grain density. The number of (silver) grains per unit length of a charged particle track at a certain point.

Hard component. That part of the cosmic radiation capable of penetrating thick absorbers, *e.g.*, 10 cm or more of lead (see page 7).

Hodoscope. A system of counters, usually involving a large number, with indicators to record which have been discharged, so that the paths of charged particles may be inferred.

Ionization. Formation of ions. When used in a quantitative sense, ionization usually means the total number of ions produced in a certain area or apparatus. Sometimes used as an abbreviation for "density of ionization."

Ionization chamber. An enclosure, normally gas-filled, with electrodes to provide a sufficient field to sweep out ions formed, thus giving a measurable current.

Knock-on (electron). An electron which has been given an appreciable amount of energy by close approach of a fast charged particle (see page 129).

λ meson. A hypothetical meson of mass about 3 to 10 electron masses (see page 59).

Latitude effect. The change in intensity of cosmic rays (or some component thereof) with latitude on the earth, caused by the bending of trajectories by the magnetic field of the earth (see page 211).

Lifetime. The characteristic time for a decay process (see page 95).

Local penetrating showers. Events in which two or more simultaneous penetrating particles occur without coincident particles at a distance.

mu meson. The meson produced in a pi-mu decay event (see page 58).

μ meson. A meson of mass about 215 electron masses, as commonly found in cosmic rays at sea level (see page 58).

Multiple production. Multiple production of mesons is used to signify the production of two or more mesons in a single nucleon-nucleon collision (see page 164).

Nucleonic component. The members of the cosmic radiation chiefly responsible for nuclear disruptions—thought to be mainly protons, neutrons, and π mesons.

Penetrating shower. A coincidence between two or more penetrating particles (see page 169).

pi meson. A meson which is observed to stop and produce another meson in a pi-mu decay (see page 58).

π meson. A meson of mass about 277 electron masses, normally produced in nuclear events.

Plural production. Plural production of mesons is used to signify the production of two or more mesons, one at a time, in a succession of nucleon-nucleon collisions, often within a single nucleus (see page 164).

Positive excess. The fractional excess of positive particles (or mesons) over negative ones (see page 204).

Primary. The particle initiating the process under consideration. If no particular process is involved, "primary" means a cosmic-ray particle incident on the earth's atmosphere from outside.

Prong. One of the tracks which make up a star (see page 185).

rho meson. A meson which is observed to stop without causing any event.

Scintillation counter. A material which emits a pulse of light when an ionizing particle passes through it. Usually used in connection with a photomultiplier tube.

Secondary. A particle produced as a result of the process under consideration. May be either produced directly by the corresponding primary, or indirectly in subsequent events. (The terms tertiary, quaternary, etc., are not often used.)

Shower. Simultaneous occurrence of two or more particles which might have been produced in a common event.

sigma meson. A meson which is observed to stop, producing a star.

Soft component. That part of the cosmic radiation not capable of penetrating a thick absorber, *e.g.*, 10 cm of lead (see page 7).

Star. An event in which one or more heavily ionizing tracks appear to come from a common point in such a way as to persuade the observer that a nucleus has been disrupted. Actual definitions vary (see page 185).

tau meson. A meson which decays to produce three π mesons.

Turbulence (in cloud chamber). Mass motion of the cloud-chamber gas introducing a spurious curvature in particle tracks in the chamber.

Varitrons. Stalinist-materialist particles with all sorts of masses (see page 57).

water equivalent (for depths under ground). Distance in water in which charged particles would have the same energy loss as in a given amount of soil or other material.

Zenith angle. Angle from the vertical or zenith.

A_{abs} Probability of absorption per unit time

$A_Z{}^N$ Arbitrary element of mass number N, atomic number Z

c Velocity of light

C   Carbon

D   Deuterium

e Charge of an electron or other singly charged particle in esu; symbol for an electron

E Kinetic energy of a particle

E_s Constant in scattering theory equal to 21 Mev

g Mesic charge

h Planck's constant

H Magnetic field

i $\sqrt{-1}$

I_v Vertical intensity

I_θ Intensity at angle θ

J_1 Flux

J_2 Integrated intensity

K Inverse range of nuclear forces

l Thickness of scatterer in radiation lengths

L Mean range before decay of π mesons

m Mass of the particle denoted by subscript; that is, m_e for mass of an electron

n Neutron

N Number; that is, number of atoms per cubic centimeter, number of events observed, number of grains counted, etc.

p Proton

P Momentum of a particle

P_x, P_y, P_z Components of momentum

r Distance from a field source

R Range of a charged particle

t Time

v Velocity of a particle

W Total energy of a particle

x, y, z Cartesian coordinates

z Charge of a fast particle in units of electronic charge

Z Atomic number

Z_0 Atomic number for which decay and absorption of μ mesons are equally probable

Z_{eff} Effective nuclear charge for calculations on μ-meson absorption by nuclei

α α particle

β Velocity in units of the velocity of light, that is, v/c

γ γ ray or photon

ϵ Ratio of frequencies of negative and positive μ mesons (Chap. 5); positive excess (Chap. 8)

θ Angle by which particle is scattered (Chap. 6); angle from vertical (Chap. 8)

λ Probability of disintegration per unit time (Chap. 5); mean free path for interaction of π mesons (Chap. 8)

Λ Probability of absorption per unit time

μ μ meson

ν Neutrino

π π meson

τ Rest lifetime of meson

τ' Lifetime of moving meson as observed in a stationary system

Φ_0 Standard cross section equal to 6.57×10^{-25} cm^2

Ψ Wave function of a meson

$F(\ ), f(\ ), g(\ )$ Undetermined functions

$I(\theta)$ Intensity at angle θ

$U(r)$ Yukawa potential

$\Phi(r)$ Coulomb potential

$\chi(E,E')$ Probability meson of kinetic energy E gives a knock-on electron of kinetic energy E'

$d\omega$ Element of solid angle

$d\sigma$ Element of area

$-\left(\dfrac{dE}{dx}\right)_{\text{coll}}$ Average energy lost by ionization per centimeter path

$-\left(\dfrac{dE}{dx}\right)_{\text{rad}}$ Average energy lost by radiation per centimeter path

∇^2 Laplacian operator

Subscripts e, μ, π, r, signify electron, μ meson, π meson, recoil particle, etc. Thus m_e is the mass of an electron, P_π the momentum of a π meson, etc.

A

Aamodt, R. L., 153
Adams, R. V., 218
Adelman, F. L., 150
Alichanian, A. I., 56
Alichanow, A. I., 56
Althaus, E. J., 110
Altmann, G. O., 207
Amaldi, E., 138
Anderson, C. D., 15, 32, 67, 113, 218, 219
Anderson, H. L., 159
Annis, M., 67
Appapillai, V., 178
Armenteros, R., 68
Auger, P., 8, 9, 59, 61, 62

B

Ballario, C., 205
Barbour, I., 54, 119, 219
Barkas, W. H., 81, 82, 88
Barker, K. H., 68, 139, 155, 173, 180
Barnothy, J., 213
Bassi, P., 204
Bastin, E., 66
Becker, J., 66
Belenky, S., 134
Bell, W. E., 103
Benedetto, F. A., 207
Benini, M., 205
Berezin, E., 112
Berger, M. J., 146
Bernardini, G., 139, 156
Bethe, H. A., 10, 34, 45, 144
Bhabha, H. J., 41
Bhattacharjee, 169
Biehl, A. T., 223
Bishop, A. S., 80, 86
Biswas, S., 194
Bjorklund, R., 89
Blackett, P. M. S., 137, 209
Block, M. M., 83

Booth, E. T., 123, 139, 156
Bothe, W., 7, 170
Bound, M., 168
Bradner, H., 77, 84, 139
Bradt, H. L., 195
Bramson, H., 113
Bridge, H., 67
Broadbent, D., 175, 182
Brode, R. B., 35, 36, 37, 55, 66
Brown, R., 133, 139, 155, 182
Burfening, J., 76
Butler, C. C., 66, 68, 139, 155, 173, 180, 186
Byfield, H., 123

C

Cachon, A., 68
Calamai, G., 205
Camerini, U., 121, 156, 188, 191–194
Carlson, A. G., 124, 196
Carmichael, H., 41
Caro, D. E., 205
Carr, T. D., 219
Cartwright, W. F., 84
Chakrabarty, S. K., 42
Chamberlain, O., 123
Chaminade, R., 100
Chang, W. Y., 144
Chanson, P., 66
Chao, C. Y., 175
Chedester, C., 156
Cheston, W. R., 150
Chou, C. N., 41
Christy, R. F., 41, 135
Clark, D. L., 159
Clay, J., 209, 213
Clementel, E., 204
Cocconi, G., 62, 148, 181
Code, F. L., 137
Cohn, H. O., 67
Conforto, A. M., 146
Conversi, M., 103, 218, 219, 223

Cook, L. J., 80, 86
Cool, R. L., 112
Cooper, D., 71, 107
Cowan, E. W., 61, 67
Crandall, W. E., 89
Crawford, F. S., Jr., 84
Crouch, M. F., 146
Crowe, K. M., 84

D

Darby, J. F., 194
Daudin, J., 59, 64
Davies, J. H., 113, 191–194
De Benedetti, S., 97
Dunlap, W. C., 131
Duperier, A., 207
Durbin, R., 159

E

Ehmert, A., 207
Ehrenfest, R., 62
Euler, H., 95
Evans, G. R., 97
Evans, J., 144, 148

F

Fainberg, J., 194
Feld, B. T., 193
Fermi, E., 159, 164
Fidecaro, G., 138
Filosofo, I., 204
Fisk, C. B., 193
Flum, R. S., 67
Forro, M., 213
Forster, H. H., 71, 159
Fowler, E. C., 112
Fowler, P. H., 156, 187, 188, 191–194
Frank, F. C., 48
Franzinetti, C., 54, 119, 191–194
Freier, P., 179
Freon, A., 59, 62, 209, 222
Fretter, W. B., 34, 55, 67, 155, 171, 179, 182
Frost, R. H., 39

G

Gardner, E., 75, 76, 88
Gardner, W. L., 117

George, E. P., 144, 148, 177
Germain, L., 207
Gilbert, W. S., 85
Gill, P. S., 41, 43, 223
Glaser, D. A., 206
Goldfarb, L. J. B., 150
Goldschmidt-Clermont, Y., 51, 54, 119, 150
Goldwasser, E. L., 36, 55
Gorodetzky, S., 32
Gottlieb, M. B., 177
Green, J. R., 175, 179
Gregory, B. P., 139, 155, 177
Greisen, K., 62, 64, 177, 181, 184, 209, 215, 222
Groetzinger, G., 146, 169, 213, 219

H

Hadley, J., 153
Hall, D. B., 219
Hall, H., 130
Halpern, O., 130
Hamermesh, B., 206
Harding, J. B., 69
Harrison, F. B., 143
Hartsough, W., 80
Hartzler, A. J., 139, 155
Havens, W. W., Jr., 83, 113
Hayakawa, S., 215
Hazen, W. E., 38, 185, 214
Heisenberg, W., 95, 164
Heitler, W., 10, 164
Henri, V. P., 123
Hershkowitz, J., 112
Hess, V. F., 207
Hill, M., 80
Hincks, E. P., 103, 110, 113
Hodgson, P. E., 70
Hooper, J. E., 124, 196
Hopper, V. D., 194
Hornbostel, J., 193
Hsiao, C., 67
Hubbard, H. W., 117

I

Ingleby, P., 170
Inoue, T., 45
Isaacs, P., 156

Ise, J., Jr., 182
Ittner, W. B., III, 146

J

Jakobson, M., 123
Janossy, L., 168, 170, 175, 177, 180, 182
Jason, A. C., 177
Jenkins, J. F., Jr., 222
Jesse, W. P., 167
Johnson, T. H., 97, 212
Jones, S. B., 79, 82, 150
Jonker, H. J., 209
Jurkiewicz, L., 214

K

Kaplon, M. F., 195
Kessler, J., 123
Keuffel, J. W., 143
King, D. T., 51, 54, 119, 124, 196
Kissinger, C. W., 107
Kolhörster, W., 7, 213
Kraushaar, W. L., 123, 203, 207
Kraybill, H. L., 223
Kusaka, S., 41, 135

L

Lagarrigue, A., 55, 113
Lapp, R. E., 43, 135
Lattes, C. M. G., 48, 75, 76, 118, 149, 186
Leavitt, C. P., 144
Lebow, I. L., 193
Lederman, L., 123, 139, 156
Leighton, R. B., 67, 113
Leprince-Ringuet, L., 9, 32, 65, 70, 159
Levy, F., 156
Lewis, H. W., 164
Lheritier, M., 65
Lloyd, P. E., 218
Loar, H., 159
Lock, W. O., 113, 156, 188, 191–194
Lord, J. J., 194
Lovati, A., 139, 155

M

McClure, G. W., 146, 213, 219
McCusker, C. B. A., 184
McKay, A. S., 133, 139, 155, 182

McMillan, E. M., 78, 85
Mailvaganam, A. W., 178
Marshak, R. E., 45, 144
Martinelli, E. A., 122
Massalski, J. M., 214
Maze, R., 59, 62, 100
Menon, M. G. K., 151
Merkle, T. C., Jr., 36, 55
Merritt, J., 77
Mezzetti, L., 177
Miesowicz, M., 214
Miller, C. E., 221
Miyazaki, Y., 213
Morris, P. A., 212
Moyer, B. J., 89
Mozley, R. F., 123
Muirhead, H., 51, 54, 113, 118, 119, 121,
    151, 156, 186, 188, 191–194
Mura, A., 139, 155, 181

N

Nageotte, E., 32, 66
Neddermeyer, S. H., 15, 32
Neher, H. V., 223
Nereson, N., 101, 107
Ney, E. P., 179
Nicholson, P., 207
Nonnemaker, G., 32

O

Occhialini, G. P. S., 48, 118, 149, 186
O'Ceallaigh, C., 70, 121
O'Connell, D. J., 77, 84
Oppenheimer, J. R., 164
Osborne, L. S., 193, 194
Owen, B. G., 204

P

Palmatier, E. D., 133
Pancini, E., 103
Panofsky, W. K. H., 91, 122, 153
Parry, J. K., 205
Passman, S., 83
Perkins, D. H., 191–194
Perry, J. P., 158
Peters, B., 195
Peterson, J. M., 78, 82, 85
Peyrou, C., 55, 113

Piccioni, O., 103, 110, 145, 156, 173, 178
Pickup, E., 194
Pomerantz, M. A., 218
Pompeia, P. A., 171
Pontecorvo, B., 110, 113
Powell, C. F., 37, 45, 48, 52, 68, 118, 121, 149, 186
Powell, W., 80, 186
Puppi, G., 204

Q

Quercia, I. F., 219
Querzoli, R., 177

R

Randall, C. A., 214
Rankin, B., 77, 84, 139
Rasetti, F., 99
Rathgeber, H. D., 205
Rau, R. R., 218
Rau, W., 207
Regener, E., 207
Regener, V. H., 168
Retallack, J. G., 36
Reynolds, G. T., 143
Richard-Foy, R., 32, 65
Richardson, J. R., 122
Richman, C., 77, 82, 84
Rispoli, B., 219
Ritson, D. M., 51, 54, 119, 121
Roberts, A., 159
Roberts, G. E., 97
Rochat, O., 151
Rochester, G. D., 66, 168, 177, 186
Roesch, W. C., 223
Rogozinsky, A., 209
Rosser, W. G. V., 68, 155, 173, 180
Rossi, B., 8, 101, 107, 168, 203, 205, 207, 217
Runcorn, S. K., 186

S

Sachs, A., 153, 156
Safonov, G., 206
Sagane, 117
Sakata, S., 45
Sala, O., 177
Salant, E. O., 193
Salvini, G., 139, 155, 181, 182

Sands, M., 218
Sarabhai, V., 207
Sard, R. D., 110, 146
Saxena, R. C., 218
Schein, M., 41, 43, 167, 194, 219, 223
Schmeiser, K., 170
Schulz, A., 123
Sciuti, S., 219
Seidl, F. G. P., 212
Seren, L., 132
Seriff, A. J., 67, 113
Shapiro, A. M., 156, 159
Sherman, N., 214
Shutt, R. P., 97, 138, 145
Sigurgeirsson, T., 107
Silverman, A., 92
Sirkar, 169
Sitte, K., 177, 184
Skinner, M., 77
Smith, F. M., 88, 150
Smith, J. E., 193
Souza Santos, M. D. de, 171
Stearns, M., 92
Steinberger, J., 80, 86, 91, 113, 123, 153, 156, 159
Steller, J., 91
Stevenson, E. C., 8, 29
Stevenson, M. L., 84
Street, J. C., 8, 29, 34, 112, 132, 144
Stroud, W. G., 222
Swann, W. F. G., 212

T

Tabin, J., 169
Tagliaferri, G., 139, 155, 181, 182
Tamm, I., 134
Taylor, H. C., 212
Thomas, J. E., 123
Thompson, R. W., 67, 112
Ticho, H. K., 107, 143
Tiffany, O. L., 214
Tinlot, J., 139, 155, 177
Tiomno, J., 148
Tongiorgi, V., 62, 148, 181
Treat, J. E., 181
Treille, P., 66
Tsai-Chou, 209, 222

V

Valley, G. E., 105, 107, 144
Van Gemert, A. G. M., 213

Vitale, J. A., 144
Voisin, A., 209, 222
Voorhies, H. G., 144
Voyvodic, L., 194

W

Wagner, N., 71
Walker, S. P., 177, 184
Walker, W. D., 177, 184
Walsh, T. G., 178
Wataghin, G., 171, 177
Weissenberg, A., 56
Wheeler, J. A., 141, 146
White, R. S., 78, 79, 82, 85
Whitehead, M. N., 84
Whittemore, W. L., 132
Wiegand, C. E., 123
Wiersma, J. T., 209
Wilcox, H. A., 82, 84
Williams, E. J., 97, 136

Wilson, J. G., 137, 204
Wilson, R., 158, 159
Wilson, V. C., 167, 213
Winckler, J. R., 222
Wollan, E. O., 167
Woodward, R. H., 8
Wouthuysen, S. A., 164

Y

Yamakawa, K. A., 108
Yekutieli, G., 191–194
Yngve, V. H., 223
York, H. F., 89, 153
Youtz, B., 77
Yukawa, H., 20

Z

Zar, J. L., 112

A

Absorption, of hard and soft components, 8, 206–208
  in atmosphere, 9, 216–218
  of heavy mesons, 70–71, 159
  of mesons in flight (see Interactions)
  of stopped μ^- mesons, 104–108, 141–148
    effect on lifetime, 106–108, 141–143
    products of, 144–148
  of stopped π^- mesons, 150–154
    in deuterium, 154
    in hydrogen, 152–154
    in nuclear emulsions, 150–152
Absorption anomaly of hard component, 95–97
Air showers, 59, 180–185
  local production of mesons in, 182–183
  μ mesons in, 181–182
  nuclear interactions in, 184
Altitude dependence, of mesons, 217–218
  of penetrating showers, 177
Angular distribution of mesons, in penetrating showers, 179
  from stars, 191–194
Anomalous scattering (see Scattering, nuclear)
Artificial mesons, 74–92
Atoms, 1–3
Auger showers (see Air showers)

B

Barometer effect, 207
β decay and meson theory, 24
Bethe-Bloch formula, 11
Bremsstrahlung, 11–15, 129, 135
  in relation to bursts, 41, 135
Bursts, 41–43, 134–135
  and air showers, 42–43
  bremsstrahlung contribution, 41, 135

Bursts, and meson spin, 41–43, 135
  and nuclear events, 42–43

C

Cascade showers (see Showers, electronic)
Charge, of μ mesons, 37–39
  measurement in cloud chamber, 38–39
  of nuclei, 2
  of π mesons, 59
Charge-exchange absorption, of stopped μ^- mesons, 146–148
  of stopped π^- mesons, 152–154
Charge-exchange scattering of π mesons, 155, 158
  by hydrogen, 159
Cloud-chamber mass measurements, 29–37, 55, 65–68
Cosmic rays, 4–5, 7–10, 201–203
  charged particles in, 8
  mesons in, 19, 201–223
Coulomb scattering, 136
Coupling of mesons to nucleons, 22–24

D

Decay, of heavy mesons, 66–70, 125
  of μ mesons, 95–118
    lifetime, 99–108
    products of, 108–118
      electrons, 109, 117
      neutrinos, 111, 118
  of π mesons, 118–124
    lifetime, 121–123
    products of, 118–121
      μ mesons, 118–119
      neutrinos, 121
  of π^0 mesons, 123–124
Decay events, 47, 66, 69, 97, 98, 119
Delayed coincidences, 101, 103, 173, 218
Density of ionization, 29, 130–132

Density effect, 130, 132
Dimensions of nuclei, 2

E

East-west effect, 212
Electronic showers (*see* Showers, electronic)
Electrons, 2
   from μ-meson decay, 97–117
      energy spectrum, 112–117
      frequency of, 105–107
      identification of, 108–109, 117
Elementary particles, 2, 27
Elements, 1
Emulsions, nuclear, 46
Energy losses, by charged particles, 10–18, 128–135
      Bethe-Bloch formula, 11
      curve for, 12
      in solid plates, 15–18
      (*See also* Bremsstrahlung; Knock-on electrons)
   of mesons by ionization, 129–132
   of shower particles, 16–18
Energy spectrum, of electrons from μ-meson decay, 112–117
      cloud-chamber results, 112–115
      counter results, 113–117
   of knock-on electrons from mesons, 132–134
   of mesons, from $a + C$, 82
      at altitude, 219–222
      from $\gamma + C$, 86
      from $\gamma + H$, 86–87
      from $p + p$, 84–85
      at sea level, 205–208
   of μ mesons from π-μ decay, 119–120
   of π mesons from stars, 188–190
Extensive air showers (*see* Air showers)

F

Flux of mesons at sea level, 203
Frequency of mesons (*see* Intensity of mesons)

G

Geomagnetic effects, at altitude, 223
   at sea level, 211–213
Grain count of mesons, 49–51
Grain density, 46

H

Hard component of cosmic rays, 8–10, 202–203
   absorption in atmosphere, 9, 216–218
   absorption anomaly of, 95–97
   mesons discovered in, 19
Hard showers (*see* Penetrating showers)
Heavy mesons, 65–71

I

Inelastic scattering of π mesons, 155–159
Intensity of mesons, at altitude, 216–218
   below ground, 213–216
      relation to π meson decay, 215–216
   at sea level, 203
Interactions, of μ mesons in flight, 148
   of π mesons in flight, 155–159
      in cloud-chamber plates, 155
      in emulsions, 156–158
   of stopped mesons (*see* Absorption)
Ionization, by charged particles, 10–12, 128–132
   density of, 29, 130–132
   by mesons, 129–132

K

Kappa mesons, 70
Knock-on electrons, 129
   energies of, 132–134
   from solid materials, 133–135

L

λ-meson hypothesis, 59–65
Latitude effect, at altitude, 223
   of penetrating showers, 177–178
   at sea level, 212
Lifetime, of mesons, 24, 95–96
      apparent, due to time dilatation, 96
   of μ mesons, 99–108, 141–143
      as affected by absorption, 106–108, 141–143
   of π mesons, 121–123
   of π^0 mesons, 124

M

Magnetic selector, 104, 146–147
Mass of meson from range of nuclear forces, 22
Mass measurements, with cloud chambers, 29–37, 55, 65–68

Mass measurements, with counter hodo-scope, 56
Masses, of heavy mesons, 65–71
  of mesons by magnetic deflection and range in emulsion, 54–55
  of mu mesons, 51, 54–55
  of μ mesons, 28–37, 88
    methods of measuring, 28–29
  of neutral mesons, 92, 154
  of pi mesons, 49–51, 54–55
  of π mesons, 88
  of π^0 mesons, 92, 154
  of rho mesons, 150
  of sigma mesons, 54–55
Mesic charge, of light particles, 23
  of nucleons, 22
Meson theory of nuclear forces, 20–25
  infinities in, 25
  and meson decay, 24
  and meson mass, 22
Mesons, definition of, 58
  existence in hard component, 19
    (For detailed data see property in question)
  from stars, 185–196
    angular distribution of, 191–194
    energy spectrum of, 188–190
    identification of, 187–189
    multiplicities of, 191–192
    π^0 mesons among, 194–196
Mu meson, definition of, 58
μ meson, definition of, 58
  properties of, 44
    (For detailed data see property in question)
Molecules, 1
Multiple production of mesons, 164, 192–194
Multiple scattering, 136
Multiplicity, of meson production, 205
  of mesons from stars, 191–192
  of penetrating showers, 178–179

N

Neutral mesons (see π^0 mesons)
Neutrinos, 6
  from μ-meson decay, 111, 118
  from π-meson decay, 121
Neutrons, discovery of, 3
  from μ-meson absorption, 146–148

Neutrons, production of mesons by, 165–169, 177, 191
Nuclear charge, 2
Nuclear dimensions, 2
Nuclear emulsions, 46
Nuclear forces, meson theory of, 20–25
  range of, 20
Nuclear scattering, 136–140
  of μ mesons, 136–138
  of π mesons, 138–140, 155–159
Nuclei, composition of, 4
Nucleus, 2–4

P

p-p collisions, production of mesons in, 84
Penetrating showers, 169–180
  altitude dependence of, 177
  angular distribution of, 179
  extensive, 170, 175
    (See also Air showers)
  latitude effect of, 177–178
  local, 170–180
  multiplicities of, 178–179
  π mesons in, 173–174
  π^0 mesons in, 174–175
  transition effect of, 175–177
Penetration, of air-shower particles, 61–64
  due to 1- to 7-Mev photons, 64
  of hard and soft components (see Absorption)
Photons, 3
  from μ-meson decay, 110–111
  production of mesons by, 165–169
Pi meson, definition of, 58
π meson, definition of, 58
  discovery of, 47–48
  properties of, 59
    (For detailed data see property in question)
Pi-mu decays, 47–51, 118–124
π^0 mesons, from absorption of π^- mesons in hydrogen, 153
  evidence for, 89–92
    (For detailed data see property in question)
Plural production of mesons, 164, 192–194
Positive excess, at altitude, 218–219
  at sea level, 204–205
Positive to negative ratio, of mesons from α + C, 82

Positive to negative ratio, of mesons
   from γ + C, 85
   of mesons from n + C, 84
   of mesons from p + C, 83
Positron, discovery of, 5–6
Production, of mesons, in air showers,
      182–183
   by α particles, 74–75
   in cosmic radiation, 163–197
   by neutrons, 77, 84, 165–169, 177,
      191
   by photons, 78, 85–86, 165–169
      yield vs. photon energy, 80
   by protons, 76, 79, 82–84, 175–177,
      188–192
      by p-p collisions, 84
   thresholds for, 81
   of π^0 mesons, 89–92
      in penetrating showers, 174–175
      by photons, 91–92
      by protons, 89–91
      in stars, 194–196
Products of decay, of heavy mesons, 68–
      70
   of μ mesons, 108–118
   of π mesons, 118–121
   of π^0 mesons, 123–124
Protons, 2

R

Radiation, energy loss from, 12–14
   (See also Bremsstrahlung)
Range, 29
   of electrons from μ-meson decay, 113–
      117
   of μ mesons from π-meson decay, 119–
      120
Relativistic rise in ionization, 129, 132
Relativistic time dilatation, 96
Rho mesons, 52, 149
   definition of, 58
Rutherford formula, 132

S

Scattering, anomalous (see nuclear, below)
   charge-exchange, 155, 158–159
   Coulomb, 136
   multiple, 136
   nuclear, 136–140
      of μ mesons, 136–138
      of π mesons, 138–140, 155–159

Scattering, of penetrating shower parti-
      cles, 139, 157
Shower particles, energy loss by, 16–18
   shower production by, 16–17
Showers, cascade (see electronic, below)
   air (see Air showers)
   Auger (see Air showers)
   electronic, 8
      altitude dependence, 17
      theory, 13–15
   extensive (see Air showers)
   of mesons from stars, 187–197
   penetrating (see Penetrating showers)
Sigma mesons, 52–55, 149–152
   definition of, 58
Soft component of cosmic rays, 8–10
   absorption in atmosphere, 9
Spin, of μ mesons, 39–43, 118
   relation to bursts, 41–43
   of π mesons, 81, 121, 159
Stars, caused by, heavy mesons, 70–71,
      159
   μ mesons, in flight, 148
      stopping, 144–148
   π mesons, in flight, 155–159
      stopping, 52, 150–152
   emitting mesons, 185–196

T

Tau mesons, 68–70
Temperature effect, 207–209
Thresholds for meson production, 81
Transition effect of penetrating showers,
   175–177

U

Ultra γ rays, 7

V

V particles, 66–68
   products of decay, 68
Varitrons, 57, 68

Y

Yield curves, for π mesons, 79–80
   for π^0 mesons produced by photons, 92
Yukawa potential, 21

Z

Zenith-angle effect, at altitude, 222
   at sea level, 209–211